SOILS AND SOIL FERTILITY

McGRAW-HILL PUBLICATIONS IN THE
AGRICULTURAL SCIENCES

R. A. BRINK, *Consulting Editor*

ADRIANCE AND BRISON · Propagation of Horticultural Plants
AHLGREN · Forage Crops
ANDERSON · Diseases of Fruit Crops
BROWN AND WARE · Cotton
CARROLL, KRIDER AND ANDREWS · Swine Production
CHRISTOPHER · Introductory Horticulture
CRAFTS AND ROBBINS · Weed Control
CRUESS · Commercial Fruit and Vegetable Products
DICKSON · Diseases of Field Crops
ECKLES, COMBS, AND MACY · Milk and Milk Products
ELLIOTT · Plant Breeding and Cytogenetics
FERNALD AND SHEPARD · Applied Entomology
GARDNER, BRADFORD, AND HOOKER · The Fundamentals of Fruit Production
GUSTAFSON · Conservation of the Soil
GUSTAFSON · Soils and Soil Management
HAYES, IMMER, AND SMITH · Methods of Plant Breeding
HERRINGTON · Milk and Milk Processing
JENNY · Factors of Soil Formation
JULL · Poultry Husbandry
KOHNKE AND BERTRAND · Soil Conservation
LAURIE AND RIES · Floriculture
LEACH · Insect Transmission of Plant Diseases
MAYNARD AND LOOSLI · Animal Nutrition
METCALF, FLINT, AND METCALF · Destructive and Useful Insects
NEVENS · Principles of Milk Production
PATERSON · Statistical Technique in Agricultural Research
PETERS AND GRUMMER · Livestock Production
RATHER AND HARRISON · Field Crops
RICE, ANDREWS, WARWICK, AND LEGATES · Breeding and Improvement of Farm
 Animals
ROADHOUSE AND HENDERSON · The Market-milk Industry
STEINHAUS · Principles of Insect Pathology
THOMPSON · Soils and Soil Fertility
THOMPSON AND KELLY · Vegetable Crops
THORNE · Principles of Nematology
TRACY, ARMERDING, AND HANNAH · Dairy Plant Management
WALKER · Diseases of Vegetable Crops
WALKER · Plant Pathology
WILSON · Grain Crops
WOLFE AND KIPPS · Production of Field Crops

The late Leon J. Cole was Consulting Editor of this series from 1937 to 1948.
There are also the related series of McGraw-Hill Publications in the Botanical Sciences, of which Edmund W. Sinnott is Consulting Editor, and in the Zoological Sciences, of which Edgar J. Boell is Consulting Editor. Titles in the Agricultural Sciences were published in these series in the period 1917 to 1937.

High yields of top-quality crops reflect a high level of soil fertility.

Soils and Soil Fertility

LOUIS M. THOMPSON, Ph.D.

Associate Dean of Agriculture
Iowa State University

SECOND EDITION

McGRAW-HILL   BOOK   COMPANY

New York   Toronto   London   1957

PREFACE

This book has been prepared for use as a text for an introductory course in soils for students in agriculture. It is the outgrowth of twenty years of experience in teaching the beginning course in soils in Texas A. and M. College and in Iowa State University. Although it is only the second edition of *Soils and Soil Fertility* published by the McGraw-Hill Book Company, this book has been in the process of development since 1937, beginning as a mimeographed supplement to available textbooks.

The chief motivating force behind the development of this book has been the need for text material organized to fit the course presented by the author. Anyone who has ever taught a course in college will certainly recognize the limitations imposed by having to skip around in a textbook for assignments that fit his outline of the course. Yet it is desirable to have the students do some outside reading on the subject to be presented.

Students have been asked to evaluate previous forms of this book, and much credit is due them for their many helpful suggestions. It was the student who was constantly kept in mind as the manuscript was developed. The approach has been to treat the material as though the student would be exposed to the subject for the first time. Concepts are gradually developed and new terms are explained as they are introduced in the text. It is recommended, therefore, that the student be expected to read the book from the beginning rather than skip around for assigned reading.

In my years of teaching experience—during the last five of which I have served as chairman of the curriculum committee for the Division of Agriculture in Iowa State University—I have been impressed by the tendency of subject matter to be expanded to cause the splitting of courses into more and more courses. That tendency is certainly true in soil science. It is a field of expansion and rapid advancement. But it must be kept in mind that most agriculture students take only one course in soils, and that course must be broad enough to generally cover the field and yet provide a foundation for the student who becomes a soils major. The more advanced courses should represent an expansion of subjects presented in the beginning course.

This edition has been expanded about fifty per cent over the previous edition at the suggestion of a number of teachers. The first twelve chapters were practically rewritten. Greater emphasis has been placed on soil structure and related physical properties. Mechanisms of aggregate formation are suggested and diagramed. The relationship of fertility to soil moisture has been developed, and emphasis has been placed on water conservation and management. Detailed descriptions of clay minerals are provided, and vermiculite is described as one of the important clay minerals. Greater emphasis is placed on weathering, and the degree of weathering is related to problems of fertility. Anion exchange relationships are given prominence, and calculations with cation exchange relationships are explained. The relation of lime to potassium release has been explained on the principle of the complementary ion effect. The chapter including minor elements has been expanded to describe chelates in iron nutrition and to include a discussion of chlorine.

The prerequisite for this course should ordinarily include inorganic and organic chemistry; however, the concepts involving chemistry are carefully developed so that one may read and understand the book with only high school chemistry as a background. The beginning course in soils in Iowa State University is a freshman course, but we know from experience that students who have had college chemistry gain more from the beginning course in soils.

While I have had access to excellent libraries, I have also had the good fortune to work in close association with the following men who have kindly read and criticised parts of the manuscript: Marvin Anderson, W. V. Bartholomew, George Browning, B. J. Firkins, Lloyd Frederick, Frank Riecken, Don Kirkham, Sterling Olsen, W. H. Pierre, Wayne Scholtes, George Stanford, and Wayne Willis. I am also grateful to other present and former associates for their discussions which have led to the development of this book. Special thanks are due to William C. Brown of Dubuque, Iowa, who published earlier versions of this book, for his contributions to its development.

I wish to make special acknowledgment to my wife, Margaret Stromberg Thompson, for her typing of the manuscript and for her invaluable assistance with the proofreading.

Louis M. Thompson

CONTENTS

CHAPTER 1

INTRODUCTION

The term *soil* is derived from the Latin word *solum*, which means floor. It is defined in Webster's Collegiate Dictionary as "the upper layer of the earth which may be dug, plowed, etc., specifically, the loose surface material of the earth in which plants grow." This is a very simple definition for a very complex material. Soils are complex because of their extreme variability in physical and chemical composition. They are formed from exposed masses of partially weathered rocks and minerals of the earth's crust. There are hundreds of different kinds of rocks and minerals with different chemical composition, different degrees of resistance to weathering, and different physical properties.

All rocks and minerals of the earth's crust are derived from primary minerals which are cooled and crystallized from a molten mass of material. The primary minerals contain all the chemical elements obtained by plants from the soil, except nitrogen. They do not contain nitrogen because nitrogenous materials are unstable at high temperatures. One important difference, therefore, between a soil capable of supporting plant growth and a mass of freshly exposed geological material is its content of nitrogen. Soil nitrogen is stored in organic matter. Another way, and a more complete way, of describing the difference between soil and the geologic materials beneath soils is that *soils are mixtures of mineral and organic matter that are capable of supporting plant life.* The organic matter, because of its being a source of nitrogen, is a necessary part of the definition and serves as the important distinguishing characteristic of soils as contrasted to geological material.

In addition to supplying nitrogen, organic matter has many other important functions which will be emphasized throughout this book. Organic matter accumulates in the soil as dark-colored, finely divided material, sometimes referred to as *humus*, which coats the surfaces of the mineral particles. And a large amount of the partially decomposed organic matter referred to as humus causes soil to be dark in color.

The Soil Profile. A characteristic common to all soils is the development of distinct layers from the surface downward. A vertical section

1

of the soil to expose the layering is called a profile. The surface layer is usually higher in organic matter and darker in color than the next layer. It is called the A horizon, or topsoil. Beneath the A horizon is a layer which may contain more clay than the topsoil and may be greatly different

Fig. 1. A characteristic common to all soils is the accumulation of organic matter in and near the surface. (*Soil Conservation Service.*)

in color. This layer is called the B horizon, or subsoil. These two horizons are referred to as the solum, the Latin word for soil. Soil, then, includes the topsoil and subsoil (the A and B horizons). The depth of the soil is a characteristic associated with the accumulation of organic matter. As a general rule, one may recognize the depth of soil development in a particular deposit of material by observing the depth to which organic matter has accumulated.

Beneath the solum is the parent material, which is referred to as the

C horizon. Collectively the A, B, and C horizons constitute the soil profile.

The A horizon of a well-developed soil has undergone many changes that make it different from its parent material, the C horizon. At one time the A horizon was similar to the C horizon, assuming a fair degree of uniformity within the original material. The A horizon gradually accumulated more organic matter than the B horizon because of the greater concentration of roots near the surface and because of the accumulation of residues on the surface. The A horizon is also more exposed to the weathering action of the sun, rain, wind, and ice. It is subjected to the many forces which tend to cause physical disintegration and chemical decomposition. The more easily decomposed materials tend to weather away, leaving the more resistant minerals and organic matter to make up the topsoil. The older the soil, that is, the longer a soil is exposed to weathering, the more resistant the material is that remains in the topsoil; a fact of greater significance than can be emphasized at this point. Strongly weathered materials are a poor source of nutrients. The weathering of minerals in the topsoil is an important source of mineral nutrients for plant growth. In strongly weathered materials the more resistant minerals remain behind, and although a source of nutrients, they may decompose too slowly to be a good source of plant nutrients. The more fertile soils are those which are younger, have suffered less weathering, and are still weathering rapidly enough to release an abundance of plant nutrients each year.

As the topsoil undergoes weathering, the particle size is reduced. Part of the sand may be reduced to silt size, and part of the silt may be reduced to clay. Part of the clay may decompose to such an extent that its constituents leach from the topsoil. This latter change is extremely drastic, however, and for the most part clay represents the residue of strongly weathered fragments of rocks and minerals.

Some of the clay of the topsoil is carried from the A horizon to the B horizon by percolating water. Where soils have formed over extremely long periods of geological time without erosion, they may have lost nearly all of the clay of the A horizon. The loss may have been due to destructive weathering in the A horizon, or movement to the B horizon, or both. Old soils are strongly differentiated; that is, they have strong differences in the clay content of the A and B horizons.

The clay content of the B horizon increases with time in comparison with the C horizon. Part of the increase is due to movement of clay from the A to the B horizon, and part of the increase is due to weathering of silt and sand in the B horizon to form clay.

In summary, soils have two characteristics common the world over. One is the accumulation of organic matter, with its greatest content in the surface.   The other is the differentiation of the clay content between the three horizons, with the greatest accumulation of clay in the B horizon.

Why Soils Differ.   Soils are formed as a result of weathering of rocks and minerals and the accumulation of organic matter.   There are hundreds of species of minerals which might occur in soils, and their distribution over the earth's surface is highly variable.   These different minerals vary in chemical composition and in the rate at which they weather. The mineral matter not only varies greatly in size of particles but also

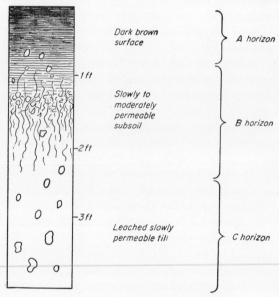

Dark brown surface — A horizon

Slowly to moderately permeable subsoil — B horizon

Leached slowly permeable till — C horizon

Fig. 2. Sketch of a Prairie soil profile.

varies greatly in chemical composition.   The variation in chemical composition reflects the variation in fertility in so far as crop production is concerned.   The variation in particle-size distribution affects water-holding capacity and aeration within the soil and many other physical properties.

The topography on which soils develop greatly affects their properties. Soils developed on slopes do not develop solums as deeply as soils developed on more level topography.   Other conditions being equal, there is greater differentiation of A and B horizons on more level areas than on more sloping areas.   Soils on more level areas are usually darker in color than soils developed on slopes.   There are many other differences in soils that may be the result of variation in topography.

The kind of vegetation which develops on a soil will affect the way in which organic matter is distributed.   The organic-matter content of forest soils is high in the immediate surface and low in the subsoil, while the organic matter of grassland soils is high in the surface but gradually decreases with depth. In other words, the organic-matter content of the B horizon of grassland soils is usually much higher than the organic-matter content of the B horizon of neighboring forest soils. The chemical composition of the organic-matter residues of plants greatly affects the soil. For example, the residues of certain coniferous trees cause soils to become acid in reaction, while the residues of certain grasses and legumes help to keep the soil from becoming strongly acid in reaction. These are only a few examples of the effect of vegetation on soils. More examples will be mentioned in Chap. 6.

Climate has tremendous effects on soil characteristics. Weathering is more rapid, and leaching of soils is more drastic, in warm humid climates. But where soils are formed under cold climates there is slower weathering and the organic-matter content is usually higher, because during the winter, when the soil is frozen, no appreciable decomposition of organic matter occurs. The amount of precipitation in drier climates determines the depth to which moisture normally penetrates into the soil material. The depth of moisture penetration may limit the depth of root penetration and the depth of organic-matter accumulation. The depth to which organic matter accumulates is the depth to which the solum is developed.

All of these changes that take place in soil development require time. Therefore we recognize time as an important factor of soil formation. The degree of profile differentiation is affected by factors other than time, as will be explained in Chap. 6. Nevertheless, strongly differentiated profiles are considered to be old soils. In areas where the parent material has long been in position for soil formation to occur, we find that soils have strongly differentiated solums. There may be local differences in degree of differentiation because of topography, but the factor of time is still a major influence.

As implied in the above paragraphs, soil is the product of five main factors in soil formation: (a) parent material, (b) topography, (c) vegetation, (d) climate, and (e) time. There are many variations within each factor, and even if there were only 10 gradations in each factor, there would be $10 \times 10 \times 10 \times 10 \times 10$ (or 10^5), or 100,000 different combinations, which would mean 100,000 different soils. It is no great wonder that there are over a thousand different soils mapped in the United States. No two soils are expected to be just alike, but soils which are similar are grouped together for purposes of classification for cultural practices and uses.

A question such as this has arisen, "Are the soils in Russia similar to those in the United States?" One answer to this is that wherever two soils have developed from similar parent materials, under similar climate and vegetation for about the same geological time on similar topography, the soils will be similar. Another question is, "How extensive is a particular soil?" Again the answer is that the soil will be as extensive as its parent material in a particular climate where the topography and vegetation are similar. The changes that occur in climate from one state to another in the United States are frequently great enough to limit the distribution of individual soils. Furthermore, the very limited distribution of certain parent materials greatly limits the distribution of the soils developed from those materials.

Naming Soils. Soils which have developed from the same parent material under similar conditions of climate, vegetation, topography, and time will be similar enough in appearance and properties so that they can be given the same name.

Soils which are alike in all their characteristics except texture of the topsoil are grouped together in a *series*. The series name like *Amarillo* or *Fargo* is a geographic name that indicates the area in which the soil is developed. One would associate the *Amarillo* soils with northwest Texas or the *Fargo* soils with North Dakota. When a soil is recognized as a separate unit for mapping, it is named after the town, county, school, church, creek, river, or some other geographic feature, as long as the name has never been used for another soil. The *series* name implies certain profile characteristics but permits some variation in the texture of the topsoil. For purposes of making maps, the *series* is separated further into *types*. A *type* includes soils which are alike in all their characteristics, including texture of the topsoil. The term *class* describes the texture and indicates the approximate proportion of sand, silt, and clay. Therefore, the *type* name would be the *series* name plus the *class* name. For example, *Amarillo silt loam* is a type name which has the *series* name of *Amarillo* plus the class name of *silt loam*.

Composition of Soil. Soils include four principal components: (*a*) mineral matter, (*b*) organic matter, (*c*) air, and (*d*) water.

Air and water occupy the pore spaces in soils. On absorbing water, soils swell to a certain extent so that it is incorrect to assume a constant pore space for a given soil; that is, air space and water space are not entirely reciprocal in relation. On the other hand, it is true that as soils absorb water the air space decreases. Approximately half of the volume of soil is occupied by air and water. Fine-textured soils generally have more total pore space than coarse-textured soils. However, fine-textured soils usually are less well aerated than coarse-textured soils. The fine-textured soils hold more water, and the spaces of fine-textured soils are smaller and many of them are isolated by water films. Generally speaking, it is desirable to have a soil which, when well drained, will have about half of its pore space filled with water. Soils which remain filled with water for several days after a rain should receive some mechanical treatment to improve the drainage so as to increase aeration.

Mineral Component of Soils. Soils include mineral matter varying in size from fine clay to large rocks. Except for gravel and rocks that occur occasionally in soils, there are three fractions, sand, silt, and clay. Sand particles are large enough to be seen by the naked eye and give soils a gritty feel. Larger silt particles can barely be seen by the eye, and the smaller silt particles can be seen only with the aid of a microscope. Silt feels smooth when rubbed between the thumb and fingers and feels much like talcum powder or wheat flour. Clay includes the fraction smaller

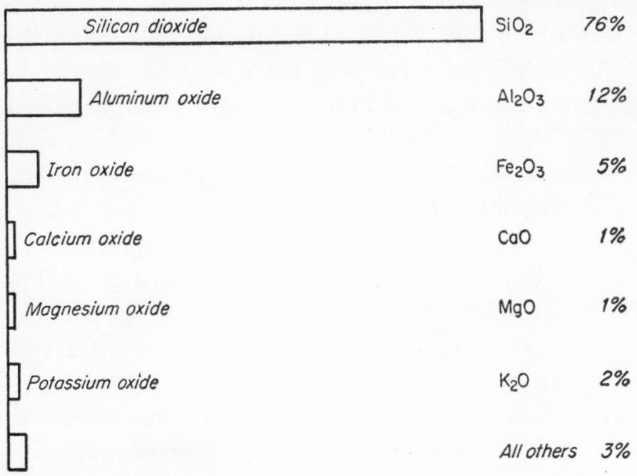

Silicon dioxide	SiO_2	76%
Aluminum oxide	Al_2O_3	12%
Iron oxide	Fe_2O_3	5%
Calcium oxide	CaO	1%
Magnesium oxide	MgO	1%
Potassium oxide	K_2O	2%
	All others	3%

FIG. 3. The percentage composition of minerals contained in a typical Prairie topsoil.

than silt and feels sticky and plastic when wet, and harsh and hard when dry. Since clay includes all particles below the size of silt, this fraction contains the available plant nutrients not contained in organic matter.

The most abundant minerals of the earth's crust are the silicate minerals and the oxide minerals. The silicate minerals include silicon and oxygen along with one or more of the following: aluminum, iron, calcium, magnesium, potassium, and sodium. The oxide minerals include oxygen in combination with silicon, aluminum, or iron. Soils represent a mixture of the various minerals of various sizes from rocks to clay. It is expected that the elements named above would make up a high proportion of the soil. Approximately 90 per cent of the mineral matter of soils includes silicon, aluminum, iron, and oxygen. Calcium, magnesium, potassium, and sodium make up about 5 per cent of the mineral component of the soil. All of the other elements found in the mineral portion of the soil make up usually less than 5 per cent of the total.

Organic Component of Soils. On a weight basis, the organic matter in the topsoil of most upland soils varies between 1 and 6 per cent, with

3 per cent being an average figure. Soils occupying old lake beds, or positions where the water table is near the surface most of the year, may have considerably more than 6 per cent organic matter. There are many areas, particularly in North Central United States, where organic matter varies between 20 and 80 per cent. Soils containing more than 20 per cent organic matter are designated as *organic* soils. Where the organic matter constitutes less than 20 per cent of the dry weight, the soil is referred to as a *mineral* soil.

The organic matter of soils is made up of undecomposed and partially decomposed residues of plants and animals and the tissue of living and dead microorganisms.

Organic matter contains appreciable quantities of nitrogen, phosphorus, and sulfur which become available to higher plants as decomposition occurs. Furthermore, the decomposition of organic matter helps to produce substances that make all of the plant nutrients more available. From a physical point of view, organic matter improves the aeration of soils and the water-holding capacity, simultaneously, a feature of great significance.

Contribution of Soil to Plant Growth. Soils provide higher plants with (a) essential elements which are referred to as *plant nutrients*, (b) a storehouse for water, (c) oxygen for root respiration, and (d) mechanical support or anchorage.

Before further consideration of the contributions of the soil it is desirable to consider a few aspects of plant physiology.

The three elements carbon, hydrogen, and oxygen make up about 95 per cent of the dry weight of plant tissue. These three elements are furnished by air and water. They become a part of plant tissue through the process of photosynthesis, an extremely complex reaction which is shown in a general way as follows:

$$\text{Energy of the sun} + 6CO_2 + 6H_2O \rightarrow$$
$$C_6H_{12}O_6 \text{ containing energy} + 6O_2$$

The water is absorbed through the root system. The carbon dioxide is absorbed through the stomates of the leaves. The simple sugar produced in photosynthesis is further elaborated along with nutrients from the soil into complex organic compounds of plant structures. All of the vitamins, hormones, and other complex *organic* compounds that are necessary in the growth of the plant are synthesized within the plant. The plant absorbs through its roots and leaves all of the 15 essential elements in simple *inorganic* form.

In the reaction of photosynthesis, oxygen is liberated. But plants also utilize oxygen of the atmosphere. Plants carry on respiration and utilize some of the energy stored in the products of their photosynthesis.

Since the atmosphere above the soil contains over 20 per cent oxygen, this necessity is practically never a limiting factor in leaf respiration. On the other hand, root respiration is sometimes limited by a low oxygen supply in the soil air. Respiration is the reverse of photosynthesis:

Energy-bearing organic matter like $C_6H_{12}O_6 + 6O_2 \rightarrow$
$$6CO_2 + 6H_2O + energy$$

Through the process of root respiration the soil air is depleted of oxygen and enriched with CO_2. Furthermore the microbial population of the soil decomposes organic matter through the respiratory process and further depletes the soil air of its oxygen supply. If the soil is well ventilated (aerated), oxygen does not become a limiting factor in root respiration. But all soils are not well aerated. Some soils have their pore space filled with water much of the time. Some soils have very fine pores, many of which are isolated by water films, and have such low oxygen supply that roots fail to develop normally. In other words, a soil may be rich in plant nutrients and filled with adequate water and still produce a poor crop because of lack of oxygen in the soil atmosphere (7). Root respiration is required in nutrient uptake and in the absorption of water (6). In other words, energy is required in the uptake of water and nutrients. A corn plant may wilt on a hot day with its roots submerged in water (5). If the roots are in a water-logged soil where the oxygen supply is used up, the roots cannot carry on respiration and the energy transfer is lacking that would permit the uptake of water.

No doubt the reader has seen plants growing in water cultures in greenhouses. The water of the cultures is changed frequently or air is bubbled through periodically so that the water will dissolve enough oxygen to permit root respiration. There are certain plants equipped to absorb oxygen through certain cell structures at the surface of the water for root respiration, but most agronomic plants require soil aeration for entry of oxygen through the root surfaces. Figure 4 illustrates the reciprocal relation of oxygen and carbon dioxide supply of the soil atmosphere.

Mechanical Support. The fact that soil provides mechanical support is rather obvious. The plant is anchored by its roots. At College Station, Texas, the predominant soil is highly differentiated. The B horizon has an extremely high clay content. Most of the pore spaces of the B horizon are so small that they do not drain free of water. In other words the pore space, although high percentagewise, is practically filled with water much of the time. The aeration of the B horizon is so poor that tree roots penetrate the B horizon only to a very small extent. The roots are anchored in a sandy topsoil. Occasionally windstorms literally uproot large tress. This is an unusual situation but illustrates the impor-

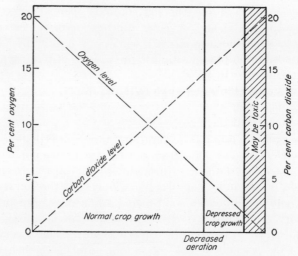

FIG. 4. The effect of decreased aeration on growth of crops.

tance of soil aeration as well as the provision of mechanical support by
the soil.

Essential Elements Provided by Soil.   There are 12 elements known
to be essential to plant growth which are provided by the soil.   They
are listed as follows:

Six macroelements		Six minor elements	
Calcium	Ca	Copper	Cu
Magnesium	Mg	Manganese	Mn
Potassium	K	Zinc	Zn
Nitrogen	N	Iron	Fe
Phosphorus	P	Boron	B
Sulfur	S	Molybdenum	Mo

The 12 elements above plus carbon, hydrogen, and oxygen make up
the 15 essential elements.   The six macroelements are used in abundance
by plants.   The six minor elements are used in trace amounts.   They
are also referred to as trace elements, and sometimes as microelements to
contrast them with the macroelements.   Collectively the 12 essential elements are usually referred to as *plant nutrients* (in preference to "plant
food").

TABLE 1. AVERAGE CHEMICAL COMPOSITION OF A LARGE NUMBER OF PLANTS
GROWN UNDER COMPARABLE CONDITIONS (3)

Analysis	K	Ca	Mg	Na	N	Cl	P	S
Per cent	1.47	0.77	0.30	0.37	1.52	0.73	0.22	0.26

Table 1 shows the average percentages of the eight most abundant elements contained in a large number of plants. Sodium and chlorine are absorbed because of their prevalence in soils. They are essential to animals, which feed upon plants, but they have not been regarded as essential to plant growth. Recent work at the University of California, however, indicates that chlorine may be essential in very minute quantities. Sodium has long been known to partially replace potassium in a potassium-deficient soil, but the essentiality of sodium has not been established.

Plants also contain appreciable quantities of silicon and aluminum, but again, these elements are not essential. These elements, like other elements, are absorbed to a certain extent in accordance with the contents that occur in the soil in available form. Where soils contain appreciable amounts of soluble aluminum, plants may absorb enough to be toxic (8).

In summary, plants grown in soils invariably contain silicon, aluminum, sodium, and chlorine, in addition to the 15 essential elements. Plants absorb these extra elements and traces of others, not because they need them, but because the elements are present in the soil in available form.

How Plants Absorb Nutrients. Plants absorb the essential elements from the soil in simple inorganic form and to the greatest extent in ionic form. For example, calcium, magnesium, and potassium are absorbed as Ca^{++}, Mg^{++}, and K^+ ions. Nitrogen is absorbed as NH_4^+ or NO_3^-. Phosphorus is absorbed as $H_2PO_4^-$ primarily, and sulfur is absorbed as SO_4^{--}. Although one might conceive of the diffusion of KNO_3 into the root as a molecule, it is probably more nearly correct to assume the diffusion of K^+ and NO_3^- separately. The plant root exchanges cations for cations and exchanges anions (or electrons) for anions (1,2). The root apparently exchanges H^+ for the essential cations. The exchanges that are made for anions are not as clearly understood as the exchange of H^+ for cations. Perhaps the OH^- produced in organic synthesis is exchanged for anions. The mechanisms of absorption of both cations and anions are not entirely clear. That cation and anion absorption is closely related to respiration, however, is generally accepted (6).

A plant root may exchange ions for those in the water in which it is surrounded, and presumably the soil water is the primary source of soil nutrients. The plant roots have much surface exposed to water throughout the growing period, and the opportunity for absorption of ions from water is probably greater for most nutrients than other means of absorption. There is ample evidence, however, to show that a very considerable amount of absorption occurs by roots exchanging ions for those which are held on the surfaces of clays and humus (4). In other words, a plant root might exchange a hydrogen ion for a potassium ion which is held on the surface of a clay crystal without the soil water serving as a diffusion medium.

The soil water is often referred to as the soil solution. It is somewhat comparable to the nutrient solutions used in growing plants in water in greenhouses. The soil water is a very dilute solution containing ions from just about every chemical compound in contact with the water. The proportion of the different ions depends on the solubility of the different compounds as well as the amounts of the more soluble compounds. But in any event, well-drained soils, particularly of humid regions, contain in solution at any one time only a fraction of the needs of the crop for a whole season. For many of the ions there is equilibrium tendency, that

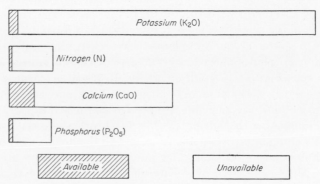

Fig. 5. Schematic relationship of available to total nutrients in the surface of a typical soil.

is, as a particular ion is removed from solution by plant absorption, another of its kind moves from the solid phase of the soil into solution.

Only a fraction of the available Ca^{++}, Mg^{++}, and K^+ occurs in solution. Most of the available quantity of these ions is held on the surfaces of clays and humus as exchangeable ions, a subject to be considered in detail in Chap. 7. Furthermore, the available nutrients represent only a small fraction of the total quantity occurring in the soil.

A third way in which soil nutrients are absorbed is through leaf surfaces. Any of the essential elements can be absorbed through the leaves, although the plant might never absorb enough of the macroelements by this means to satisfy the total needs. The minor elements can be sprayed directly on the leaves of the plants periodically to satisfy the total needs. The reasons for such practice are described in Chap. 14.

Requirements of a Productive Soil. In order for a soil to be productive, it should have adequate water-holding capacity, good aeration, and a supply of decomposing organic matter in the presence of minerals which are dissolving at a rate sufficiently rapid to meet crop needs. Obtaining the right combination of the above conditions is the objective of the farmer in soil management.

REFERENCES

1. Broyer, T. C., The Nature of the Process of Inorganic Solute Accumulation in Roots, Chap. 8 in E. Truog (ed.), "Mineral Nutrition of Plants," University of Wisconsin Press, Madison, Wis., 1951.
2. Burström, Hans, The Mechanism of Ion Absorption, Chap. 9 in E. Truog (ed.), "Mineral Nutrition of Plants," University of Wisconsin Press, Madison, Wis., 1951.
3. Cooper, H. P., J. H. Mitchell, and N. R. Page, The Relation of the Energy Properties of Soil Nutrients to the Chemical Composition of Plants, *Soil Sci. Soc. Amer. Proc.*, **12**:359–363, 1947.
4. Jenny, H., and R. Overstreet, Cation Interchange between Plant Roots and Soil Colloids, *Soil Sci.*, **47**:257–272, 1939.
5. Kramer, Paul J., "Plant and Soil Water Relationships," McGraw-Hill, New York, 1949.
6. Meyer, B. S., and D. B. Anderson, "Plant Physiology," Van Nostrand, New York, 1952.
7. Page, J. B., and G. B. Bodman, The Effect of Soil Physical Properties on Nutrient Availability, Chap. 6 in E. Truog (ed.), "Mineral Nutrition of Plants," University of Wisconsin Press, Madison, Wis., 1951.
8. Pierre, W. H., G. G. Pohlman, and T. C. McIlvaine, Soluble Aluminum Studies. I. The Concentration of Aluminum in the Displaced Soil Solution of Naturally Acid Soils, *Soil Sci.*, **34**:145–160, 1932.

CHAPTER 2

THE PHYSICAL PROPERTIES OF SOILS

Soils are classified and mapped generally on the basis of physical characteristics which the surveyors can recognize by visual inspection. Many of the important chemical and biological properties are reflected by the physical properties of the soil. Furthermore, the physical properties of soils determine to a large extent their productive capacity. The aeration and moisture relations, as well as area of root penetration, are determined largely by the physical make-up of the soil profile.

Some of the physical properties emphasized in this chapter are texture, structure, porosity, color, and temperature relations.

Soil Texture. Texture refers to size of soil particles. Based on size of soil particles there are three fractions, *sand*, *silt*, and *clay*. The sand fraction is further divided into five groups, resulting in a total of seven size groups. The seven groups are designated as seven *soil separates*. Table 2 gives the size of each separate.

TABLE 2. SIZE LIMITS OF SOIL SEPARATES*
(U.S. Department of Agriculture)

Fraction	Soil separate	Size, mm.	"Memory aid"
Sand...........	Very coarse sand	2 –1	$2.00–$1.00
	Coarse sand	1 –0.5	1.00– 0.50
	Medium sand	0.5 –0.25	0.50– 0.25
	Fine sand	0.25–0.10	0.25– 0.10
	Very fine sand	0.10–0.05	0.10– 0.05
Silt............	Silt	0.05–0.002	0.05– 0.002
Clay..........	Clay	Below 0.002	Below 0.002

* The size limits established by the International Society of Soil Science are as follows: coarse sand, 2.0 to 0.2 mm.; fine sand, 0.2 to 0.02 mm.; silt, 0.02 to 0.002 mm.; and clay, below 0.002 mm.

Stones and gravel larger than 2 mm. are not considered in the determination of the percentages of sand, silt and clay in a sample of soil. The presence in a soil of an amount of gravel or stones large enough to affect the use or management of the soil would be indicated by the surveyor in mapping the soil. This is usually done by adding a *phase* name to the *type* name; for example, *Houston clay, gravelly phase,* or *Houston clay, stony phase.*

The determination of the proportionate amounts of sand, silt, and clay is called particle-size analysis. There are two laboratory methods of

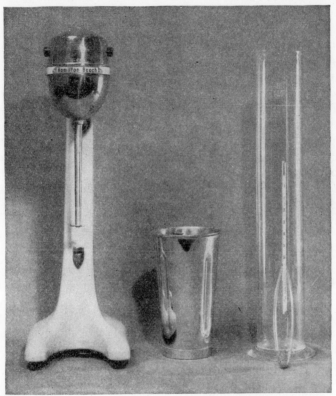

FIG. 6. Equipment used in the hydrometer method of particle-size analysis. This figure shows the improved hydrometer described by Bouyoucos in the November issue of *Soil Science,* 1953. (*Courtesy of G. J. Bouyoucos.*)

analysis which will be described below. Both methods are based on the determination of the settling velocity of suspended particles in water. The coarse materials settle rapidly, while the fine materials settle slowly.

Methods in Particle-size Analysis. *Bouyoucos Method.* The method of analysis usually demonstrated during a laboratory exercise is called the Bouyoucos method, named for Professor Bouyoucos, who developed it at Michigan State University (3). It is also the *hydrometer* method. The method is briefly as follows: A sample of soil is mixed with water, a deflocculating agent (sodium silicate) is added, and the sample is agitated in an electric milk shaker.   The sample is then transferred to a tall cylinder of about 1-liter capacity, and water is added to fill the cylinder.   The cylinder of muddy-looking water is shaken end over end a few times, and the specific gravity of the suspension is determined after 40 sec., with a special hydrometer.   At the same time the temperature of the suspension is measured so as to correct for expansion of the volume due to room temperature, which is usually above 67°F.   The cylinder and hydrometer are calibrated for a temperature of 67°F. when they are manufactured. The first reading of the hydrometer (after correction for temperature, which is 0.2 added for each degree above 67°F.) expresses the percentage of silt and clay in suspension.   The sand settles during the first 40 sec. The second reading is made (and corrected for temperature) at the end of 2 hr.   The second reading expresses the percentage of clay in suspension. It is assumed that all the silt settles in 2 hr.

This procedure gives only the percentage of the three fractions.   It is necessary to use a set of sieves to determine the percentage of each sand separate.

Pipette Method.   The pipette method (11), which is considered the official method, consists of suspending a weighed sample of soil in a cylinder of water as in the Bouyoucos method.   Instead of estimating the density of the suspension by a hydrometer, a sample is pipetted from the suspension and then evaporated and weighed.   The sampling with the pipette is done at a specified depth in the suspension and in accordance with a specified time schedule.   From data thus accumulated, one may calculate the percentages of sand, silt, and clay.[1]

Determination of Class Name.   The class name designates the proportionate amounts of sand, silt, and clay.   Each class name has maximum and minimum percentages of each fraction.   A triangle showing the range in limits for each fraction is shown in Fig. 7.

In using the triangle, the following procedure is recommended: Assume that the sample of soil contains 30 per cent clay, 61 per cent silt, and 9 per cent sand.   First, consider clay.   The base line at the bottom of the triangle is 0 per cent clay.   Read up the left side of the triangle to 30 per cent clay.   Draw a pencil line parallel to the base line for clay and through the 30 per cent point for clay.   Next, consider silt.   The zero line for silt is along the left edge of the triangle.   Read down the right side of the triangle to just past 60 per cent silt, and draw another line parallel to the zero line for silt.   You will note that the lines cross in the area designated *silty clay loam.*   This is the class name of the soil.   To check on your accuracy, it is a good idea to draw the line for sand.   The zero line for

[1] For a discussion of methods in particle-size analysis see L. D. Baver, "Soil Physics," Wiley, New York, 1956.

sand is along the right side of the triangle. Read to the left along the bottom of the triangle to 9 per cent. Draw a line parallel to the zero line for sand. You will note that all three lines cross at the same point.

If *sand* or *sandy* is part of the name, it is necessary to state whether there is a predominance of very coarse sand, coarse sand, medium sand, fine sand, or very fine sand. In accurate mechanical analysis, it is necessary to determine the proportion of each of the sand separates by use of sieves

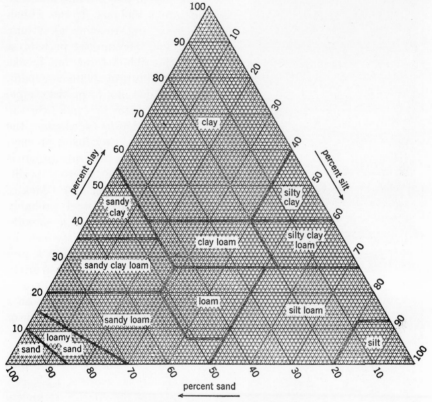

Fig. 7. Guide for textural classification.

of various dimensions. The sand separate which occurs in an amount greater than any other separate is used to indicate the name; for example, fine sandy loam indicates a predominance of fine sand.

If case lines cross on a line between two class names, it is customary to use the name in favor of the finer fraction. For example, if the lines all cross at 40 per cent clay, then the name *clay* is used rather than *clay loam.*

Determination of Texture by Feel. In mapping soils, it is necessary to acquire the ability to estimate texture by feeling the sample between the thumb and fingers. The following procedure is recommended (it is advisable to learn this technique with a copy of the texture triangle for reference): Moisten a sample of soil which is about as large in diameter as a dime. There should be just enough moisture so that the consistency is about like that of workable putty. Press and squeeze the sample between the thumb and forefinger. Gradually press the thumb forward and press the sample into a ribbon. If the ribbon forms easily and remains as a long plastic ribbon, the sample is probably a clay. If the ribbon forms but breaks easily, the soil is probably a clay loam. If the ribbon does not form, the sample is probably a loam or sand. So the first thing to decide is whether the sample is a loam, clay loam, or clay. The next problem is to decide if there is a predominance of either sand or silt. If there is a gritty feel and a lack of smooth, talclike feel, sand probably predominates. If there is a smooth, talclike feel and lack of gritty feel, silt predominates. If there is not a predominance of either the smooth or gritty feel, the sample should be considered a clay, clay loam, or loam. Suppose a sample feels quite smooth, with little or no grit in it, and will not form a ribbon; the sample would be called a silt loam.

FIG. 8. A profile of Edina silt loam from southern Iowa. This soil has a light-colored layer of silty material over a heavy clay subsoil. It is highly differentiated. (*Courtesy of Roy W. Simonson.*)

For a soil surveyor to become proficient in classifying textures, it is necessary to practice on samples of known percentages of sand, silt, and clay and of sand separates.

If a sample is judged to be a sandy loam, loamy sand, sand, sandy clay loam, or sandy clay, it is necessary to estimate which separate of the sand fraction predominates in the gritty feel.

Relation of Texture to Soil Productivity. Soils with high percentages of sand and low percentages of clay are frequently low in fertility and water-holding capacity. A high proportion of sand is often associated with strong differentiation of the A and B horizons. The sand in this instance might represent a residue of highly resistant minerals, which would weather further so slowly as to be a very poor source of plant nutrients. Sometimes a sandy soil may have formed from a deposit of sandy parent material. Sandy deposits are often associated with stream action in river valleys and along coastal plains. Sand and coarser material are usually deposited where the water moves more swiftly. Silt and clay are usually deposited in areas where water moves more slowly. In dry climates where there is much wind erosion the finer materials are removed

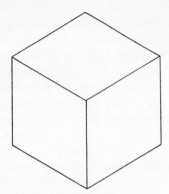 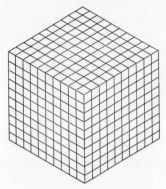

A block one millimeter in diameter (25 times natural size)

The same block sliced vertically and horizontally into blocks .1 of a millimeter in diameter

FIG. 9. The block 1 mm. in diameter has 6 sq. mm. of surface. The block sliced to smaller ones 0.1 mm. in diameter would result in 1000 blocks with 60 sq. mm. of surface exposed. Slicing the block into smaller ones, 0.001 mm. in size, would result in 1 billion particles, and the surface would be 6000 sq. mm.

and the coarse material remains. The sand may drift into large dunes which shift with the wind.

Sandy soils are generally well aerated and absorb water very readily. They have two important limitations. One is that they do not hold enough water, and the second is that they represent a poor storehouse for plant nutrients. They must receive frequent additions of water and plant nutrients in order to be productive. Organic matter improves the capacity of sands to hold water and plant nutrients.

Where sprinkler systems of irrigation may apply all of the water that is needed, sandy soils can be made extremely productive. Fertilizers, of course, must be added frequently under such a system. Applying large amounts of fertilizer at one time might mean serious losses by leaching.

As mineral matter decreases in size, its rate of weathering increases, because of its increased area of surface exposed to solutions. To illustrate the magnitude of the difference in surface of large and small particles, the diagrams in Fig. 9 are used.

Clays have the capacity to hold plant nutrients in available form on their surfaces. Although these nutrients might be displaced and removed by leaching, the loss is small compared to the losses that might occur if the same amount of nutrients were added to a soil high in sand. Clays not only have the capacity to attract and hold nutrients on their surfaces, but they also hold much more water than sands. An amount of water which might cause leaching of a sandy soil might not wet a clay soil deep enough to cause leaching. Where leaching is a problem, the nutrients are leached out of the feeding zone of the plant roots, into the water table, and into drainage water.

In humid regions, the medium-to-fine-textured soils (those with about 20 per cent or more clay) usually outyield sandy soils. Water is not the most important limiting factor under ordinary systems of management in humid regions. The lower yields from sandy soils compared to finer-textured soils can usually be explained on the basis of fertility differences. In subhumid regions, however, soils with lower clay contents frequently outyield the heavier-textured soils, particularly in the production of crops, like corn, which normally do better in humid regions. The reason appears to be related to the water intake and storage. A fine-textured soil with a high water-holding capacity may hold an inch of rain in the top 4 to 6 in., and much of the water is soon lost by evaporation from the surface. On the other hand, some sandy soils may permit an inch of rain to soak down about 1 ft. With deeper penetration, a lower per cent of the rainfall is held in the top 2 to 3 in. which dry so readily by evaporation. The heavy-textured soils of the dry regions lose much of their water supply by holding the water near the surface where evaporation occurs so readily.

In humid regions or under irrigation, clays have the desirable properties of high water-holding capacity, high capacity to hold plant nutrients in available form, and a high surface exposure for further weathering and release of nutrients to available form. Too much clay, however, may cause too much water-holding capacity and not enough aeration. This property of too much clay depends greatly on the arrangement of the particles. If there is good aggregation with large connecting pores for aeration, soils with very high clay content may be highly productive. On the other hand, if aggregation is poor and the pore spaces are tiny and filled with water, the soil may be unproductive because of poor aeration.

Under most conditions, a clay content of about 20 to 25 per cent provides desirable qualities of aeration, water-holding capacity, and nutrient-holding capacity. However, there are exceptions. The *Houston clay* soils of the blackland prairies of Texas have over 50 per cent clay and are highly productive. These soils are unusually granular with good aeration.

Accumulation of Clay in Subsoils. Most soils have a higher percentage of clay in the B horizon than is found in the A horizon. As soils become older, the difference in clay content between the A and B horizons becomes greater. Figure 10 illustrates the general relationship between time and profile differentiation with regard to distribution of clay in the different horizons. In very old soils which have claypan B horizons, there is an abrupt change in texture between the A and B horizons. The A horizon may have as low as 10 per cent clay, while the upper part of the B horizon may have over 50 per cent of clay in very old soils.

Profile differentiation with respect to texture is due to three conditions primarily. One is the transfer of dispersed clay from the A to the B horizon by percolating water. Another condition is that of chemical decomposition of clay in the A horizon and a removal of the soluble products in

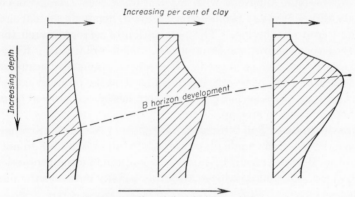

FIG. 10. Schematic diagram showing increase in percentage of clay in the B horizon. (*After data of Ulrich.*)

drainage water. Still another condition is the weathering of silt and sand in the B horizon to form clay. To what extent each of the three conditions contributes to profile differentiation is difficult to learn. It has long been assumed by most people that movement of clay from the A to the B horizon accounted for most profile differentiation; however, it seems that the trend is to believe that weathering accounts for a high proportion of the differentiation. The very sandy topsoils of the soils of the Southeastern part of the United States appear to have formed as residues of chemical weathering. The silicate minerals that produce clay on weathering suffered almost complete decomposition through long periods of exposure in the warm humid climate. More discussion of this aspect of soils will appear in Chap. 5.

The older soils of the Northern part of the United States have also suffered greatly from weathering, and many soils occur with strongly differentiated profiles.

Older and more strongly differentiated profiles contain in the topsoil those minerals which are most resistant to decomposition.   The remaining resistant minerals are a poor source of plant nutrients.   In soils where fertilizers are not used, the weathering of minerals is the primary source of nutrients for crop production (except for nitrogen which is not ordinarily contained in rocks and minerals).   Younger soils are usually richer soils.

If geological erosion is not active enough to gradually remove some of the surface, the topsoil becomes an accumulation of silt or sand composed of the most insoluble minerals in the soil profile.   The topsoil literally becomes infertile with long exposure to weathering where there is little or no geological erosion, and the B horizon accumulates a high proportion of clay.

As will become apparent with later studies, the strongly developed (strongly differentiated) profile offers a great handicap to soil management and crop production.   The percolation of water through the subsoil is very slow.   Aeration of the subsoil is slight or lacking.   Root penetration of the subsoil is limited.   The soil is droughty because of the limited area of root penetration and limited water-holding capacity of the surface soil.   Furthermore, a soil with a heavy clay subsoil on a slope is very susceptible to erosion.

A Classification of Soil Structure.   Structure refers to the arrangement of soil particles.   Soils made up of practically all sand or silt do not show any structural arrangement because of lack of the binding properties provided by clay.   A well-developed structure usually indicates the presence of clay.

Soil structure is classified as follows:

I. Structureless
   A. *Single grain.*   Common in very sandy surface soils where each "grain" of sand appears to separate from all others on drying.
   B. *Massive.*   Common to sandy loams, loamy sands, and silt loams. The soil clings together because of the small amount of clay and organic materials but shows no definite lines of cleavage.
II. With structure
   A. *Granular.*   Particles of soil aggregated into more or less rounded granules somewhat uniform in shape and size.   This is the desirable structure in soils, and the development of a granular structure is the aim of every farmer who manages soil containing enough clay to permit granulation.   The term *crumb* is related to *granular* and indicates a similar type of aggregation but with more porous aggregates, irregular in size and shape; also characteristic of surface soils.   Right after plowing of a bluegrass sod or oats and clover sod, one will notice a more *granular* condition than will be observed after several continuous years of cultiva-

tion. The *crumb* structure is more characteristic of surface soils
that have been cultivated a number of years.

B. *Platy.* A platy structure is sometimes found in uncultivated
soils either in the A or the B horizons. Platy structure is not
ordinarily developed under cultivation. A platy structure
appears as aggregates with horizontal dimensions greater than
vertical dimensions. The occurrence of a platy structure is associated with presence of such platy minerals as muscovite and
biotite, commonly known as mica.

C. *Blocky.* A blocky structure is common in subsoils, particularly
in forest soils or strongly differentiated prairie soils. A blocky
structure may be described as angular aggregates with about the
same vertical as horizontal dimensions. The size may vary from
about ⅛ in. to somewhat greater than 3 in. in diameter.

D. *Prismatic.* A prismatic structure appears as vertically elongated
aggregates in the shape of prisms. The prismatic structure is
common in subsoils of deep and strongly differentiated profiles.
The prisms may vary up to as large as 6 in. in diameter. Where
the prisms are rounded at the top, they are designated *columnar*.
A columnar structure is common in subsoils of arid regions where
the sodium content is high, or was high in the soil during its
formation.

III. Structure destroyed

A. *Puddled.* When soils containing clay are plowed when wet, they
become puddled or "run together." Puddling greatly reduces
pore space and leaves the surface of the soil in an undesirable
cloddy condition.

Importance of Structure in Subsoils. Structure of the B horizon is of
particular importance in the absorption of water and the circulation of air.
A desirable structure of the B horizon should have a high proportion of
medium-sized aggregates (approximately 5 mm. in diameter) and an
appreciable number of large pores through which water and air can move
readily. Soils with claypan subsoils are serious problems in management.
They absorb water slowly during rainstorms, but once they do take up
all the water they can absorb they drain slowly. Furthermore, root penetration may be limited because of lack of oxygen for root respiration.
There is not much that a farmer can do to improve the structure of a
heavy clay B horizon. Chemical soil conditioners are too expensive for
treatment of subsoils. Deep plowing, subsoil plowing, and chiseling are
frequently tried. Figure 11 shows a type of implement used for this purpose. There are soils with brittle material in the subsoil which can be
shattered to improve aeration and drainage, but most experiences with

subsoil cultivation have been disappointing.   The high cost of such practice is not repaid by sufficiently high increase in yields.   Some good is
done, of course, and yields are improved temporarily following the deep
tillage, but the costs are generally too high for the practice to be profitable
under present cost-income relations.

Deep-rooted perennials, particularly alfalfa, help to open up channels
for air and water movement in heavy clay subsoils.   As the large roots

Fig. 11. An implement designed to loosen a subsoil.   It is referred to as a chisel and is
pulled through the soil on the contour at intervals of about 6 ft.   (*Courtesy of Glen
Cunningham.*)

decay they leave temporary channels between the usually close-fitting
aggregates.

One of the most important lessons in the study of soils is gaining the
appreciation of the limitations placed on soil productivity by a dense and
poorly aerated subsoil.   The appraised value of any soil should be based
to some extent on the physical properties of the subsoil.   The topsoil can
be altered much more easily and more economically than can the subsoil.

Importance of Structure in Topsoils.   Structure of topsoils has received
a great deal of attention because of (*a*) the relation to seedbed preparation,
(*b*) the relation to erosion, (*c*) the relation to aeration, and (*d*) the relation

to water absorption versus runoff. Furthermore, topsoils can be treated with materials which can be added economically, while the same treatment of the subsoil would be so costly as to be prohibitive for ordinary field-crop production.

Soils are plowed to kill vegetation, to bury crop residues, to loosen the soil for preparation of a seedbed, and to increase absorption of air and water. The stirring of the soil by plowing is like opening the draft on a furnace. The increased oxygen supply hastens the decomposition of organic matter and hastens the liberation of available nutrients. Figure 12 illustrates the difference in available nitrogen that one might expect

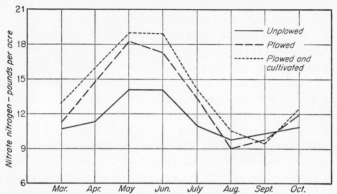

Fig. 12. Nitrate nitrogen under corn during the growing season as influenced by plowing and cultivation (1). (*Reproduced with permission of William A. Albrecht.*)

in soils plowed and unplowed. Nitrogen is made available as organic matter decomposes in the soil. It has also been shown in Iowa studies that plowing increased the potash availability, or at least the uptake of potash, in the production of corn, compared to methods of tilling only the surface 2 in. (4).

The seedbed must be prepared in such a manner that the seed can be placed in the soil at a desired depth and to a uniform depth, so that there will be enough small aggregates fitting around the seed to keep it moist and so that oxygen will be available to the seed and, later, to the seedling. There should be a minimum of competition between the planted seed and weeds. Furthermore, the seedbed should have a minimum of residues with a high carbon to nitrogen ratio, a subject to be discussed in Chaps. 4 and 9. These requirements of a seedbed mean that some tillage will be necessary. The depth to which the tillage should be done depends on the compactness of the soil and the nature of the crop to be grown. The practices which help to fit a seedbed tend to develop a granular or crumb arrangement. The first impression one receives in examining a good seedbed is that a desirable structure has been developed. Unfortunately, however, the tillage required to produce a desirable crumb or granular structure destroys some of the binding materials which cause aggregates to be stable in water.

There are three most important aspects of soil structure, (a) the arrangement into aggregates of a desirable shape and size, (b) the stability of the aggregate, and (c) the configuration of the pores, that is, whether or not they are connected by channels or isolated, a characteristic emphasized by Page (12). Aggregates which are stable in water permit a greater rate of absorption of water and a greater resistance to erosion. Aggregates which are unstable in water tend to slake and disperse. Aggregates exposed to the impact of falling raindrops are particularly subject to dispersion. The finely dispersed material moves into the pores of the surface soil to clog them and render them impermeable to air and water. Furthermore, the dispersed soil is easily suspended in the water, which cannot soak in the surface soil but must run off down the slope. When the surface dries out following a rain on a freshly planted seedbed with unstable aggregates, a crust is likely to form. In some instances the crust becomes a deterrent to seedling emergence.

The stability of aggregates is due to the kind of clay, the chemical elements associated with the clay, the nature of the products of decomposition of organic matter, and the nature of the microbial population. Some clay crystals expand like an accordion on absorbing water; other clays do not expand appreciably on becoming wet. The expanding type of clay is much more likely to produce unstable aggregates, other things being equal. An excess of sodium associated with clays tends to cause dispersion. A high proportion of hydrogen and/or calcium is associated with aggregation. The mycelial growth of fungi appears to have a binding effect on soils. Furthermore, it has been demonstrated that certain species of fungi are much more effective than others in causing aggregate stability (6).

It has long been known that organic matter improves structural arrangement and aggregate stability. The mechanism of structure formation by organic matter is gradually being elucidated.[1] Bits of plant residues obviously make a soil easier to till. Mixing organic matter with soil has an immediate effect of keeping the soil from "running together" following a rain. But the mixing of organic matter has little to do with aggregate stability until some decomposition occurs. It appears that certain products of decomposition cause the binding together of the clay particles. These products are suspected to be chainlike organic compounds which attach themselves to clay particles by a chemical binding process. Clay particles have many negative positions and some positive

[1] See references (10,12) for review papers which list the important contributors to this field of endeavor.

positions.   Organic compounds of humus also have negative and positive positions.   These negative and positive positions on clays and humus are usually satisfied by the attraction of cations like Ca^{++}, Mg^{++}, H^+, and anions like OH^- and $H_2PO_4^-$.   The chainlike organic compounds probably form bridges across from one particle to another through chemical bonding.   The naturally occurring organic compounds which have this binding effect appear to decompose rather easily.

The binding properties are estimated by measuring the percentage of soil aggregates of a specified size which remain on a sieve after repeated dipping in a container of water for a specified period of time.   The water stability, measured in such manner, declines rapidly in soils which are

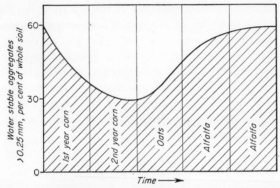

Fig. 13. Schematic diagram showing effect of time and crop on soil structure (5).

planted to a clean-tilled crop.   The water stability of aggregates increases while the soil is in a sod crop like alfalfa and brome grass.   The graph in Fig. 13 indicates that the greatest loss of stability occurs during the first year of a clean-tilled crop and that the loss in stability is less during the second year.   Succeeding years of cultivation should result in very little change in stability.   In other words, an equilibrium is reached, finally, where continuous cultivation keeps the aggregate stability about the same, year after year.

Aggregate stability is more closely related to runoff and soil losses by erosion than to yields.   In other words in most soils the aggregate stability can decline somewhat without influence on yields if the fertility is maintained by the use of fertilizers and if water is not a limiting factor. There are some very fine textured soils, however, which run together easily and crust on drying that do show marked relation between yield and aggregate stability.

The loss in aggregate stability must be great enough to cause poor seedling emergence or poor stand or to cause aeration or water storage to be limiting factors before crop yields are affected.   In other words, water stability of aggregates is only an indication of possible effects of the associated conditions of structure, *i.e.*, seedling emergence and stand, aeration, runoff of water, and erosion.

Suggested Mechanisms Associated with Aggregate Stability. There is much speculation as to how soil particles are bound together. There is probably no single mechanism, but many mechanisms, operating in the same soil. The importance of one mechanism is probably greater in some soils than in others. It is very difficult to isolate materials from soils so as to measure the effects of one mechanism without interference of others. The following mechanisms are suggested.

I. Biological
   A. The physical binding together of soil particles by the presence of interwoven mycelial (threadlike or filamentous) tissue of fungi and actinomycetes.
   B. The chemical bonding of positive charges on clay particles by chainlike organic compounds which have negative charges. The chain is illustrated with brackets in the following diagrams. There are some positive charges on the edges of clay crystals, but the over-all charges are predominately negative.

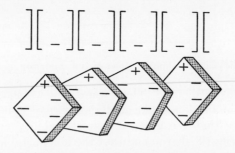

   C. The chemical bonding of negative charges on clay particles by negatively charged chainlike organic compounds through cation linkage, including calcium, iron hydroxide, and through hydrogen.

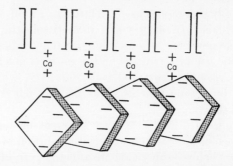

D. The chemical bonding of negative charges on clay particles by positively charged chainlike organic compounds. The amino groups in proteins and amino acids are positively charged under certain conditions (associated with acidity and alkalinity). These organic compounds may attach themselves to negatively charged clay crystals. There are also other positively charged groups exposed by organic compounds, which may affect soil structure.

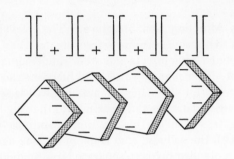

II. Chemical

It is recognized that aggregates can be formed by stirring a moist mixture of sand, silt, and clay in the absence of organic matter. The following mechanisms envisage clay without organic matter.

A. The chemical bonding of negatively charged particles of clay through cation linkage. This mechanism is visualized by Russel (14) as associated also with water molecules which appear to be polar (negative on one end and positive on the other). As the water molecules evaporate, the particles of clay are pulled closer together. Calcium is used as the cation for illustration, but other cations like the positively charged hydroxides of iron may also have a part in this mechanism.

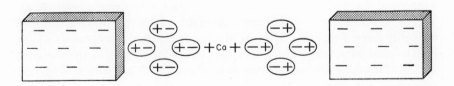

B. The chemical bonding of negative positions on one clay particle to positive positions on another. Where several positive and negative positions exist on the surfaces of clay crystals, this mechanism would be most effective. A certain amount of orientation or rearrangement is necessary to permit the maximum binding by this mechanism. Page (12) suggests that puddling increases the opportunity for orientation of clay crystals.

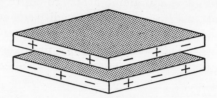

Other Factors Affecting Soil Structure. The following factors have long been known to improve structure: freezing and thawing, wetting and drying, action of burrowing insects and other small animal life, the growth of root systems of higher plants. It should be borne clearly in mind that these factors loosen the soil; they do not increase aggregate stability. The factors wetting and drying and freezing and thawing have been shown to reduce aggregate stability (19). Action of animal life helps to mix organic matter with the soil and also helps in causing aggregation. The growth of plant roots also helps to separate large aggregates, or "clods," into smaller ones.

The loosening of the soil is a necessary part of aggregate formation. So much emphasis has been placed on the binding properties of organic matter that we lose sight of the value of the loosening effect. Clay can be caused to "run together" to form very large aggregates, so large, in fact, that one would choose to call them clods.

Organic matter helps to reduce the size of clods by forming lines of weaknesses that cause smaller aggregates to be formed. The lines of weaknesses are caused by two conditions that exist in soils. (a) The clay particles are bound together by various forces associated with ionic attraction. The internal surfaces of clays (the surfaces inside the aggregate) are attracted to each other by various mechanisms described on page 28. (b) The external surfaces of the clays (those surfaces on the outside of the aggregate) have electrical charges that could cause one aggregate to adhere to another to build larger aggregates. But the outside surfaces probably have protective coatings of adsorbed organic compounds which help to keep the aggregate as a unit; that is, the forces binding the particles within the aggregate are greater than the forces that would bind two aggregates together (12).

A certain amount of "breaking apart" of soils is necessary to develop aggregation of particle size favorable to aeration and water intake and storage. The size judged best runs from about 0.25 to 5 mm. in diameter. Soils which do tend to form clods require a certain amount of tillage to develop aggregation, but overtillage may reduce the size too greatly and cause reduction in stability.

Use of Chemical Soil Conditioners. One of the most significant developments in soil science during the past decade has been the preparation of soil conditioners. One of the early attempts to use a chemical compound was made by Van Bavel in 1950 (18). He stated that organic chemicals could be used to increase the water stability of aggregates effectively, but the materials he used were too expensive to be used on a field scale. Among other materials, he used a mixture of dimethyldichlorosilane and methyltrichlorosilane which he called "MCS." These chemicals exist as volatile liquids, and the gas formed from them combines with the soil moisture. The compounds thus formed render the aggregates more water-stable.

In 1952 the Monsanto Chemical Company announced the preparation of a successful soil conditioner sold under the trade name of Krilium. W. P. Martin and George Taylor, soil microbiologist and soil physicist, respectively, of the Ohio Experiment Station, tested the materials for the Monsanto scientists. The early publications on this subject by Martin and Taylor, the Monsanto scientists, and others are contained in the June, 1952, issue of *Soil Science*.

There are many other products now available. Some of them are the same as Krilium under different trade names. To illustrate the general nature of the chemical soil conditioners one of the first products called Krilium is described as follows. The compound is a sodium salt of hydrolyzed polyacrylonitrile (8). This may appear to be a formidable description, but since the terms have appeared in advertisements in popular magazines, it might be of interest to the reader to break this description down to its component parts.

Acrylonitrile has the formula

$$
\begin{array}{cc}
\text{H} & \text{H} \\
| & | \\
\text{C} & = \text{C} \\
| & | \\
\text{H} & \text{C} \\
& ||| \\
& \text{N}
\end{array}
$$

The double bond between the two carbons is broken in polymerization to form a chainlike compound called polyacrylonitrile.

$$
\left[
\begin{array}{cc}
\text{H} & \text{H} \\
| & | \\
-\text{C} & -\text{C}- \\
| & | \\
\text{H} & \text{C} \\
& ||| \\
& \text{N}
\end{array}
\right]
\left[
\begin{array}{cc}
\text{H} & \text{H} \\
| & | \\
-\text{C} & -\text{C}- \\
| & | \\
\text{H} & \text{C} \\
& ||| \\
& \text{N}
\end{array}
\right]
$$

On hydrolysis, two molecules of water are added to each unit to form ammonium acrylate or ammonium salt of the hydrolyzed polyacrylonitrile. The compound may be changed to polyacrylic acid by the substitution of hydrogen for ammonium.

$$
\begin{bmatrix}
\begin{array}{c}
H \quad H \\
| \quad\;\; | \\
-C-C- \\
| \quad\;\; | \\
H \quad C \\
\;\;\; \diagdown\diagup \\
\;\; O \;\; O \\
\;\; | \\
\;\; H
\end{array}
\end{bmatrix}
\begin{bmatrix}
\begin{array}{c}
H \quad H \\
| \quad\;\; | \\
-C-C- \\
| \quad\;\; | \\
H \quad C \\
\;\;\; \diagdown\diagup \\
\;\; O \;\; O \\
\;\; | \\
\;\; H
\end{array}
\end{bmatrix}
$$

The $-C\overset{O}{\underset{O-H}{}}$, or (COOH), is known as a carboxyl group. The H of this group is exchangeable. By exchanging sodium for the hydrogen one gets the sodium salt of the hydrolyzed polyacrylonitrile.

This material is referred to in soils literature as HPAN. This long-chain organic compound is negatively charged as the sodium ions move away from the compound. The compound may link clay particles together in one or more of the following ways.

The negative positions of the organic compound may attach themselves to the positive positions on the clay, or the compound may bind clay particles together through hydrogen bonding or cation linkage.

Chemical soil conditioners have a tremendous effect on aggregate stability. The effect is also long-lasting in that the material is highly resistant to microbial attack (10). The permeability to rainfall is greatly increased by the treatment, and erosion is reduced to a very low figure. The high cost of the material, although cheaper than when it was first introduced, is still prohibitive for broadcasting on a field scale. It is being used profitably with vegetable crops on tight clay soils where the application is made in the row next to the seed to prevent the soil from crusting over the seed.

Perhaps the greatest use that has been made of soil conditioners is in fertility research on the effects of soil organic matter on soils. Before the introduction of soil conditioners it was not possible to tell whether the effects of organic matter were largely due to structural changes or to changes in nutrient availability. A researcher may use soil conditioners with and without fertilizers, and fertilizers alone in comparison to organic-matter additions, to evaluate the effects of organic matter on various soils. Another important contribution of soil conditioners is their usefulness in studying the mechanism of structure formation.

Porosity of Soils. The calculation of pore space in soils is ordinarily accomplished after the determination of bulk density and particle density.

Bulk Density (Volume Weight). For many years the term volume weight was used instead of bulk density. For all practical purposes they are the same. The data in the literature for volume weight can be used for bulk density with no appreciable error. The two properties are different only to a very slight degree. Volume weight is determined by dividing the weight of a given volume of oven-dry soil by the weight of the same volume of water. Bulk density is determined by dividing the weight of oven-dry soil in grams by its volume in cubic centimeters. Since one gram of water occupies (practically) one cubic centimeter of water, the two definitions are, for all practical purposes, the same.

Bulk density refers to the weight of the oven-dry soil with its natural structure arrangement. The pore space is a part of the volume of soil measured for bulk density. This property is usually measured by pressing a metal cylinder of known volume into a soil. The edges of the cylinder are sharpened on the outside edge, which allows the cylinder to enter the soil with no appreciable alteration of the structure of the soil within the cylinder. The sample of soil thus collected is oven-dried, and the oven-dry weight in grams is divided by the volume (in cubic centimeters) of the cylinder.

The bulk density of uncultivated soils usually varies between the limits of 1.0 and 1.6. The variation is due largely to the differences in total pore space. As a general rule, the finer the texture of a soil the greater is its per cent of total pore space. By the same generalization, the finer the texture of a soil, the less it will weigh for a given volume. In other words, finer-textured soils have smaller bulk-density values than do coarser-textured soils. Clay soils have bulk densities ranging from about 1.0 to 1.3. Clay loams and silt loams have bulk densities ranging from about 1.1 to 1.4; loams, sandy loams, and sands have bulk densities ranging from about 1.2 to 1.6. A representative silt loam soil is assumed to have a bulk density of 1.32. Of course, the same soil may have considerably different bulk-density values in accordance with changes in pore space. The packing of a soil decreases the pore space and increases its weight per unit of volume.

Loss in organic matter may increase the weight of soils in two ways. One is that organic matter is much lighter in weight than mineral matter, and the second influence is that a loss in organic matter is usually associated with loss of total pore space. Of the two influences the latter one is by far the more important in increasing the bulk density of a given soil; that is, the loss in pore space through loss of organic matter is more effective in changing bulk density than the change in the weight of the solid matter.

The bulk-density values for paired uncultivated and cultivated soils are given in Table 3. Two of the soils in Table 3 showed no change in

Fig. 14. A machine used in collecting a deep core of soil without disturbing the natural structure. A sample of soil which resembles a post is lying above the wheel in the foreground. (*Texas Agricultural Experiment Station.*)

bulk density under the conditions of cultivation. Four of the soils showed considerable increase in bulk density under cultivation compared to the uncultivated soil. All of the soils lost considerable quantities of organic matter under cultivation.

The weight of a cubic foot of soil (oven-dry) can be estimated by multiplying the bulk density by the weight of a cubic foot of water (62.4 lb.),

TABLE 3. BULK DENSITIES AND ORGANIC-MATTER CONTENTS (2)
For several cultivated and uncultivated soils

Soil type	Bulk density		Organic matter, per cent*	
	Uncultivated	Cultivated	Uncultivated	Cultivated
Webster loam.........	0.91	1.14	10.9	8.4
Carrington silt loam...	1.13	1.13	7.8	7.2
Ida silt..............	1.19	1.36	5.2	1.7
Marshall silt loam.....	1.08	1.08	5.5	3.8
Grundy silt loam......	1.02	1.20	8.5	5.4
Edina silt loam.......	1.04	1.36	5.9	4.2

* Calculated by multiplying total nitrogen by 20.

For example, a cubic foot of a representative silt loam soil weighs about 82 lb. (1.32 × 62.4 = 82.37 lb.).

An average acre furrow slice is assumed to weigh (oven-dry basis) about 2 million lb. The weight is calculated as follows:

$$\frac{\text{Bulk density} \times 62.4 \times 43{,}560 \times 6.67}{12} = \text{weight of acre furrow slice, lb.}$$

where 62.4 = weight of cu. ft. water
43,560 = number of sq. ft./acre
6.67 = depth of furrow slice, in.
12 = depth of cu. ft., in.

It should be obvious that the 2 million lb. weight of an acre furrow slice is just an average weight and that the weight of any given soil might be greatly different from the average. The 2 million lb. value is quite useful in agronomy for the following reason. Most analytical data are reported as parts per million (p.p.m.). If a soil has 10 p.p.m. available phosphorus, then it would have 20 lb. in 2 million lb., or 20 lb. per acre furrow slice. In other words, one only has to multiply parts per million by 2 to estimate pounds per acre.

Particle Density. Particle density is defined as the average density of the soil particles not including fluid space. Particle density is usually expressed in grams per cubic centimeter.

For all practical purposes one may use particle density and specific gravity interchangeably. Specific-gravity figures are available for a great many soils in the literature. Specific gravity is defined as the weight of the oven-dry soil divided by the weight of the water displaced by the soil. Since one cubic centimeter of water weighs approximately one gram, there is little difference between specific gravity and particle density, but *particle density* is a term preferred by soil physicists.

Particle density can be estimated by the *pycnometer method*, which makes use of a small flask known as a pycnometer. The flask is weighed full of water. The oven-dry weight of the sample of soil is determined. The flask is emptied of water, and the soil is poured in; then water is added to fill the flask about two-thirds full. The flask of soil and water is placed in a vacuum desiccator to remove the air from the soil. More water is then added to fill the flask. The flask, soil, and water together are weighed. The weight of the soil (separate) plus the weight of the flask full of water minus the weight of the flask containing both soil and water equals the weight of water displaced. The weight of the oven-dry sample divided by the weight of the water displaced gives a close estimate of particle density.[1]

The particle densities of different soils vary to some extent but not nearly so much as bulk densities. The particle densities of most soils will fall within the narrow limits of about 2.6 to 2.7. The value of 2.65 has been assumed to be the average particle density of soils.

The density of quartz is 2.65, and quartz is the predominant mineral in soils. The densities of several important silicate minerals are orthoclase, 2.56; plagioclase, 2.6 to 2.76; muscovite, 2.76 to 3.0; biotite, 3.0. The iron and aluminum in soils are heavy and light, respectively, but the two components averaged together in most soils will average about 2.6 to 2.7. Organic matter, being light in weight, causes A horizons to have usually somewhat lower particle densities than C horizons, other factors being similar. It should be emphasized that particle density is not affected by size of the particle or the changes in pore space.

The following data were obtained by Swanson and Peterson (13) from a Marshall silt loam:

Soil	Particle density	Bulk density
Uncropped............	2.49	0.93
Cropped.............	2.59	1.13

The loss in organic matter of this soil caused an increase in particle density. The loss in pore space accounts for most of the increase in bulk density.

Per Cent Pore Space in Soils. Pore space is calculated in the following manner:

$$100 - \left(\frac{\text{bulk density}}{\text{particle density}} \times 100 \right) = \text{per cent pore space}$$

[1] By applying the appropriate corrections for temperature and the density of water, the precise value for particle density could be calculated.

Dividing bulk density by particle density gives the fraction of soil solids. Multiplying by 100 changes the fraction to per cent of soil solids. The per cent of soil solids must be subtracted from 100 to give per cent of pore space.

Example:

$$100 - \left(\frac{1.06}{2.65} \times 100\right) = 60\% \text{ pore space and } 40\% \text{ soil solids}$$

A soil with particle density of 2.65 and a bulk density of 1.325 would have 50 per cent pore space. Decreasing the bulk density would increase the pore space. Conversely, an increase in bulk density in the same soil would reduce the pore space.

A cubic foot of oven-dry soil with a bulk density of 1.32 weighs about 82.4 lb. (1.32 × 62.4 = 82.4 lb.). Assuming the soil has 50 per cent pore space, the cubic foot of soil would have a particle density of 2.64. The particles of *soil solids* occupy only one-half the volume occupied by the *soil plus the pore space.*

A cubic foot of soil with 50 per cent pore space could hold 6 in. of water if all the pore space were filled. If this soil were to drain to where it had half of the pore space filled with water, it would have a capacity for 3 in. of water and one-fourth of the volume would be occupied by air.

The following are approximate average values for bulk density, pore space, and weights of soils of different textures. Finer-textured soils have

TABLE 4. RELATION OF TEXTURE TO BULK DENSITY
Per cent pore space and weight per cubic foot of soil

Soil class	Bulk density	Pore space, %	Lb./cu. ft.
Sand...............	1.6	40	100.0
Sandy loam..........	1.5	43	93.6
Loam...............	1.4	47	87.3
Silt loam............	1.3	50	81.2
Clay loam...........	1.2	55	74.9
Clay...............	1.1	58	68.6

lower bulk densities and greater percentages of pore space than coarser-textured soils. The weights per cubic foot run from about 65 to 70 lb. for clays up to about 90 to 100 lb. for very sandy soils.

Numerous studies in recent years have shown that many soils placed under cultivation suffer losses in pore space. The following data show changes in pore space that occurred in several different soils. These soils were collected in pairs. A cultivated-soil sample was collected a few yards away from the same soil type under natural conditions of grass cover. Four of the soils suffered losses of total pore space and aeration pore space. Two of the soils, Carrington silt loam and Marshall silt loam, showed some improvement in aeration pore space and no change in total pore space under cultivation.

TABLE 5. CHANGES IN PORE SPACE RESULTING FROM CULTIVATION OF
SEVERAL SOILS (2)

Soil type	Total pore space*		Aeration pore space†	
	Uncultivated	Cultivated	Uncultivated	Cultivated
Webster loam.........	65.6	57.0	19.3	7.9
Carrington silt loam...	57.3	57.3	9.5	10.3
Ida silt..............	55.0	48.8	8.3	4.8
Marshall silt loam.....	59.2	59.2	7.1	9.1
Grundy silt loam......	61.5	54.7	7.2	5.4
Edina silt loam........	60.8	48.8	9.0	7.1

* Calculated from bulk-density values assuming a particle density of 2.65 in all soils.

† Pore space drained under a tension of 40 cm. of water (see page 51).

Capillary and Aeration Porosity. Total pore space is really a poor measure of aeration. A soil may have a high percentage of total pore space and be poorly aerated. As a general rule, the finer-textured soils have the highest percentage of total pore space, yet the finer-textured soils are those which usually require the most care in maintenance of aeration, and some clay subsoils have nearly 60 per cent total pore space and yet are so poorly aerated that they almost inhibit root penetration by field crops.

Sandy soils generally have lower percentages of total pore space than the finer-textured soils, but they are almost invariably well aerated. Sandy soils drain readily and do not hold large amounts of water. The pore spaces in sands are not particularly large, but they are large enough for air circulation, and there is a minimum of isolated pore spaces which air circulation is prevented from reaching.

Clay loams and clays have high total pore space, but they hold large amounts of water even when subsoil drainage is good. Most of the pore spaces are tiny and may be no thicker than capillary water films. Many of the large pores are isolated from circulating air because they are surrounded by tiny pores which are filled with water much of the time.

To characterize the porosity that permits aeration is an extremely difficult problem. An arbitrary definition of aeration porosity is necessary because the degree of aeration depends on the content of soil water. The usual method of characterizing aeration porosity is that of allowing a saturated soil to drain under a specified "tension." The loss of water would represent the water that drained from the aeration pore space. The amount of tension used to drain the pore space varies usually from 40 to 60 cm. The saturated soil (all pore space filled with water) is placed on a porous absorption plate which is in contact with a column of water adjusted to the desired tension. If a tension of 60 cm. of water is developed, it would represent the same tension that would exist in a well-drained soil at a point 60 cm. above a water table. This amount of tension causes the larger pore spaces, through which air would ordinarily circulate, to be drained free of water.

The tension method of evaluating porosity is popular among soil physicists, but they recognize its limitations. The tension applied will cause water adjustments to occur so that water will drain out of the larger pores and yet the pores may be isolated after the adjustment occurs. In other words, the isolated pores may not have the opportunity to exchange gases with other pores. As a consequence, oxygen may be used from the isolated pores, causing isolated anaerobic conditions in a soil with a fair amount of aeration porosity. Various techniques have been devised to measure air circulation in soils as a means of evaluating soil aeration, but none are in use as standard procedures at the present time.

Cultivated soils usually have less total pore space than adjacent uncultivated soils of the same type. The most significant loss in porosity is the reduction in aeration porosity. Conditions of cultivation are associated with reduction in organic-matter content, compaction by heavy machinery, and exposure to the direct impact of falling raindrops. These factors cause reduction in size of larger aggregates. As the aggregates decrease in size, the pore spaces are also reduced in size. Furthermore, some of the dispersed material resulting from exposure to raindrops filters into pores of the subsurface.

Figure 15 shows the pore-size distribution of two soils. The Minden is a silt loam soil with slight profile differentiation. The aeration porosity (A.P.) is quite high in the soil to a depth of 3 ft. and tapers off in the C horizon. The Edina is a silt loam in the surface, but has a B horizon of high (usually above 50 per cent) clay content. The aeration porosity of the B horizon is very low. The B horizon has the gray subsoil associated with poor aeration. As will be described in the next section, gray colors are associated with conditions of reduction.[1]

Practices that help to improve soil structure also help to improve aeration. The use of grass-legume meadows in the rotation helps greatly

[1] The iron is in reduced form because of lack of oxygen. A simple classroom demonstration can be used to illustrate this relationship. A sample of red subsoil can be placed in a flask to which sugar is added as a source of energy for microorganisms. If the soil is kept saturated with water for several weeks, the soil will turn gray in color. The microorganisms reduce the ferric oxide (Fe_2O_3), which is red in color, to ferrous iron oxide (FeO), which is gray in color.

to develop aeration porosity. Plowing at the right moisture level helps to loosen a soil for better aeration, but overtillage tends to reduce aggregate stability and may also reduce aeration porosity. Maintenance of organic matter through incorporation of crop residues also helps to maintain aeration and a supply of oxygen. It is unfortunate that oxygen should be allowed to become a limiting factor when oxygen constitutes over 20 per cent of the air above the ground.

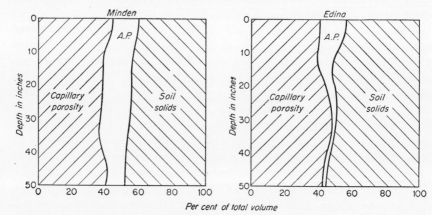

FIG. 15. The capillary and aeration porosity in a slightly differentiated Minden profile and in a strongly differentiated Edina profile (17).

Soil Color. Color in soils is an important characteristic. Not only is color an important feature in recognizing different soil types, but color is also an indicator of certain physical and chemical characteristics.

Color in soils is due primarily to two factors, humus content and the chemical nature of the iron compounds present in the soil. Humus has a dark-brown, almost black, color. Humus exists in very finely divided condition on the surfaces of soil particles. A very high content of humus may mask the color of the mineral matter to such an extent that the soil appears almost black regardless of the color status of the iron compounds. This would be rather extreme, however, and the usual situation is that the color of the mineral matter and the humus color blend together. The blending might well be likened to that of colors in a tweed suit. A brown tweed has a mixture of red and black threads primarily. A gray tweed has a mixture of black and white threads. The closer one gets to the tweed the more the two colors stand out, but the farther away they are the more the two colors blend as one. The same is true of soils. If one examines a soil with a magnifying lens under a strong light, one will see specks of black humus on a red, yellow, or gray background. Without the close examination the two colors blend as one.

Iron is an important color material because iron appears as a stain on the surfaces of mineral particles. About 5 per cent or more of mineral soils is iron. Some of the iron exists as a constituent of the unweathered minerals. In such form the iron has no important influence on color. Some iron occurs as a part of the crystal lattice of clay and may have a slight effect on the clay color in this form. The iron that has the great effect on color is that which has weathered from primary minerals and exists in the oxide or hydroxide form. In the oxide or hydroxide form, the iron is more or less a part of the clay fraction; that is, it is very finely divided and occurs as a coating on surfaces of mineral particles. This latter condition of iron exists in three main forms as follows:

Form	Chemical formula	Color
Ferrous oxide	FeO	Gray
Ferric oxide (hematite)	Fe_2O_3	Red
Hydrated ferric oxide (limonite)	$2Fe_2O_3 \cdot 3H_2O$	Yellow

There are various degrees of hydration, and the color varies between red and yellow. It is important to note that the yellow iron is in the oxidized form as well as hydrated. This means that a supply of oxygen must be associated with moist conditions to cause yellow colors to form. Too much water and an absence of oxygen cause anaerobic microorganisms to reduce the ferric iron to ferrous form, and a gray color would be the result. The red color is associated with good aeration, and a generally lower amount of water is present than is found in yellow materials. The red color might be thought of as a state of dehydration.

Silicon dioxide, in the form of quartz or as colloidal silica, is almost colorless but would give soils a light-gray, almost white, appearance. The aluminum in soils is generally a part of the unweathered minerals in the silt and sand fraction or part of the crystal lattice of the clay and is light gray in color.

The unweathered minerals in the sand and silt fractions may be gray, black, red, yellow, or other colors, but the mixture is generally grayish in color. Clay particles consisting primarily of oxides of silicon and aluminum are gray in color.

It has been implied so far that soil mineral colors vary between red, yellow, and gray with the superimposed color of humus. This is generally what one finds. However, there are some soils with various other shades. Some soils have an olive-drab or greenish-yellow color, others have bluish or purplish tinges. These are the unusual soils. The usual combinations are dark brown to black with gray, red, or yellow or their intermediates.

The soils in the Southern part of the United States have much brighter colors due to iron than do soils of the Northern part of the country.   Soils of the tropics and subtropical regions have even greater intensities of red and yellow.   This difference in color of soils in the Northern and Southern parts of the United States is due mostly to the higher content of humus masking the iron colors in the Northern part and to greater content of free iron in the Southern part.   Moving from North to South in the Northern Hemisphere one finds an increasing amount of weathering.   The higher temperatures have the effect of speeding the rate of weathering; it is a principle well known to any student of chemistry that applying heat increases the speed of most chemical reactions.   Soils of Iowa, Minnesota, and Michigan have brownish colors but none of the reds and yellows characteristic of Georgia, Alabama, or Mississippi.

In the Southeastern part of the United States, many of the topsoils are high in quartz sand and the color is due to the gray background of quartz with shading in color due to humus.   Most subsoils are higher in clay content and have accumulated iron and aluminum that moved from the A horizon.   The colors of the subsoils are generally distinctly red, yellow, gray, or mottled.   On the upper well-drained slopes the iron on weathering has become dehydrated and is red in color.   Down the slope one finds, with more moisture in the subsoil, that there has been less dehydration and the iron is yellow.   Between red and yellow soils there may be varying degrees of red and yellow mottling.   On the flats that are poorly drained one often finds the subsoil to be gray in color due to the iron occurring in the reduced form.   The gray color is a distinct indication of poor aeration in areas where red and yellow colors prevail.   Also associated with poorly drained subsoils are mottled spots of yellow or concretions of iron compounds.   Sometimes these concretions look like black pellets from a shotgun shell.

In the Northern part of the United States, the brown soils are associated with good drainage while black soils are usually associated with slow drainage.   A distinctly gray subsoil below a black topsoil is a good indication of poor aeration in the subsoil.

There are some black soils in the Southern part of the United States and in other warm countries.   These soils have formed generally from calcareous deposits and are fine in texture.   Their organic-matter contents are not particularly high, although higher than found in the red and yellow soils of the same regions.   The black color is associated with a fair amount of humus on a gray background.   Removal of the humus with hydrogen peroxide leaves a dark-gray background.   Heating of the soil to cause oxidation develops a red color.   Apparently the iron remains in ferrous form in the soil in association with the high content of calcium carbonate, and probably much of the iron exists as ferrous carbonate, which is dark gray in color. The solubility of ferrous carbonate is low in the presence of excess calcium carbonate.

Red and yellow colors are associated with a moist and warm climate. The presence of these colors in a presently dry or cool climate is a carry-over from a former age when the climate was moist and warm, or the materials may have been transported to their present location. Grayish colors, obtained by mixing and grinding of a variety of minerals, are those associated with a dry climate. In other words, the grayish colors of well-aerated soils of dry climates indicate little chemical weathering.

Soil Temperature. Soil temperature is important from several points of view, but the main points of interest in this chapter are the relation of temperature to microbial activity, seed germination, and plant-root extension; factors that affect soil temperature; and the relation of temperature to some soil characteristics.

Microbial Activity. The range of microbial activity of interest in soils is that from about 32 to about 105°F. When the soil is frozen there is practically no biological activity. Soil temperatures often reach 120°F. and even higher at times during the summer. There are certain organisms that are most active at the higher temperatures, but they are relatively unimportant in soil fertility. The soil temperatures above 105°F. are usually associated with drying conditions, and the drying of the surface causes a reduction in microbial activity. As long as the surface is moist enough to maintain high microbial activity, the high rate of evaporation has a cooling effect and prevents the soil from reaching the high temperatures that are unfavorable to the microorganisms. Consequently, the generalization can be made that under conditions of favorable aeration and favorable moisture the microbial activity increases as the temperature increases.

The increase in microbial activity with increase in temperature is a logarithmic curve as indicated in Fig. 16.

Some organisms reach the peak of their activity at about 95°F. Good examples of this group are the nitrifying bacteria that oxidize ammonia to nitrates. Some organisms are more numerous at somewhat lower temperatures, others prefer a higher temperature than 95°F. Incubation studies by Thompson (16) have shown that CO_2 evolution (a good index of microbial activity) is greater at 104° in moist soils than at 95°F. Thompson (16) has also shown that the decomposition of organic phosphorus compounds in soils is greater at 104° than at lower temperatures.

While a higher rate of organic-matter decomposition is a good index of microbial activity, it may not indicate maximum numbers of microorganisms. Some studies have indicated that maximum numbers of organisms occur between 85 and 95°F. The higher temperatures above 95°F. are associated with higher rates of respiration.

The increase in microbial activity takes place gradually as the temperature rises to about 50°F.   Above 50°F. the activity increases greatly with increase in temperature.   The low microbial activity in the early spring and late fall causes nitrogen, and to some extent phosphorus, to be a limiting factor in plant growth.   Nitrogen made available as organic matter is decomposed by microorganisms.   Phosphorus is affected in the same

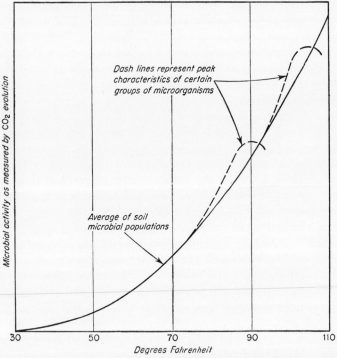

Fig. 16. A schematic diagram showing the relation of CO_2 evolution to soil temperature.   The peak in the biological range is about 125°F. CO_2 evolution continues to increase through a peak of about 160°F. (16), but the decomposition is probably more chemical than biological at temperatures above 125°F.

manner but to a lesser extent.   A good share of the phosphorus of soils is in the inorganic form, but practically all of the available nitrogen must come from the decomposition of organic matter.   Sulfur availability is likewise affected; that is, most of the sulfur in soils is stored in organic form.

Seed Germination.   The temperature favorable to seed germination varies with the species of the plants.   Oats, alfalfa, and brome grass germinate when the daily soil temperature of the top 2 in. averages about 50°F.   Corn germinates when the average daily temperature of the top

2 in. of soil is about 60°F. Cotton germinates when the temperature of the seedbed reaches about 70°F.

Throughout most of the United States corn is planted as early as germination will permit. Occasionally this means frost damage to the young plants in Texas in March and in May in Iowa. It is generally desirable to get the corn in early to escape the hot and dry part of the summer in the Southern states and to escape frost damage in the late summer or early fall in the Northern states. Having a warm seedbed, then, is of particular importance to corn.

Drainage is perhaps the factor of soil temperature that is most amenable to management. Table 6 illustrates the difference in temperature found in drained and undrained soils. A high content of water keeps a soil

TABLE 6. TEMPERATURES OF DRAINED AND UNDRAINED SOILS (9)

Day of month	Time of day, P.M.	Air temperature, °F.	Drained soil, °F.	Undrained soil, °F.
Apr. 24..........	4	60.5	66.5	54.0
Apr. 25..........	3	64.0	70.0	58.0
Apr. 26..........	2	45.0	50.0	44.0
Apr. 27..........	2	53.0	55.0	50.7
Apr. 28..........	8	45.0	47.0	44.5

from warming up because of the high capacity that water has for absorbing heat. As a general rule, one finds that soil temperatures are inversely proportional to clay content (other factors being equal) because of the higher water-holding capacity associated with soils high in clay.

One usually thinks of dark-colored objects absorbing heat and of light-colored objects reflecting heat. If aeration and water content were held constant, one would expect black soils to be warmer than light-gray soils. This is not always the case, however, because darker-colored soils are often finer in texture and have more water-holding capacity than have lighter-colored soils. "Warm soils" are generally well-drained soils.

Root Growth and Extension. Root growth is greatly affected by temperature, and subsoil temperatures are particularly important for early spring growth. Soils with well-drained subsoils warm up quicker at the lower depths than do soils with high water content. A gram of water requires about five times as much heat to raise the temperature 1°F. compared to a gram of mineral matter in soils. Furthermore, the heat capacity for clays is somewhat higher than for sandy soils at the same water content.

There is a considerable time lag in the warming of the subsoil in the spring compared to that of the surface soil. Likewise, there is a lag in cooling of the subsoil in the fall.   This lag is of particular interest in daily marches of temperature curves.   The greatest daily fluctuation is in the surface soil, and the daily fluctuation decreases with depth.   On a different scale, one finds that the monthly variation in temperature decreases in depth of the soil profile until a depth is reached where the temperature remains about constant.   This depth is about 3 or 4 ft. in the tropics and about 50 ft. in Iowa, and the temperature of this depth is the same as the average annual temperature of the atmosphere above the soil.

Soils of very cold climates, such as certain soils in Alaska, have a layer of *permafrost*, or frozen subsoil, which occurs even in summer months. Thawing begins at the surface, and depth of thawing gradually increases until midsummer, but the thawing does not occur deep enough to thaw the frozen subsoil.

Slope Factor.   The fact that southern exposures are warmer in the United States has greatly influenced selection of garden and orchard sites.   The southern slopes receive the sun rays more perpendicularly and therefore receive more heat per unit area than do northern slopes. Southern slopes are warmer and dry out faster.   The degree of dehydration of iron compounds is greater on southern exposures, and the soils are redder or browner than soils on north slopes.   The organic-matter content is less on southern slopes because of more evaporation, less water available for plant growth, and more rapid decomposition of plant residues.   The north slopes lose less water by evaporation and have more water leaching through the solum.   This difference in soil characteristics due to slope exposure is greater on steep slopes than on gently rolling topography.

Temperature Effect on Soil Properties.   The relation of temperature to soil properties has already been mentioned and is summarized here.   Soils of warmer climates contain less organic matter because of more microbial activity and more rapid decomposition of plant residues.   Weathering occurs more rapidly in the warmer climates.   The accumulation of the oxides of iron are greater in warmer climates, and the colors due to iron are more intense.

REFERENCES

1. Albrecht, W. A., Why Do Farmers Plow? *Better Crops with Plant Food*, **27**(6):23, 1943.
2. Anderson, M. A., and G. M. Browning, Some Physical and Chemical Properties of Six Virgin and Six Cultivated Iowa Soils, *Soil Sci. Soc. Amer. Proc.*, **14**:370–374, 1949.
3. Bouyoucos, G. J., A Recalibration of the Hydrometer Method of Making Mechanical Analysis of Soils, *Agron. J.*, **43**:434–438, 1951.
4. Browning, G. M., and R. A. Norton, Tillage, Structure and Irrigation: Tillage Practices with Corn and Soybeans in Iowa, *Soil Sci. Soc. Amer. Proc.*, **12**:491–496, 1947.

5. Browning, G. M., R. A. Norton, A. G. McCall, and F. G. Bell, Investigation in Erosion Control and the Reclamation of Eroded Land, *U.S. Dept. Agr. Tech. Bull.* 959, 1948.
6. Downs, S. C., T. M. McCalla, and F. A. Haskins, *Stachybotrys atra*, an Effective Aggregator of Peorian Loess, *Soil Sci. Soc. Amer. Proc.*, **19**:179–181, 1955.
7. Gieseking, J. E., The Clay Minerals in Soils, *Advances in Agron.*, **1**:159–204, 1949.
8. Hedrick, R. M., and D. T. Mowry, Effect of Synthetic Polyelectrolytes on Aggregation, Aeration, and Water Relationships of Soils, *Soil Sci.*, **73**:427–441, 1952.
9. King, F. H., "Physics of Agriculture," 6th ed., published by Mrs. F. H. King, Madison, Wis., 1914.
10. Martin, W. P., J. P. Martin, and J. D. DeMent, "Soil Aggregation: Microbiological and Synthetic Conditioner Effects," Mimeographed proceedings of the Soil Microbiological Conference, Purdue University, 1954.
11. Olmstead, L. B., L. T. Alexander, and H. E. Middleton, A Pipette Method of Mechanical Analysis of Soils Based on Improved Dispersion Procedure, *U.S. Dept. Agr. Tech. Bull.* 170, 1930.
12. Page, J. B., Role of Physical Properties of Clays in Soil Science, *Calif. Dept. of Nat. Resources Bull.* 169, pp. 167–176, 1955.
13. Swanson, C. L. W., and J. B. Peterson, The Use of Micrometric and Other Methods for the Evaluation of Soil Structure, *Soil Sci.*, **53**:173–185, 1942.
14. Russel, E. W., "Soil Conditions and Plant Growth," 8th ed., Longmans, New York, 1950.
15. Smith, Guy D., W. H. Allaway, and F. F. Riecken, Prairie Soils of the Upper Mississippi Valley, *Advances in Agron.*, **2**:157–205, 1950.
16. Thompson, Louis M., "The Mineralization of Organic Phosphorus, Nitrogen and Carbon in Virgin and Cultivated Soils," Ph.D. Thesis, Iowa State College, 1950.
17. Ulrich, Rudolph, "Some Physical and Chemical Properties of Planosol and Wiesenboden Soil Series as Related to Loess Thickness and Distribution," Ph.D. Thesis, Iowa State College, 1949.
18. Van Bavel, C. H. M., Use of Volatile Silicones to Increase Water-stability of Soils, *Soil Sci.*, **70**:291–297, 1950.
19. Willis, Wayne O., Freezing and Thawing, and Wetting and Drying in Soils Treated with Organic Chemicals, *Soil Sci. Soc. Amer. Proc.*, **19**:263–267, 1955.

CHAPTER 3

SOIL MOISTURE

The management of soil moisture is becoming increasingly important with better knowledge of fertility practices. Soil fertility has been the most important limiting factor in crop production in the humid part of the United States. But with improved fertility on many of the humid-region soils, other factors, such as lack of moisture and poor physical condition of the soil, are limiting crop production.

Soil-moisture control has reached its greatest development in irrigated regions, where successful crop production requires that the right amount of water be added at the right time along with provisions for adequate drainage.

Forms of Soil Water. Water contained in soil is classified as follows:

1. Chemically combined water, as in water of hydration (example: limonite, which has the formula $2Fe_2O_3 \cdot 3H_2O$). This form of water is not generally considered in studying the physical properties of soils. Chemically combined water can be entirely removed only by heating the soil to very high temperatures. It is not removed by drying the soil in an oven at the temperature of boiling water.

2. Hygroscopic water is contained in an air-dry soil and can be removed by drying in an oven at the temperature of boiling water. In order to hasten the removal of hygroscopic water and to allow for the increased boiling point of the water due to the presence of dissolved salts, the drying oven is set at 105 to 110°C. and the sample is left in the oven for several hours or overnight. For very precise determination of hygroscopic water, the sample of soil before oven-drying must be at 98.2 per cent relative humidity, which is accomplished by leaving the sample of soil for a given period of time in an atmosphere above a solution of 3.3 per cent sulfuric acid. The hygroscopic water is obtained by subtracting the oven-dry weight from the weight at 98.2 per cent relative humidity.

The hygroscopic coefficient is the amount of hygroscopic water in a soil expressed as per cent of the oven-dry weight of the soil.

Example:

$$\text{Weight of air-dry soil} = 100 \text{ g.}$$
$$\text{Weight of oven-dry soil} = 90 \text{ g.}$$
$$\text{Weight of hygroscopic water} = 10 \text{ g.}$$
$$\frac{10}{90} \times 100 = 11.1\% \text{ hygroscopic water}$$

3. Capillary water can be removed by air-drying, or plant absorption to a certain extent, but resists movement out of the soil by force of gravity. Capillary water can move from the soil into plant roots or move within the soil. Not all capillary water is available to plants. This form of water is held as a film around soil particles and in spaces between soil particles.

As water is withdrawn from the soil the films of water around particles become thinner. And as water is withdrawn the larger spaces between soil particles are drained first. The spaces between particles are referred to as capillary spaces. The finer the capillary spaces, the more resistant they are to forces which would drain them of capillary water. Plants absorb water rather easily when the soil is holding all of the capillary water it can hold against gravitational drainage. As plants reduce the amount of water in a soil, they exert more and more pull (or negative force) in order to withdraw the water from the finer capillary spaces. At the same time that the plant is absorbing water from soil it is also losing water to the atmosphere through transpiration. As the water content of the soil is reduced, the plant takes up less and less water during a given period of time. If the plant loses water faster than it can absorb it, the cells lose their turgidity and the plant wilts. As the atmosphere cools down during the night and the humidity goes up, the plant may absorb water rapidly enough to restore turgidity of its cells and continue to grow. If no more water is added to the soil, however, a point is finally reached when absorption of capillary water is so very slow throughout the root zone that the plant wilts and cannot recover. In other words, permanent wilting occurs. At the time permanent wilting occurs there is still some capillary water present in the soil which can be removed by air-drying.

The wilting coefficient is the amount of water in the soil at the time permanent wilting occurs. It is expressed in per cent of the oven-dry weight of the soil. Wilting point is a term frequently used instead of wilting coefficient and means the same.

A soil must be reduced to the wilting point throughout the root zone before permanent wilting occurs. During a prolonged drought the top several feet of a soil may be at the wilting point (or below, in terms of water percentage) without serious damage to the crop as long as some of the roots are withdrawing subsoil moisture.

4. Gravitational water is that water which drains out of a soil by the force of gravity. Gravitational water may be absorbed by plants, but if all the pore space of the soil is filled with water, the crops cannot grow normally, and with prolonged waterlogged conditions (no aeration) crops will die. On nearly level or depressed areas where the water table is high, it is necessary to install drainage tile or some other system to remove the excess water.

Field Capacity. Field capacity is the moisture condition of the soil when downward movement of capillary water into dry soil has virtually ceased. This condition develops (usually in 2 or 3 days) after a rain in a well-drained soil. Quantitatively, field capacity is expressed as the percentage of water based on the oven-dry weight of the soil.

When an inch or so of rain falls on a relatively dry soil, the surface few inches will, at first, contain all the capillary water possible for it to hold plus some gravitational water. The gravitational water soaks down rather rapidly, and for several days the water will continue to soak down until the thickness of the capillary films is greatly reduced. When the rate of downward movement due to capillarity becomes essentially zero, the soil is considered to be at field capacity.

The amount of water contained in a soil at field capacity can be estimated by centrifuging a wet sample of soil at 1000 times gravity. The amount of water in the soil determined by this method in the laboratory is called moisture equivalent. Moisture equivalent and field capacity have about the same value in percentage of water.

Under field conditions of good drainage, the best estimate of available water in a soil can be determined by subtracting the wilting-point percentage from the field-capacity percentage. For example, the Marshall silt loam in Table 7 has 11.3 per cent available water at field capacity or moisture equivalent. This value is obtained by subtracting 12.7 from 24.0 per cent. The moisture equivalent of soils can be readily measured in the laboratory, but the determination of the wilting point is a difficult procedure. Briggs and Shantz (6) suggest that moisture equivalent may be divided by 1.84 to give a fairly good estimate of the wilting point. This means that slightly less than half the water is available to plants at field capacity in some soils.

Energy Relationships. An energy concept of soil-moisture measurement has been developed in recent years. As previously indicated, the greater the amount of water in a soil the smaller the amount of energy required to reduce the moisture content. If a small sample of soil is laid in a pan of water until completely saturated and then lifted out of the water and allowed to drain a few seconds, it will be noted that a drop of water tends to hang to the wet sample and yet fails to fall off. A very slight amount of energy would be required to reduce the water content of the soil sample. If the soil is air-dry it still has a small amount of water, but to reduce the amount of water in the air-dry soil would require a large amount of energy, expressed in terms of negative pressure. The amount of negative pressure required to reduce the water in an air-dry soil is equal to about 30 atm. The negative pressure of 30 atm. is equal to the weight of a column of water about 31,000 cm. long hanging on the surface of the air-dry soil. The negative pressure required to reduce the moisture in a soil at field capacity is equal to about 0.33 atm., or about 340 cm. of water tension. The term *tension* is introduced at this point to indicate a negative pressure. The tension required to reduce the moisture in a soil at the wilting point is about 15 atm. Note that the term *reduce* is used instead of *remove*. Applying a tension of 15 atm. will reduce the moisture to a small extent but will not remove all of the water. A tension of about 30 atm. would be required to reduce the moisture to air dryness. The more water removed, the greater the amount of tension required to remove the next increment of water.

When working with soil moisture at high tension values it is more convenient to express tension in atmospheres.[1] But in working with soil moisture at low tension values it is frequently more convenient to express tension in centimeters of water or centimeters of mercury. Soil-moisture tension at low tension values (high moisture content) of about 0.5 atm. or less is usually measured with a mercury tensiometer. A simple mercury tensiometer is shown in Fig. 17. This simple tensiometer is very useful in a classroom for showing the increase in development of tension with a decrease in moisture content of the soil. As the moisture moves down into the dry soil, the moisture content of the soil surrounding the clay bottle is reduced. The clay bottle is full of water, as is the glass tubing leading to the beaker of mercury. As the moisture is reduced around the clay bottle, a tension is developed which is strong enough to pull water out of the clay bottle. As water is pulled out of the clay bottle, more water is pulled into the bottle from the glass tubing. Consequently, the mercury is pulled up as the tension increases. Mercury is 13.6 times heavier than water. When the mercury column rises 10 cm., this represents a tension equal to a column of water 136 cm. in length. When the mercury rises to a height of 25 cm., the moisture surrounding the clay bottle is considered to be at field capacity. This tension is equal to 340 cm. of water, or approximately 0.33 of an atmosphere. It should be

[1] Schofield (18) suggested that the logarithm of the centimeters of water tension be used to express the tension with which moisture is held by the soil. He introduced the term pF as an expression of the free energy required to reduce the moisture in a soil at a given moisture content. The logarithms of 31,000 and 15,500 and 340 cm. of water (4.5, 4.2, and 2.5) would be pF values and would represent hygroscopic coefficient, wilting point, and field capacity, respectively. While the pF values were frequently used in literature 10 to 15 years ago, they are seldom used at the present time.

remembered that 1 atm. is equivalent to 76 cm. of mercury, which is also equivalent to 1033 cm. of water.   Multiplying 76 cm. of mercury by 13.6, which is the specific gravity of mercury, one obtains 1033 cm. of water.

Considerable work has been done in developing tensiometers for measuring soil-moisture conditions.   Some are constructed with a vacuum gauge to show the tension which is developed in the moist soil.   The popular practice is to place a tensiometer, as shown in Fig. 18, in the soil to measure the tension at a depth of several feet.   Tensiometers are particularly useful in irrigated soils where it is essential that only enough

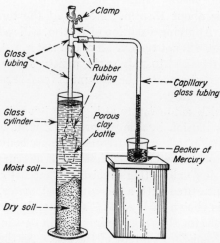

Fig. 17. A simple mercury tensiometer.   The clay bottle and glass tubing are filled with water.

moisture be used to satisfy the needs of the growing crop.   Too much water is costly and may cause a high water table to form.   If the water table rises to within a few feet of the surface, there may be a considerable rise of capillary water to the surface.   The rising capillary water may carry salts to the surface in sufficient quantity to cause detrimental effects on the crop and on the physical condition of the soil.

The tension with which water is held by the soil above the water table is equal to the height in centimeters above the water table once equilibrium is reached (16).   At 10 cm. above the water table, the tension is equal to 10 cm. of water.   At 136 cm. above the water table, the tension is equal to 136 cm. of water, or 10 cm. of mercury.   At a height of 340 cm. above the water table (assuming equilibrium with the water table), the moisture will be held with a tension of 25 cm. of mercury, which corresponds to about 0.33 of an atmosphere.   This is the tension with which water is held at field capacity or moisture equivalent.

When the amount of water is reduced to the amount held at field capacity, the capillary movement is practically nil. As the amount of water is increased above field capacity, the rate of capillary movement increases. Soil moisture held at tensions of 2 or 3 cm. of mercury will move rather readily to an area of soil containing less moisture held at a higher tension. The moisture near the water table is held at low tension values. The moisture (in equilibrium with the water table) 10 ft. above the water table would be held at a high tension and would move very slowly, if at all. A height of 10 ft. above the water table corresponds to a height of 306 cm., which is almost the tension of field capacity; field

FIG. 18. These tensiometers were photographed at the experiment station in the Rio Grande Valley, Weslaco, Texas. The tension is indicated by a vacuum gauge rather than a mercury tensiometer.

capacity is 340 cm. of water tension. Water may rise by capillarity in fine-textured soils to heights of 10 ft. or more, but the rate of movement is so slow at such a high tension that evaporation may occur as rapidly as the water moves upward. For all practical purposes, 10 ft. may be considered the upper limit of rise of capillary water even in clay soils. Water will not rise as high in sandy soils (compared to clay soils) because the capillary pores are larger. Figure 25 indicates the effect of size of capillary openings on the rise of capillary water.

Figure 19 indicates the difference in tension with which water is held in the soil where the water table varies in height. If the water table is deeper than about 12 ft., or if the substratum is permanently dry, the water from rainfall or irrigation will soak down until field capacity is reached in the surface soil. If the water table is shallow (less than 10 ft.), the moisture in the surface soil cannot be reduced to field capacity by drainage alone.

If the water table is 5 ft. from the surface, or 153 cm., the added water will adjust itself with the water table so that it will be held with a tension of 153 cm. (5 ft.) of water in the surface soil, which will mean more water than would be held at field capacity. However, rapid evaporation and plant absorption can reduce the water to the wilting point or below, even though the water table may be only a few feet deep.

It was pointed out in the previous chapter that aeration pore space is that space in the soil from which water drains readily. It was pointed out

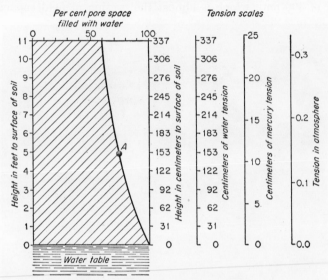

Fig. 19. A schematic diagram showing the relation of soil moisture and tension at different heights above the water table. It is assumed that the soil has uniform texture and that the moisture is in equilibrium with the water table. At point A the tension is 5 ft. of water (= 153 cm. of water = 11.2 cm. of mercury = 0.15 atm.) and the pore space is filled to 75 per cent of the pore volume.

also that a tension of 40 to 60 cm. of water is required to drain the water from the aeration pore space. This means that at a height of about 40 to 60 cm. above the water table in a soil one would expect the aeration pore spaces to be drained. This is of practical significance to farmers in the Corn Belt in the early spring, according to Professor Don Kirkham of Iowa State College,[1] because, as a consequence of heavy precipitation, a crop may grow with a water table within 1 ft. of the surface during parts of the season.

Measuring Moisture Availability by the Electrical-resistance Method.[2] Professor G. J. Bouyoucos, of Michigan State University,

[1] Personal communication.

[2] For a nontechnical article on this method see the December, 1954, issue of *Market Growers Journal*, a Babcox publication, Akron, Ohio.

has developed a moisture meter which indicates the percentage of available water by measuring the electrical resistance. The instrument includes a (dry-cell battery-powered) portable meter which can be attached to two wires leading to a gypsum block (Fig. 20). One instrument may be used for determining moisture availability at many different locations. At each location, the gypsum block is buried at a desired depth and left in place. The wires leading from the gypsum block are left in place with sufficient length extending above the ground for easy attachment to the portable meter. The wires are usually tied to a stake which marks the location.

Fig. 20. Moisture meter developed by G. J. Bouyoucos of Michigan State University.

The meter is based on the principle that electricity flows through a moist soil with less resistance than through a dry soil. The gypsum block which remains in contact with the soil gains or loses water in proportion to the changes in moisture content in the surrounding soil. The meter is calibrated so that it reads about 100 per cent at field capacity and about 0 per cent at the wilting point. In other words, the meter expresses the percentage of available water in the range from wilting point to field capacity. The meter does *not* express the amount of water, which would vary, of course, with soils of different textures and different organic-matter contents. The meter is calibrated in such a manner that it indicates the percentage of available moisture in all textures of soils.

The meter is widely used in both experimental plots and in irrigated fields of commercial growers. Experimental data with irrigation are often reported on the basis of applying water when the soil reaches a certain level of available water. Usually such measurements of available water are made with the electrical-resistance method.

Factors Affecting Water-holding Capacity of Soils. The principal factors affecting water-holding capacity are texture, structure, and organic matter.

Texture. In a well-drained soil, water is held in capillary spaces between aggregates, or between particles, and is also held as films on the surfaces of aggregates or particles as indicated in Fig. 21. Finer-textured soils have greater surface, more capillary spaces, and finer capillaries. Therefore, finer-textured soils hold more water than coarse-textured soils. This relationship holds for hygroscopic water and water held at the wilting point and at field capacity; that is, the content of each form of water increases as the texture goes from sand to clay. Table 7 shows the percentages of three forms of water that exist in four soils when drained to field capacity. These percentages are based on the oven-dry weight of the soil. By subtracting the per cent of water at the wilting point from

TABLE 7. PERCENTAGE OF WATER IN DIFFERENT SOILS (17)

Soil type	Percentage of oven-dry weight of soil			Per cent available water
	Hygroscopic water	Wilting point	Moisture equivalent*	
Dickinson fine sand.............	3.41	3.7	7.6	3.9
Clarion sandy loam.............	6.93	7.2	15.5	8.3
Marshall silt loam..............	10.40	12.7	24.0	11.3
Wabash silty clay loam.........	16.10	20.6	30.4	9.8

* Essentially the same as field capacity.

moisture equivalent (or field capacity) one obtains the per cent of available water. As texture becomes finer, soils hold more water and usually more available water. As a general rule, this relation holds, but the Wabash silty clay loam has such a high per cent water at the wilting point that its available water is less than found in the Marshall silt loam.

To convert per cent of water to pounds of water per cubic foot of soil, the per cent water can be multiplied by the weight of a cubic foot of the soil. Where the soil weight is not available, one may use the estimated weights for different textures found in Table 4 on page 37.

Available water per cubic foot is estimated in the following manner:

$$\text{Bulk density} \times 62.4 = \text{lb./cu. ft. of oven-dry soil}$$

Example:

$$1.32 \times 62.4 = 82.37 \text{ lb. oven-dry soil/cu. ft.}$$

Per cent of available water $\times$ wt. of cu. ft. of oven-dry soil

$$= \text{lb. water/cu. ft. of soil}$$

Example:

$$11.3\% \times 82.37 \text{ lb.} = 9.31 \text{ lb. water/cu. ft. of soil}$$

To convert pounds per cubic foot to (surface) inches of available water, use the following procedure:

$$62.4 \text{ lb.} \div 12 = 5.2 \text{ lb. water 1 in. deep over a sq. ft.}$$

Therefore:

$$\text{Lb. water/cu. ft.} \div 5.2 = \text{in. of equivalent surface water}$$

Example:

$$9.31 \div 5.2 = 1.79 \text{ in. of water}[1]$$

Once the inches of water is calculated for 1 cu. ft. the same figure would apply to a square acre 1 ft. deep. In other words, there would be required 1.79 in. of water over an acre to soak the top foot of the acre to field capacity if the top foot of this soil were at the wilting point before adding the water.

The amounts of water, expressed in inches per foot of depth, that one might expect in soils of different texture are shown in Table 8. These are estimated ranges, but such figures are often useful in calculations for water requirements. These values vary greatly with the organic-matter content and structural arrangement. As a general rule, organic-matter contents are greater in soils of finer textures so that organic matter is taken into consideration in estimating these values. Also, the relation of texture to bulk density is taken into consideration.

TABLE 8. APPROXIMATE NUMBER OF INCHES OF AVAILABLE WATER PER
CUBIC FOOT
For several soil classes

Soil class (texture)	Available water, in. per cu. ft.
Fine sands, loamy fine sands, fine sandy loams..........	0.50–1.5
Loams, silt loams.....................................	1.25–2.0
Sandy clay loams, clay loams.........................	1.75–2.5
Silty clay loams, sandy clays, silty clay, clays..........	2.25–3.0

A soil with a capacity of 2 in. of available water per foot to a depth of 5 ft. will store half the needs of a 100-bu. crop of corn, assuming adequate fertility and good management. It takes about 20 in. of water to produce 100 bu. of corn on a fertile soil. If 10 in. of water is in storage in the top 5 ft. ahead of planting, then a 100-bu. crop of corn will need,

[1] For simplicity of computation the above procedure may be combined as follows: in. equivalent surface water = 12 $\times$ bulk density $\times$ per cent water $\div$ 100. Thus in the example above, 12 $\times$ 1.32 $\times$ 11.3 $\div$ 100 = 1.79 in.

during the growing season, 10 additional inches of water which must soak deep enough in the soil to escape losses that occur through evaporation from the surface.

The capacity of the soil to store water is of great significance. Soils with low storage capacities are droughty; that is, they must receive rains more frequently than the finer-textured soils in order to be productive. A soil with 0.5-in. storage capacity of available water per foot will hold only 2.5 in. of available water to a depth of 5 ft.

Deep sandy soils, overlying clays, or sandy clays are often too droughty for grasses and field crops to prove successful in most years in the humid regions. Yet these soils grow trees quite satisfactorily. This is due to the nature of the root system of trees compared to grasses and most field crops. A tree has much of its root system located in the lower part of the soil profile where the water storage is greater. Furthermore, where a deep sandy soil overlies a clay or sandy clay one finds that a greater per cent of the precipitation is transpired than on adjacent fine-textured soils. The reason for this is that the sandy topsoil absorbs rainfall rapidly with little runoff. The water drains down into the underlying fine-textured material with a minimum amount of water left in the top 2 in. to be lost by evaporation and more to be available for transpiration. From the standpoint of tree production, the soil is not a droughty soil, but for annual crops the soil may prove droughty and unproductive.

Another aspect of managing sandy soils is that the drought damage appears worse on soils low in available nitrogen. The roots must extend themselves to considerable depth in order to use water which has drained deeply in sandy soils. If the plant runs out of nitrogen, it cannot produce the protein for further extension of its root system. Therefore the plant starves for water simply because its roots cannot extend themselves to the available water.

Structure. The ratio of the specific surface of a silt loam to the specific surface of a sandy soil is much greater than the ratio of the respective amounts of available water of these soils. The fact that fine particles lie so close together causes proportionately less water to be held in the silt loam in available form. If the particles are very loosely arranged with a very high percentage of pore space, there is greater opportunity for each particle to hold its own film of water. Therefore it can be stated very simply that within practical limits a fine-textured soil can store greater amounts of available water when its pore space is greatest, that is, when its bulk density is least.

The water-holding capacity of soils has been considered in relation to treatment with soil conditioners. It should be emphasized that chemical soil conditioners stabilize structure. They do not necessarily improve the arrangement. As a matter of fact, chemical soil conditioners will stabilize a poor structure. If the structure is improved in a dense soil simultaneously with addition of a soil conditioner, then water-holding capacity is increased. If the structure is not changed, then it is not expected that the water-holding capacity will be changed following the addition of a soil conditioner.

Coarse sandy soils have such large pore spaces that they have few tiny capillaries that hold water at field capacity. By compacting a sandy soil it is possible to rearrange the particles to such an extent that there will be more fine capillaries that hold water against drainage. See Fig. 21 to

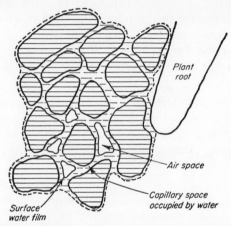

Fig. 21. Water is held in capillary spaces between soil particles or aggregates and as films on their surfaces.

get the distinction between water held as surface films and that held in capillary spaces.

Organic Matter. Organic matter will hold water equivalent to an amount several times its weight. One per cent of organic matter in a soil would represent 0.8 lb. in a cubic foot of a silt loam soil. If the organic matter holds twice its weight as water, then 1 per cent of organic matter would represent a capacity of $(0.8 \times 2) \div 5.2 = 0.3$ in. of water-holding capacity per foot depth of soil.

To a soil with low water-holding capacity to begin with, organic matter has a tremendous influence on water-holding capacity. Many soils have lost as much as 1 per cent of organic matter under cultivation. They have suffered a serious loss in water-holding capacity, not only because of the water-holding capacity of the organic matter, but also because of changes in rate of infiltration.

The addition of 10 tons of manure per acre would represent about 5000 lb. of dry matter, much of which decomposes the first year. But even with calculations based on 5000 lb. of dry organic matter, 10 tons of manure holding twice its dry weight as water would increase the water-holding capacity of an acre furrow slice by only about

$$10,000 \div (5.2 \times 43,560) = 0.04 \text{ in. of water}$$

And only about half of this amount would be available water. Thus one can see that ordinary applications of organic matter have little benefit to water-holding capacity as a direct influence. On the other hand, organic matter influences water-holding capacity indirectly by increasing the pore space in fine-textured soils and by helping to fill in between large pores to increase the numbers of capillaries in coarse-textured soils; that is, the capillary capacity of the mineral portion of soils is increased by the addition of organic matter.

Availability of the Forms of Soil Water. The forms of soil water are diagramed in Fig. 22. The terms *wilting point* and *hygroscopic point*

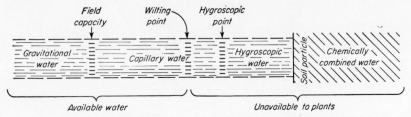

FIG. 22. Forms of soil water in relation to their availability to plants.

are misleading to a certain extent. They represent points on a curve as indicated by Fig. 23. The forms differ with respect to the amount of tension required to remove an increment of water. There is no difference in the nature of the water held as hygroscopic water compared to capillary. The boundaries between them are arbitrary in that the (loose) definition of hygroscopic water, as that held at air dryness, determines the boundary. They appear to have different properties because the one form evaporates under ordinary conditions while the other form remains in the soil. But the amount of water that evaporates is determined by the temperature and humidity of the evaporating atmosphere. Therefore the distance up to the boundary for the hygroscopic coefficient will depend on the temperature and humidity. There can be no sharp boundary line for the hygroscopic point. Furthermore, in the determination of wilting point one would find variation in results obtained with different plants. These differences, however, are slight, and it is necessary to select a plant that would most nearly represent the average of field crops. Young sunflower plants are normally used for the determination. The plants are allowed to grow in a moist soil until they permanently wilt; that is, the addition of water after wilting would not restore turgidity. At the time that permanent wilting occurs, a tension of about 15 atm. is developed. The plant is still absorbing a tiny bit of water but not enough to maintain the plant, and it dies. So, again, there is no sharp boundary between the kinds of water held in the soil after permanent wilting occurs and that which was absorbed by the plant.

There has been much speculation as to the relative availability of water near field capacity as compared to that near the wilting point. Data can be found that support the view that water is equally available throughout

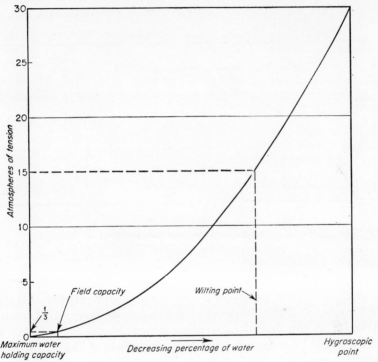

FIG. 23. A schematic relation of the forms of water to the tension with which they are held in soils.

the range from field capacity to the wilting point. The more recent trend in thinking is that the water near field capacity is more available. This view is expressed by Kramer in his book "Plant and Soil Water Relationships" (12). The recent studies with high fertility and irrigation indicate that higher yields are obtained where the moisture is maintained at near field capacity.

Gravitational water, which includes all water in excess of field capacity, is quite readily available to plants as long as there is adequate aeration to permit root respiration, which is necessary for water absorption.

The point of field capacity on the curve in Fig. 23 is an arbitrary point also; it is shown at ⅓ atm., which is about 25 cm. of mercury tension. The ⅓-atm. point seems to fit most soils better than any other point. Figure 24 indicates the reason for the selection of the term field capacity. The tension that is developed in a soil, as the moisture drains down after a rain, increases rapidly during the first day. The rate of increase becomes less and less with succeeding days. After about the third day one observes little change in the tension developed by further drainage. Field capacity is a point on the curve where it obviously flattens out. Soils may vary slightly as to the time when the curve flattens out.

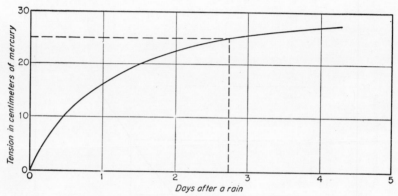

Fɪɢ. 24. The relation of soil-moisture tension to time required for drainage after a rain.

In the first 3 days after a rain, in a well-drained soil on which a crop is growing, much of the water utilized by the crop is that which might have drained to lower depths had there been no crop growing. Water is probably most available where the least amount of energy of the plant is used in its absorption. Under this concept, water in excess of field capacity would be more available than water held in the soil after field capacity is reached. The difference in availability would probably be too small to measure. As tension serves as a measure of energy, Fig. 23 can serve to indicate the relation between availability and energy. The diagram indicates that there could be quite a change in water content with only 1 atm. of pressure difference in the high range of water content. In the low range of water content, a slight change in water content would represent a large change in tension.

Movement of Soil Water. Gravitational water is free to move downward under the force of gravity. Hygroscopic water has no movement as a liquid and is held in a soil at air dryness. Capillary water moves as a liquid and may move in any direction in response to capillary tension. Capillary water may also move as a vapor from one part of the soil to another, and such movement may be of much greater importance than generally thought. Water may vaporize in one part of the soil, move as a vapor to another part, and condense to become liquid capillary water.

The rise of capillary water may be illustrated by standing glass tubes of different dimensions in a vessel of water; see Fig. 25. The smaller the capillary diameter, the higher the water will rise. Water rises higher in a clay soil than in a sandy soil, but more slowly.

The movement of capillary water in soils is in response to capillary tension. The fact that water moves from films on soil particles into plant roots simply means that plant roots exert a tension great enough to pull the water from the soil. If the water film is thinner on one particle than on an adjacent particle, there is unequal tension. The water tends to move in the direction of greatest tension. As soon as the films adjust themselves to the point where tension is equal, no movement occurs. Although capillary movement of water in soils can be readily demonstrated in the laboratory, the significance of capillary movement of water to plant roots has long been overemphasized. It can be demonstrated that capillary movement is appreciable in soils where the water table is near the surface. On the other hand, the *movement* of water by capillarity *from* a

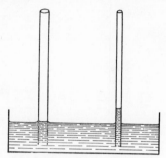

FIG. 25. The effect of size of the capillary on the rise of water.

water table is of questionable importance in the growth of crops. Water may move several feet from a water table, but this rise is not so important when one realizes that movement is slow and roots grow fast, the result being that plant roots will grow rather close to the water table if it is not too deep and provided that there is adequate aeration in the soil above the water table.

If there is no water table within 10 or 15 ft. of the surface, the water soon drains down after a rain, so that the moisture level in the soil is at field capacity. Further movement of water by capillarity is possible but important only for slight distances in the soil. The water is removed by plants by virtue of the fact that the root system is extensively developed. The distance that water moves in the soil by capillarity at field capacity or below is limited to only a few millimeters. To see this more clearly, imagine having a soil wet to field capacity for a depth of 5 ft. and dry below this depth. The plant gets the moisture down as deep as 5 ft. because the root system grows to such depths. It would not be possible for the roots to grow only to a depth of 1 ft. and the moisture to move up by capillarity from lower depths, where the amount of water below does not exceed field capacity.

Figure 26 shows a section of soil typical of subhumid and semiarid lands. In regions of low rainfall it is possible to store water by *fallowing*. When rain falls, the moisture soaks into the ground and drains down until the moisture level is at field capacity. When more rain falls, the water soaks down deeper until the soil is again at field capacity. The surface dries out by evaporation, and the top 3 or 4 in. may become air-dry. The water does not move down, because the tension of the soil is great enough to hold the moisture at field capacity. The moisture does adjust itself for a slight distance at the upper side of the moist layer and on the lower side of the moist soil layer. Another reason that the moisture cannot move

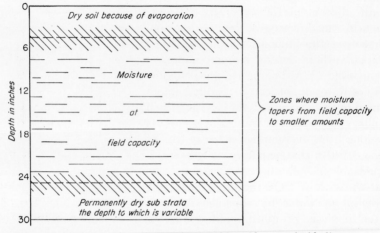

FIG. 26. Diagram of a soil profile in a subhumid or semiarid climate.

downward is the resistance of the drier soil to moisture flow. The drier soil below tends to pull the moisture down until the whole soil body is equally moist, but this resistance of the drier soil to movement is so great that the movement is negligibly small for a tension value larger than ⅓ atm. The same resistance keeps it from moving up. The result is that water may be held from one year to the next if weeds are prevented from growing on the land. The only way the water can move out of the soil, if there are no weeds, is by air-drying, which takes place from the surface downward. A dust mulch would be of no aid in preventing the water from getting out. The surface would dry anyway. Mulching by cultivation could have two effects in conserving moisture, both of which, however, are indirect: one would be to keep weeds from growing, and the other might be filling cracks or preventing them from forming in the soil. If cracks form, there may be severe moisture loss by evaporation along the walls of cracks. With cracks filled and no weeds growing, cultivation would have no value in conserving water.

The Amounts of Air Space in Soils at Field Capacity. A cubic foot of clay loam with 50 per cent pore space would contain 0.5 cu. ft., or 31.2 lb., of water if all the pore space were filled with water. If such a soil weighed 80 lb. (oven-dry) and had a field capacity of 30 per cent, it would contain 24 lb. of water. This amount of water would occupy 77 per cent of the pore space (24 × 100 ÷ 31.2).

A cubic foot of silt loam soil with 50 per cent pore space, with 20 per cent water at field capacity and weighing 80 lb. (oven-dry), would contain 16 lb. of water, which would occupy 51 per cent of the pore space.

The proportion of pore space occupied by water at field capacity increases with increase in clay content but decreases with increase in total pore space. A clay soil weighing 78 lb. per cu. ft., containing 50 per cent pore space and capable of holding 40 per cent water at field capacity, would have all pore space filled with water while at field capacity. If the same soil were to have its pore space increased to 60 per cent, it would have 66 per cent of its pore space filled with water while at field capacity.

It may be recognized, then, why some soils with clay subsoils have apparently no root penetration into the subsoils. Some soils which have been strongly differentiated have no air space in the subsoil at the time when they are moist to field capacity. Even with crops growing on the soil, the roots do not grow into the moist layer because of lack of oxygen.

Absorption of Nutrients from Relatively Dry Soil. The amounts of available plant nutrients are usually greater in the topsoil than in the subsoil. At the same time, the greater part of the root system of crops is concentrated in the topsoil. On the other hand, it is well known that the topsoil dries out more quickly than the subsoil, owing to both evaporation and plant absorption.

It has been shown by several workers (5,23) that plants can absorb nutrients from a soil where the moisture has been reduced below the wilting point if the subsoil is supplying plenty of water to keep the plant turgid. In other words, nutrients in the topsoil may be taken up by plants during droughty periods when the topsoil is apparently dry. Figure 27 illustrates this phenomenon. The tomato plant was grown for $3\frac{1}{2}$ months with its root system in a pot of moist soil and with its stem encased in an apparently dry soil. At the end of the experiment the originally dry soil had increased from 2.3 per cent moisture to 18.8 per cent moisture. Furthermore, roots were found to be growing in the originally dry soil. This interesting experiment is rather simple and is easy to duplicate. The author has used this technique for classroom demonstrations. It illustrates very effectively the principle of water movement in response to greater tension.

The movement of water from soil into the plant is due to the fact that tension is greater inside the plant roots than in the soil.   In like manner, water may diffuse from the plant roots into a dry soil if the tension of the soil is greater than that exerted by the plant.   Stating it another way, water moves from a location of lower tension to a location of higher tension.   It is possible, then, for water to move through the plant root system from moist soil with low tension to drier soil above with higher tension. As the water diffuses into the dry soil, it becomes possible for the plants to obtain nutrients.

It is not expected that a significant amount of water will move from moist subsoil through the root system into dry surface soil in the field as illustrated in Fig. 27.   Water supply was never limiting in the growth of the tomato plant used in the experiment.   Under field conditions, where evaporation and plant absorption tend to reduce the water content of the surface soil to the wilting point or below, it is not expected that water would increase in content above the wilting point in the topsoil through the process illustrated by Fig. 27.   The important feature is that diffusion of water may occur in either direction, soil to plant or plant to soil, in response to tension gradients that might be developed. When the roots in the topsoil are surrounded by soil which is at the wilting point, there still may be slight movement of water back and forth from root to soil.   With such movement of water, though ever so slight, there may be movement of cations and anions from the roots to soil and soil to roots.   In other words, there might be considerable absorption, through contact exchange, of plant nutrients from the surfaces of clay and humus in the topsoil when it is at the wilting point. There is no doubt, however, that much greater feeding would occur from the topsoil if it were maintained at a higher moisture content.

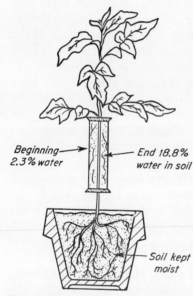

Beginning — 2.3% water

End 18.8% water in soil

Soil kept moist

FIG. 27. Illustrating development of roots on a tomato stem when placed in dry soil (5).

Relation of Fertility to Water Utilization.   There have been many figures published that show the water requirements of different crops. These requirements are expressed as pounds of water required to produce a pound of dry matter.   The requirement is also called the transpiration ratio.   Several hundred pounds of water are transpired in the production of a pound of dry matter.   Different crops require different amounts of water, and the same crop will vary in its requirements in accordance with growing conditions.

The water requirement of any crop is influenced in particular by factors that affect transpiration (wind, temperature, and humidity) and by the productivity of the soil. A fertile soil will produce more pounds of dry matter than will a poor soil if both receive the same amount of water and enough to produce a crop.

Much emphasis has been placed on the fertility factor in recent years to show greater efficiency in the use of a limited amount of water (19). Unfortunately, many farmers have been disappointed with their investments in fertilizers because they considered fertilizer as a partial substitute for water.

In 1953, much of the Corn Belt of the United States suffered a summer drought following a wet spring which had left subsoils well supplied with water. The crops on soils which were well fertilized came through the drought in good shape, while crops on poor soils, which did not receive fertilizers, failed or yielded very poorly.

In 1954, a great many people in the same area fertilized heavily, thinking that fertilizers might help to make more efficient use of a limited supply of water in the event that the drought were to continue. The drought did continue in the southwestern part of the Corn Belt in 1954, in an area where subsoil moisture had been depleted the previous year. The fertilizers gave the crop, particularly corn, a good start, which caused a greater need for water than would have been required had the crop not been fertilized. The fertilized crops fared worse in the drought area where the subsoil had been depleted of moisture. On August 2, 1954, the continuous corn plots without fertilizers looked the best of all treatments of corn on the Sanborn plots in Columbia, Missouri. In 1953 they had suffered worse. But in 1953 they did not exhaust the subsoil of moisture as much as did the better treatments. The continuous corn had little fertility and grew slowly and gradually utilized some of the subsoil moisture in 1954.

An experiment conducted in 1953 in southern Iowa (in the drought area where the rainfall was 11 in. below normal for the growing season, April through September) is described, as follows, to explain the relation of fertility to water utilization (14). Plots of continuous corn (which were started in 1952) were grown side by side with different nitrogen treatments (Fig. 28). All plots received the same amounts of other nutrients. Plot A received no nitrogen. Plot B received 120 lb. of elemental nitrogen per acre. When the corn was about waist-high it received its last rain. The fertilized corn continued to grow without signs of drought damage until the ears started filling out. The unfertilized corn started to show nitrogen-starvation symptoms before the time of

tasseling.   The lower leaves turned yellow, a symptom farmers associate
with dry weather.

To a certain extent, dry weather caused the lower leaves to turn yellow
(to "fire").   In the unfertilized soil the crop depended on the decomposition of organic matter for a source of available nitrogen.   When the
upper part of the soil, which contained the organic matter, became dry

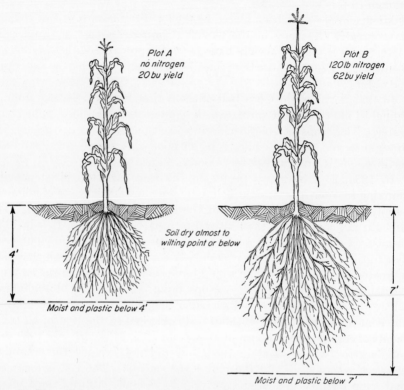

Plot A
no nitrogen
20 bu yield

Plot B
120 lb nitrogen
62 bu yield

Soil dry almost to
wilting point or below

4'

7'

Moist and plastic below 4'

Moist and plastic below 7'

Fig. 28. The relation of water removed from the soil and the yield of corn, as also
related to nitrogen treatment in an experiment in Iowa (14).

to the wilting point, the decomposition slowed to a very low level.   The
plants virtually ran out of nitrogen.   In response to needs of new growth
some nitrogen moved from older (lower) leaves toward new growth.   This
loss of nitrogen caused the lower leaves to turn yellow.   The plant did
not have enough nitrogen to build the proteinaceous material for an
extensive root system.   The roots grew slowly as nitrogen was made
available through very slow decomposition of organic matter.   By the
end of the growing season the roots in the unfertilized plot had extended
themselves to a depth of 4.0 ft., and below 4.0 ft. there was plenty of
moisture still available.   The moisture was near field capacity and had

been held tightly enough so that it could not move upward rapidly enough to replace the water that was absorbed in the top 4.0 ft.

In plot B, which received 120 lb. of nitrogen, there was quite a different story. During the time there was a plentiful supply of water in the topsoil, the plant took up an excess amount of nitrogen, a typical plant response to high-nitrogen fertilization. When the drought got under way, the plant was utilizing subsoil moisture. There was adequate nitrogen so that the plant could provide proteinaceous material for extensive root development. As the roots extended themselves, they withdrew the water stored deeply in the subsoil. The soil was depleted of available water to a depth of nearly 7 ft.

Just how the plants from plot B took up sufficient nitrogen is a matter of interest here. The same treatment was followed the year before, and there may have been some nitrogen that had leached to lower depths and was left there from the previous crop. This could account for only a minor part, however. The plant, no doubt, contained an excess of nitrogen when the drought started. By the time a corn plant has produced one-third of its final weight of dry matter it may have taken up 50 per cent of its nitrogen needs (see graph on page 359). About one-third of the dry weight had been produced by the time the topsoil was dry after the last rain. Another fraction of the nitrogen may have been absorbed from the relatively dry topsoil as indicated in the previous section (page 66). The nitrogen-fertilized corn yielded 62 bu., while the corn without nitrogen fertilizer yielded only 20 bu. per acre. The nitrogen-treated corn maintained the green color right up to the time of permanent wilting in late August.

The important point from this study is that an adequate supply of *available* nitrogen in the soil has tremendous value in utilization of subsoil water during droughty periods. The nitrogen is much more effective if in mineral form (ammonia or nitrate) than in the organic form. Decomposition of organic nitrogen is very slow at the wilting point.

An inventory of subsoil moisture should be taken as one plans the fertilizer program each year. If a farmer ordinarily has half of his water needs for a crop stored in the soil to a depth of 5 ft., he is running a big risk if he fertilizes heavily on a soil which is depleted of subsoil moisture at the beginning of a crop season.

Supplemental Irrigation. There is considerable interest in supplemental irrigation in the humid part of the United States. Where farmers have a source of water from a river, well, or reservoir, they find supplemental irrigation to be profitable in dry years even with ordinary field crops.

In 1954, the rainfall at Clemson, South Carolina, was about one-third of normal. Unirrigated plots of corn failed to produce a marketable crop.

The average yield of three irrigated plots receiving an average of 8.1 in. of water was 78 bu. of corn.   One set of plots was irrigated when wilting was observed by 10 A.M.   The treatment included during the season a total of 8.3 in. of water, and the yield was 75.0 bu. per acre.   One set of plots was irrigated when the available moisture dropped to 25 per cent of the capacity for available water.   The treatment required 9.2 in. of water, and the yield was 90 bu. per acre.   The water cost an average of about $4 per acre-in.   The net returns on the two treatments just described were $86.80 and $107.20, respectively, figuring corn at $1.60 per bushel (1).

On the average, it takes about 20 in. of water to produce 100 bu. of corn under good management on a productive soil.   This would mean 5 bu. of corn per inch of water.   But an inch of water at a critical time can mean about 10 bu. or more.   The South Carolina experiments illustrate this point.   The data in Table 9 further illustrate this relation.   Three

TABLE 9. CORN YIELDS ASSOCIATED WITH THREE IRRIGATION PRACTICES
AND NO IRRIGATION
Blacksburg, Va., 1954 (11)

Period of irrigation	Irrigation applied, in.	Yield per acre, bu.	Increase per acre from irrigation, bu.
No irrigation	0	64.6	
Tasseling through milk stage	3.0	102.4	37.8
Early growth plus tasseling through milk stage	6.0	119.15	54.51
Continuous through season	10.5	128.17	63.53

inches of water during the time the ear was forming increased the yield by 12.6 bu. for each inch of water.   The increase in yield per inch of water was 6 bu. of corn where water was supplied throughout the season. This was a relatively dry year.   A total of 12.58 in. of rain fell during the growing season, May to September.

Table 10 shows the results of an experiment involving extra nitrogen and supplemental irrigation of corn near Temple, Texas.   The soil is calcareous and has a very high clay content.   The soil is high in available potassium.   Additional water increased the yield of continuous corn about 10 bu. where no extra nitrogen was applied.   Nitrogen without water increased the yield of continuous corn about 4 to 6 bu., depending on the stand.   But the additional water on nitrogen-treated plots increased the yield about 34 bu. for the high-stand level and about 23 bu. for the low-stand level.

Table 10 also shows the effect of water on a fertile plot in a corn–sweet clover rotation.   The fertility was high enough so that no response was obtained by adding extra nitrogen.   Extra water increased the yield about 20 bu. of corn on the low-stand and about 38 bu. on the high-stand plots.

This experience at Temple, Texas, emphasizes the importance of having adequate fertility and high-stand level for maximum benefits from supplemental irrigation.

Where a farmer has water available for irrigation he must decide from which of his *soils* he will get the greatest return and from which *crop* he will

TABLE 10. CORN YIELDS AS INFLUENCED BY SUPPLEMENTAL IRRIGATION, NITROGEN FERTILIZER, PLANT POPULATION, AND CROPPING SYSTEMS ON HOUSTON BLACK CLAY AND AUSTIN CLAY, 1951–1954
(Unpublished data of Blackland Experiment Station, Temple, Tex.)*

Cropping system	Nitrogen and water treatment	Plants per acre, thousands	Yield, bu. per acre				Average yield total (4 or 3 yr.)
			1951	1952	1953	1954	
Continuous corn with adequate phosphorus fertilizer annually	O-O	6	42.9	50.4	32.6	29.4	38.8
		12	56.6	54.3	31.5	28.6	42.7
	O-W	6	53.4	57.9	47.3	34.6	48.3
		12	64.0	68.0	53.7	27.5	53.2
	N-O	6	48.9	54.8	31.5	36.4	42.8
		12	60.0	64.5	28.5	40.3	48.3
	N-W	6	56.3	79.2	48.3	60.9	61.2
		12	70.2	86.3	63.8	86.3	76.5
Corn after 1 year of sweet clover with adequate phosphorus fertilizer	O-O	6	....	60.0	42.6	44.0	48.8
		12	....	71.9	34.7	48.4	50.8
	O-W	6	....	77.0	61.8	67.1	68.6
		12	....	93.4	84.9	88.8	89.0
	N-O	6	....	58.4	31.0	41.0	43.4
		12	....	66.1	29.6	43.7	46.5
	N-W	6	....	73.4	67.5	64.3	68.3
		12	....	91.8	81.6	84.8	86.0

N = 90 lb. N per acre.
W is supplemental irrigation.

* In 1951 only 3 in. of water was applied in three applications. During 1952, 1953, and 1954, the root zone was kept below 5 atm. and 7 to 14 in. was applied in four to seven applications.

get the greatest return with irrigation. Ordinarily, sandy soils will give the greatest differences in yields, when comparing irrigated with unirrigated soils. Likewise, fertilizer response is greater on sandy soils than on finer-textured soils. This may not mean a higher profit from a sandy soil compared to a finer-textured soil because the finer-textured soil might produce a fair crop without fertilizers or irrigation, while the sandy soil might result in a crop failure without fertilizer and irrigation. The question then arises as to what a farmer should grow on a soil where he can regulate fertility and water supply. As a general rule one finds the intensive production of high-income crops where fertility and water can be regulated.

Irrigation of Burley tobacco in Blacksburg, Virginia, in 1954, increased the average yield 857 lb. per acre and the average market value of all grades by $4 per 100 lb., resulting in an average increase in value of the crop $513 per acre. During that year, 3.5 in. of water applied between knee-high to bloom was just as effective in increasing yield as irrigation with 8.0 of water throughout the season. This is a very-high-income crop. The yield of tobacco without fertilizer was 2879 lb., and its value was $1214 per acre (11).

In general, yields are related to amounts of water applied in the same manner that yields are related to fertilizer treatment. That is, the smaller rates give the greatest increase per unit applied. In the following experiment (see Table 11), however, the yield plotted against inches of water is almost a straight-line relationship.

TABLE 11. COTTON YIELDS PER ACRE AND CONSUMPTIVE USE OF WATER
WITH FOUR IRRIGATION PRACTICES
Tulia, Tex., 1954 (21)

Treatment	Water applied after planting		Total water*	Yield of lint per acre	Yield of lint per acre-in. of water
	No irri-gation	In.			
Preplanting only..................	0	0	13.9	326	23.5
Maintain 27% available water in 0–24 in. depth to Aug. 15..........	2	8.0	21.9	477	21.8
Maintain 50% available water in 0–24 in. depth to Aug. 1...........	2	7.5	21.4	519	24.3
Maintain 50% available water in 0–24 in. depth to Aug. 15..........	3	11.5	25.4	562	22.1

* Includes 0.9 in. available water in the soil at the time of applying 6.5 in. of pre-planting irrigation in late April, 2.3 in. of rain in May prior to planting, and 4.24 in. during the growing season, a total of 13.9 in. At the time of planting the soil profile was at field capacity to a depth of 60 in. throughout the field and to 72 in. in some places. The 72-in. profile was at the wilting point at harvesttime.

The yield of cotton with only preplanting irrigation yielded 326 lb. of lint, while the addition of 11.5 in. of water increased the yield by 236 lb. of lint, an increase of 22.1 lb. of lint per inch of water applied. At 30¢ per pound for cotton and $4 per inch of water, the net return was $24.80 for 11.5 in. of additional water. This return appears small compared to the return expected from the production of such irrigated crops as citrus, tobacco, tomatoes, and other vegetable crops. But for field crops where prices are stable, or guaranteed, there might be no more risk in growing them with supplemental irrigation than there is in growing the unprotected very-high-income crops under systems of irrigation.

While high-income crops receive priority on water available for irrigation, there is an increasing interest in supplemental irrigation of ordinary field crops like cotton and corn.

Water Conservation. The conservation of water is becoming increasingly more important. Twenty years ago, the emphasis in conservation was on soil loss resulting from runoff. Today the emphasis is on those conservation practices that make the best use of available water. Erosion control is still important, but the change in emphasis has come about largely as a result of improved fertility practices. The higher the soil fertility is raised, the greater becomes the value of an inch of water conserved.

Throughout the humid region of the United States, about half of the water reaching the soil through precipitation is lost in so far as crop utilization is concerned. The water is lost through evaporation from the surface, by transpiration from weeds, runoff over the surface, and percolation to depths beyond the root-feeding zone. Some of the losses are unavoidable, as will be described subsequently, but a good share of the losses can be avoided.

At conservative average figures, it is estimated that an inch of water saved is enough to produce 2 bu. of wheat, 5 bu. of corn, or 25 lb. of lint cotton. There are times, of course, when an inch of water applied at a critical time would mean much more yield of these crops than indicated. And there are times, of course, when more rain falls than the soil can hold. But over a period of years, it is estimated that, through good soil management, 2 in. of water could be saved in the United States which is now being wasted. This amount of water conservation would raise the yield of corn in the United States as much as did the introduction of hybrid seed.

Runoff. Runoff accounts for most of the water lost that could be saved.

The chief problem in the United States is that much of the rainfall comes faster than the soils can absorb the water. Soils vary tremendously in the rates with which they can absorb water. Some soils can absorb less than 0.1 in. per hr., while other soils can absorb water at a rate of more than 2.0 in. per hr. Even the most absorptive soils may have rain falling on them faster than they can absorb it at times.

A soil which has an intake rate of 0.25 in. per hr., assuming adequate storage capacity available, would require a 2-in. rain to fall slowly over an 8-hr. period if no runoff is to occur. Obviously, if 2 in. of rain fell on the same soil in a 2-hr. period, there would be 75 per cent runoff. Another soil with an intake rate of 1 in. per hr. may absorb all of a 2-in. rain falling in 2 hr. with no runoff.

Runoff is also a serious problem under irrigation systems where the soils are sloping. During a 14-year period an average loss of 62 per cent of irrigation water was sustained on plots of the Owybee Irrigation Project in eastern Oregon. As much as 50 per cent runoff occurred on some plots because of low rate of intake (22). Part of the loss is due to overirrigation in some parts of the plots, causing percolation beyond the area of root development.

The development of sprinkler systems of irrigation has greatly improved efficiency of the use of water. The rate of application can be regulated to a certain extent in accordance with the rate of intake by the soil. They are especially helpful on sandy soils where lateral flow of water would be slow. Water tends to soak down in a sandy soil, because of high rate of intake, rather than flow through and over the surface, and percolation losses are high.

In 1954, on sloping irrigated plots near Caldwell, Idaho, 44 per cent of the applied water was held in plots where furrows were down slope, while sprinkler irrigation caused 64 per cent absorption (15).

Runoff, which might be saved for crop use, can be reduced most significantly by increasing the rate of intake and by holding the water on the soil for a longer period of time to permit more intake. A good structure with water-stable aggregates protected from falling raindrops by a straw mulch or crop residues offers one of the best solutions to the problem. Runoff was reduced by one-third in Ohio by plowing only 3 to 4 in. deep and only partially covering the sod of a meadow crop compared with conventional methods of plowing (3).

Figure 29 shows a tillage implement that has been developed to loosen the surface soil and leave residues on the surface of a soil. This system of culture got off to a poor start, however, because of the fertility problem associated with it. The mulch system requires a high level of fertility, particularly with respect to nitrogen. Much research is needed to adapt the system to wider variety of soil conditions, but it is most promising from the standpoint of water conservation on soils with low rate of intake. Mulches of straw applied to the surface are very effective in conserving water in dry years. In eight experiments in North Carolina, in 1944 to 1947, straw mulch applied after the second cultivation increased corn yields an average of 21 bu. under dry conditions (13). The average yield without the mulch was 59.8 bu. The soils were adequately fertilized, which included at least 150 lb. of nitrogen in addition to phosphorus and potassium. The mulching made little difference under good moisture conditions. The yields during 1944 to 1947 averaged 100.3 and 105.7, respectively, for unmulched and mulched soils, both receiving adequate fertilizer. The mulch was applied at the rate of 3 tons per acre, but it is known from other studies that applications of 1 to 2 tons are also effective in conserving water.

FIG. 29. A tillage implement designed to kill vegetation, loosen the surface soil, and leave much of the crop residues on top of the soil. (*Courtesy of M. S. Anderson.*)

Crop rotations including a grass-legume crop maintain the soil in better condition for absorbing water than the continuous culture of a clean-tilled crop. Table 12 shows the results of 9 years' study of runoff from variously treated plots at Zanesville, Ohio. The continuous corn lost 6.5 in. more water per year than did the rotation corn.

TABLE 12. RUNOFF LOSSES FROM CONTINUOUS CORN AND 4-YEAR
ROTATION PLOTS
Zanesville, Ohio, 1934–1942 (3)

Total rain-fall, in.	Annual runoff, in.				
	Continuous corn	Rotation corn	Rotation wheat	Rotation meadow	
				1st yr.	2d yr.
33.9	15.7	9.2	9.7	0.58	0.22

Subsoil-moisture studies in Iowa, in the spring of 1955, showed that soils in grass-legume cover the previous year had accumulated more moisture to a depth of 5 ft. during the fall, winter, and early spring months than adjacent soil in corn the previous year. There had been several rains since the previous crop season to restore much of the water removed by previous crops. By some spring-planting dates, the preseason rains are so limited that one finds less water in soils which had a grass-legume cover the previous year. Grass-legume crops often exhaust the subsoil moisture in the fall more than corn does. A dry preseason, then, might cause corn to produce better after corn than after a grass-legume sod. This is not the usual experience, however.

Contour listing is one of the most effective mechanical practices for holding water on sloping soils to allow more time for infiltration. The

Fɪɢ. 30. Small contour ridges or furrows are especially desirable in reducing runoff and erosion. The water that cannot be held in the furrows is caught above the terrace. Under conditions of high rainfall, the terrace is built with enough grade to conduct the excess water off the field. (*Soil Conservation Service.*)

listing practice provides a deep furrow which impounds considerable water where the furrows are on the contour. Runoff on Marshall silt loam in Iowa was only one-fifth that from rows up and down hill (8). During the period of 1933 to 1939, contour listing saved over 2 in. of rainfall per year compared to rows up hill. The contour-listed plots produced 71.22 more bushels of corn and had 14.14 fewer inches of runoff during the 7-year period. Each inch of water saved produced an average of 5.03 bu. of corn. During the 7-year period 13 storms caused runoff on contour-listed plots, while 48 storms caused runoff on plots with rows up hill.

Planting on the contour has little effect on runoff unless there is some means of impounding the water. In Ohio, contour tillage was practiced on the Soil Conservation Experiment Station in comparison to rows up hill for corn. Contour planting with flat cultivation did not reduce runoff. Contour cultivation to form ridges, however, reduced runoff by 40 per cent compared to rows up hill.

A ridge type of terrace is an effective means of controlling runoff and reducing erosion but is less effective than contour cultivation in conservation of water. On steep topography, only the channel is benefited, and sometimes the extra water in the channel is a detriment. On nearly level topography (less than ½ per cent slope), at Spur, Texas, rows up hill lost an average of 1.41 in. of rain by runoff from 1927 to 1939 (10). The field produced an average of 102 lb. of lint cotton. On a contoured field the water loss was 0.88 in. and the yield was 123 lb. of lint cotton. On

Fig. 31. Subsoil cultivation is effective in reducing runoff and increasing infiltration, but on most soils the effect on water conservation is only temporary. (*Des Moines Register and Tribune*.)

a field with closed level terraces the loss of water by runoff was zero and the yield of cotton was 150 lb. of lint. The average annual rainfall was 18.74 in. These data have received wide recognition, but it should be recognized that a level terrace 18 in. high can hold water back for a width of 300 ft. on the 0.5 per cent slope which existed at Spur, Texas. A terrace on a 6 per cent slope with 18 in. of effective height can hold water back over an area only 25 ft. wide.

There are conflicting ideas on the relation of cultivation to runoff. If the soil is bare and left uncultivated, it will permit more runoff than will occur if the soil is cultivated. This statement is supported by studies at Spur, Texas (10), and at Clarinda, Iowa (8). On the other hand, if the soil is protected by a cover of residues like shredded cornstalks or wheat stubble, there is less runoff than would occur if the soil were plowed and all of the trash buried. The advantage to early fall plowing for water conservation is usually from killing of vegetation that might deplete the available water supply.

Evaporation Losses. It is estimated that about one-fifth of the total precipitation falling on cropland of the United States is lost by evaporation. A high proportion of this loss is unavoidable. Much of the precipitation comes as light showers, and only the top 2 or 3 in. of soil is moistened. A soil that can hold 2 in. of available water per foot at field capacity will require ½ in. of rain to wet the soil to a depth of 3 in. A high proportion of a ½-in. rain or less is lost by evaporation during the growing season if the surface soil is dry to the wilting point at the time of the rain.

Evaporation increases as the humidity decreases and as the temperature increases. Wind also hastens evaporation. When the surface is very moist the rate of evaporation is about as rapid as from an open-water surface, but as the water content of the surface decreases, the rate of evaporation decreases so that by the time the top 2 in. is air-dry the moisture loss by evaporation is very slight. If the soil is at field capacity below the dry surface layer, there is no capillary movement to the surface. Further losses by evaporation result from the vapor movement from the moist soil below. The air in the soil is practically at 100 per cent saturation, and as the moist air is exchanged with the drier atmosphere above the soil there is some further loss by evaporation. This latter loss is very slight, however, unless large cracks form in the soil.

Cultivation immediately after a rain merely hastens the loss of water from the surface. The dry layer on top of the soil will form without cultivation. Cultivation to form a dust mulch or soil mulch is not recommended as a means of reducing evaporation losses.

Mulching with straw or manure usually reduces the temperature of the surface soil, which would reduce the rate of evaporation. A bare soil often reaches a temperature of several degrees above air temperature in the daytime during the summer. In the mulch studies in North Carolina (cited on page 74), Krantz reported that when the air temperature was 95°, the soil temperature at ½ in. depth was 81°F. in the mulched area and 118°F. in the ummulched area. Krantz considered a part of the increased yield from mulching to be due to saving of water from evaporation.

The Horticulture Department of Iowa State College has found that ground corncobs make an excellent mulch for flower beds. The mulch reduces soil temperature, reduces evaporation losses, and will practically control weed growth if applied thickly enough.

Where mulching with straw or ground corncobs is practiced, the surface soil must be maintained at a high nitrogen level through fertilization (see page 90).

Losses from Transpiration by Weeds. Weeds can reduce the water content of a soil to the wilting point throughout the zone of their root extension. The conservation of water where fallowing is practiced requires that weeds be controlled.

Along the western edge of the Corn Belt water conservation is a particularly important problem in soil management. Corn usually follows a legume-grass meadow in rotations. It is desirable to store as much

FIG. 32. Strip cropping to control wind erosion and conserve water in Nebraska. These are alternate strips of wheat and summer fallow. (*Soil Conservation Service.*)

preseasonal moisture as possible for the corn. Where erosion will not be too serious, the meadow should be plowed after the last hay crop is removed so that transpiration losses will cease.[1] The runoff might be increased by the plowing, but the water loss will be considerably less by runoff than would occur through a combination of runoff and transpiration if the vegetation were allowed to grow until killed by a hard freeze.

Percolation Losses. Losses of water by percolation are most significant under conditions of irrigation. The loss of water is also accompanied by

[1] Ordinarily, in most Corn Belt soils there is too much water in the spring, so that a carry-over from the preceding fall is not important. Experience in Iowa has shown that fall plowing is preferable to spring plowing (except on soils subject to erosion or for sandy soils). See, for example, M. F. DeBoodt, A. J. Englehorn, and D. Kirkham. Fall vs. Spring Plowing and Soil Physical Conditions in a Rotation Experiment, *Agron. J.*, **45**:257–261, 1953.

loss of available plant nutrients.   The avoidable losses under irrigation are those resulting from the method of applying water.   In the furrow irrigation system, the end first receiving the water may be overirrigated by the time the opposite end of the furrow receives adequate irrigation. This problem is particularly serious on very permeable soils.   Another problem is the irregularity of slope.   Water runs to low places, and the low places may receive entirely too much water.   The latter problem is usually solved by land-leveling technique on river-bottom lands, but on the more rolling topography a system of contour areas resembling bench-type terraces is developed.   Where the leveling or bench terracing is impractical, the sprinkler type of irrigation system is becoming more and more popular.   The system can be used on rolling sandy land that could not be irrigated satisfactorily by any other system.   In irrigated regions there is an effort toward reducing all percolation losses except where necessary to leach excess salts from the surface soil.   Overirrigation in dry climate may cause enough percolation to build a water table near enough to the surface to cause alkali soils to form.

Percolation losses in humid regions are difficult to control.   Practices which reduce runoff may also increase percolation losses.   In lysimeter studies of Marshall silt loam it was observed that the amount of runoff saved by application of manure was about equal to the increase in percolation collected at the depth of 3 ft. (8).   The water percolating to the depth of 3 ft. would not be considered a loss, however.   Most field crops, particularly corn, wheat, and cotton, will deplete the moisture to a depth of 5 ft. or more during a dry year.

When a soil is drained to field capacity to a depth of 3 ft., for example, additional water causes the soil to hold more than field capacity in the top 3 ft. for a few days, but the additional water finally drains down, extending the depth of field capacity.   When the percolation causes water to extend beyond the depth of root development, there may be economic losses.

In humid regions the loss of nutrients by percolation is more serious than the loss of the water.   There is little that can be done to reduce the loss of the water by percolation in humid regions.   But the magnitude of losses should be recognized.   Table 13 shows the extent of leaching losses from Cornell lysimeters.   Losses are greater from bare soils than from cropped soils.   The greatest difference in nutrient loss from bare and cropped soil was nitrogen.   In managing soils to reduce economic losses from leaching, nitrogen receives first consideration.   It is the most expensive of the fertilizer elements and most easily leached from the soil. See Chap. 9 for information on nitrogen losses by leaching.   The losses of the bases, calcium, magnesium, and potassium are unavoidable, and a management program must be developed with these losses in mind.

Liming of a soil replaces the calcium and magnesium and is a practice that requires some degree of regularity on most humid-region soils.

Table 14 shows results of lysimeter studies with Marshall silt loam in southwestern Iowa. These studies show that manuring of the soil greatly increased the rate of nutrient loss by leaching. The anions (nitrates,

TABLE 13. ANNUAL LOSS OF NUTRIENTS FROM BARE AND CROPPED SOILS
BY LEACHING (2)

Measured by Cornell lysimeters. Average of 10 years' results on
Dunkirk silty clay loam

Treatment	Pounds per acre per year					
	N	P_2O_5	CaO	MgO	K_2O	SO_3
Bare.........	69.0	Trace	557.2	104.4	86.8	132.5
Rotation.....	7.8	Trace	322.0	73.2	69.1	108.5
Grass........	2.5	Trace	364.0	83.1	74.5	111.1

sulfates, chloride, and bicarbonates, in particular), produced on decomposition of the manure, leach from the soil and carry with them an equivalence of cations (calcium, magnesium, and potassium, in particular). As a general rule, one must accept the fact that soils at a high level of fertility will lose more nutrients by leaching than soils at a low level of fertility.

Leaching losses in subhumid regions (usually below 30 in. of precipitation in the United States) are of little importance. They do occur in

TABLE 14. CALCIUM AND MAGNESIUM IN PERCOLATE FROM LYSIMETERS IN
MARSHALL SILT LOAM

In pounds per acre (8). Precipitation: 1935, 32.35 in.; 1936, 22.02 in.

Crop and treatments	1935		1936	
	Ca	Mg	Ca	Mg
Fallow..............................	175.5	42.5	39.8	12.1
Fallow plus 16 tons of manure...........	394.0	105.1	112.3	30.4
Corn..................................	173.7	37.7	4.5	1.3
Corn plus 16 tons of manure.............	211.9	48.9	51.0	12.2

some depressed areas, but in general, the underlying parent material of subhumid and drier regions is permanently dry. The nutrients that leach from the solum accumulate in the underlying material at a depth to which moisture normally penetrates.

Drainage. The removal of excess water from soils is desirable in order to improve aeration and to prevent excessive movement of dissolved salts to the surface layer. The problem of accumulation of dissolved salts is of particular importance in arid regions where evaporation is high and irrigation is practiced.   In a typical irrigated valley in an arid region there are two systems of ditches; one carries the fresh water for irrigation, the other carries the salty drainage water away.   Unless a drainage system is provided, there is great risk of overirrigating and raising the water table high enough to cause capillary rise of water to the surface.   The rising capillary water carries sodium, and some potassium and magnesium, salts to the surface to cause alkalinity.   Finally, enough salts may accumulate to cause injury to plant growth.   The tiles under irrigated fields empty into deep ditches.   The drainage system must be quite deep to keep the water table low enough to prevent salts from rising to the surface. Tiles are usually placed at depths ranging from 5 to 10 ft. in irrigated soils.

The lowering of the water table to facilitate aeration is a problem of importance throughout much of the Corn Belt, along the Gulf Coast, and in isolated areas elsewhere in this country.   There are several undesirable conditions resulting from a high water table, even though the pore space of the soil is not completely filled with water.   The little pore space just above the water table is likely to have a low percentage of oxygen and a high percentage of carbon dioxide.

Both low oxygen and high carbon dioxide content of soil air create problems in absorption of water and nutrients by crops [9].   Either the absence of oxygen or the presence of high carbon dioxide will reduce absorption of water, so that in spite of the roots being in a wet soil, plants may actually wilt on dry hot days in the presence of excessive soil moisture [12].

The low aeration accompanying excessive water reduces absorption of potassium by some crops, particularly corn [4,7].   Again, the retardation of potassium uptake may be due to the ill effects of too much carbon dioxide and not enough oxygen.

The decomposition of organic matter and the release of nitrogen are retarded by lack of aeration.   Ammonia nitrogen cannot be oxidized to nitrate nitrogen under anaerobic conditions, and nitrate nitrogen may be reduced to elemental nitrogen or nitrous oxide and lost from the soil as a result of waterlogged conditions.   The yellowing of corn in poorly drained spots is frequently due to nitrogen starvation, although the starvation may be for potassium under some conditions, particularly in high-lime soils [20].

The presence of wet spots is particularly objectionable to the farmer, because the spots cannot be planted as early as adjacent better-drained soils.   Wet spots may represent a loss in so far as a crop is concerned, besides the trouble in plowing around them and keeping down weeds that grow up with lowering of the water table with advancement of dry weather.

Soil characteristics determine to a large extent the depth and spacing of tile. It is common practice to place tile 4 ft. deep in light open soils and 2½ to 3 ft. deep in heavy soils. In very tight clay soils the tile should be spaced not more than 30 to 40 ft. apart. In heavy clay soils having high porosity the tile may be spaced 70 to 80 ft. apart, and in lighter-textured silt loam and sandy soils overlying poorly drained subsoils the tile should be placed about 100 ft. apart. Sandy soils overlying clay at 3 to 4 ft. may be drained by placing tile lines 100 to 150 ft. apart.

It has frequently been observed that tile systems which were effective at the time of installation may later be inadequate. The gradual destruction of the natural soil structure has caused soils to run together, with loss of large pore spaces through which water moved readily. Inclusion of grass and legumes in rotations helps to increase aeration porosity and improves the rate of drainage.

REFERENCES

1. Beale, O. W., and C. M. Lund, Quarterly Report on Progress in Soil and Water Conservation Research, U.S. Department of Agriculture, March, 1955.
2. Bizzell, J. A., and T. L. Lyon, Composition of Drainage Waters from Lysimeters at Cornell University, *Proc. Intern. Congr. Soil Sci.*, **2**:342–349, 1927.
3. Borst, H. L., A. G. McCall, and F. G. Bell, Investigations in Erosion Control and the Reclamation of Eroded Land, Zanesville, Ohio, 1934–1941, *U.S. Dept. Agr. Tech. Bull.* 888, 1945.
4. Bower, C. A., G. M. Browning, and R. A. Norton, Comparative Effects of Plowing and Other Methods of Seedbed Preparation on Nutrient Element Deficiencies in Corn, *Soil Sci. Soc. Amer. Proc.*, **9**:142–146, 1944.
5. Breazeale, J. F., and F. J. Crider, Plant Association and Survival, and the Build-up of Moisture in Semi-arid Soils, *Ariz. Agr. Expt. Sta. Tech. Bull.* 53, 1934.
6. Briggs, L. M., and H. L. Shantz, The Wilting Coefficient for Different Plants and Its Indirect Determination, *U.S. Dept. Agr. Bur. Plant Ind. Bull.* 230, 1912.
7. Browning, G. M., and R. A. Norton, Tillage, Structure, and Irrigation: Tillage Practices with Corn and Soybeans in Iowa, *Soil Sci. Soc. Amer. Proc.*, **12**:491–496, 1947.
8. Browning, G. M., R. A. Norton, A. G. McCall, and F. G. Bell, Investigation in Erosion Control and the Reclamation of Eroded Land, *U.S. Dept. Agr. Tech. Bull.* 959, 1948.
9. Chang, H. T., and W. E. Loomis, Effect of Carbon Dioxide on Absorption of Water and Nutrients by Roots, *Plant Physiol.*, **20**:221–232, 1945.
10. Dickson, R. E., B. C. Langley, and C. E. Fisher, Water and Soil Conservation Experiments at Spur, Texas, *Tex. Agr. Expt. Sta. Bull.* 587, 1940.
11. Jones, J. Nick, Jr., and John E. Moody, Quarterly Report on Progress in Soil and Water Conservation Research, U.S. Department of Agriculture, March, 1955.
12. Kramer, Paul J., "Plant and Soil Water Relationships," McGraw-Hill, New York, 1949.
13. Krantz, B. A., Fertilize Corn for Higher Yields, *N.C. Agr. Expt. Sta. Bull.* 366, 1949.

14. Nicholson, R. P., John Pesek, and W. D. Shrader, Unpublished data, Iowa Agricultural Experiment Station, Ames, Iowa.
15. Pair, Claude H., Quarterly Report on Progress in Soil and Water Conservation Research, U.S. Department of Agriculture, March, 1955.
16. Richards, L. A., Uptake and Retention of Water by Soil as Determined by Distance to a Water Table, *J. Am. Soc. Agron.*, **33**:778–786, 1941.
17. Russell, M. B., Soil Moisture Sorption Curves for Four Iowa Soils, *Soil Soc. Amer. Proc.*, **4**:51–54, 1939.
18. Schofield, R. K., The pF of the Water in Soil, *Trans. Third Intern. Congr. Soil Sci.*, **2**:37–48, 1935.
19. Smith, Dwight D., Fertility Increases Efficiency of Soil Moisture, *Better Crops with Plant Food*, **38**(6):11, 1954.
20. Stanford, George, Joe B. Kelly, and W. H. Pierre, Cation Balance in Corn Grown on High-lime Soils in Relation to Potassium Deficiency, *Soil Sci. Soc. Amer. Proc.*, **6**:335–341, 1941.
21. Swanson, Norris P., Quarterly Report on Progress in Soil and Water Conservation Research, U.S. Department of Agriculture, March, 1955.
22. Tileston, Fred, Quarterly Report on Progress in Soil and Water Conservation Research, U.S. Department of Agriculture, March, 1955.
23. Volk, G. M., Significance of Moisture Translocation from Soil Zones of Low Moisture Tension to Zones of High Moisture Tension by Plant Roots, *J. Am. Soc. Agron.*, **33**:93–107, 1947.

CHAPTER 4

THE ORGANIC MATTER OF SOILS

Considerable emphasis has already been placed on the importance of soil organic matter. The relations of organic matter to water absorption and aeration have been stressed in particular. This chapter will be devoted to a consideration of the composition and properties of soil organic matter and factors affecting the distribution of organic matter in soils. Subsequent chapters will deal with the relation of organic matter to the availability of the different plant nutrients derived from the soil.

The residues of higher plants provide the parent material of soil organic matter. There is great variability in the nature of plant residues that become a part of soil organic matter, and yet soil organic matter is surprisingly similar in quality from one location to another. However, the mixture of a great many different kinds of organic compounds makes the study of the chemistry of soil organic matter most difficult. It is only in general terms that one can characterize soil organic matter.

The residues of higher plants provide an excellent source of food for microorganisms. Very soon after residues are left in the soil, the microorganisms start decomposing the material as a source of nutrients and energy. The more easily available organic compounds soon disappear. The more resistant organic compounds persist for longer periods. A very high proportion of the residues of higher plants that exist in the soil is in very finely divided condition. This finely divided material along with the microbial material has long been termed humus. Waksman (15) defined humus as "all of the material which is in the process of decomposition and which has lost its original structure."

Only a very small per cent of the soil organic matter would be considered outside of the humus fraction. A soil with 3 per cent organic matter would have about 30 tons of organic matter in the acre furrow slice. Less than 1 ton of this material, on the average, would have its structure unchanged, and the unchanged material would not persist for any appreciable time as such. Furthermore, for analytical work, soil is usually crushed and passed through a 20-mesh sieve. Such screening removes most of the undecomposed residues, and for all practical purposes there is no need for differentiating between organic matter and humus. Norman (9) stated that "I avoid entirely the use of the word humus, preferring instead to speak of the organic matter fraction, which in most soils will not in fact be easily recognizable as of plant origin."

Composition of Soil Organic Matter. As the residues of higher plants are decomposed, microbial cells are synthesized, which in turn die and are decomposed by other microorganisms. A large part of the material of plant residues is actually consumed as food for the microorganisms.

FIG. 33. Dark-colored soils are generally high in organic-matter content, while light-colored soils have low contents of organic matter. (*Soil Conservation Service.*)

None of the organic compounds of plant residues would be considered indestructible. But apparently part of the material is so resistant to microbial decomposition that it persists long enough to build up to rather large quantities. Organic material which does succumb to microbial attack becomes a part of the tissue of the microorganisms or is released as simple end products of decomposition, including carbon dioxide and water.

Just what proportion of the organic-matter fraction is represented by resistant organic compounds of plant tissue and what proportion is represented by living and dead microbial tissue is a matter of speculation. Norman (9) suggests that one-third to one-half of the organic matter formed under aerobic conditions in soils is microbially derived. Norman's opinion is shared by a great many soil microbiologists.

Nitrogen in Soil Organic Matter. The existence in the soil organic matter of about 5.0 per cent nitrogen is the most important clue to the belief that soil organic matter is about half microbial tissue.

If the nitrogen were all proteinaceous, one could use the conventional factor of N × 6.25 and calculate that soil organic matter contains 5 × 6.25, or 31.25, per cent protein. This percentage of protein is far higher than that of plant materials which reach the soil as residues. Moreover, the proteins of plant materials are readily decomposed by microorganisms. If one assumes that the nitrogen in the soil is proteinaceous, one could not account for its presence on the basis of the persistence of plant proteins. It would be more logical to suggest that the proteinaceous material represents residues of microbial tissue. If all the nitrogen were microbial proteins, microbial tissue were 60 per cent protein, and the organic matter fraction were 30 per cent protein, then half the organic matter would be microbial tissue.

Waksman and Iyer (13) and later Waksman (15) have stressed the proteinaceous character of nitrogen in soil organic matter. More recently Broadbent (6) has challenged the concept that a high proportion of the nitrogen exists in the soil as protein. He suggests that less than half of the nitrogen exists in protein form. Evidence of Bartholomew and Goring (2) indicates that a very small share of the nitrogen would exist in the form of nucleic acid (which also contains phosphorus). Broadbent (4) cites the evidence of Bremner and Shaw (3) in suggesting that an important part of the nitrogen of soil organic matter exists as chitin (an amino sugar), a constituent of fungal tissue.

The resistance to decomposition of the nitrogenous materials in soil organic matter is of great concern to agronomists. A soil with 3 per cent organic matter contains about 3000 lb. of nitrogen in the acre furrow slice, yet the soil may release no more than 60 lb. in a year through decomposition. Unless commercial fertilizer is added, the decomposition of organic matter is necessary as the source of nitrogen for crop production. On many soils, although high in total nitrogen, extra fertilizer nitrogen must be added to the soil in order to raise satisfactory yields.

Carbon in Soil Organic Matter. The carbon in plant material is derived from the carbon dioxide of the atmosphere and is reduced in the process of photosynthesis, the energy for which is derived from the sun. The carbon compounds are elaborated by the plant into many complex forms. The principal compounds, however, are (a) the polysaccharides, (b) lignin, and (c) proteins. These, and other carbon compounds, are sources of energy. The oxidation of the carbon to produce carbon dioxide is the principal source of energy for the microbial population of the soil.

During decomposition of plant residues the microorganisms use a part of the carbon in synthesis of their own body tissue, and a part of the carbon is oxidized to carbon dioxide as a source of energy. Then as the organisms die, their bodies undergo decomposition. Again the principle applies that a part of the carbon would be resynthesized and a part would be oxidized.   Without a fresh supply of plant residues the organic matter of the soil would eventually go through cycle after cycle of microbial life and death until eventually the organic carbon of the soil would virtually all be oxidized to carbon dioxide.

The fact that organic matter accumulates in soils is due to the resistance of a fraction of the plant residues and to the resistance to decomposition of part of the microbial tissue.   Under natural conditions of soil formation the organic matter gradually accumulates until an equilibrium is reached. The level remains about the same as long as the factors of formation remain unchanged.   During the equilibrium period the decomposition rate is equal to the rate of income of organic matter.   This relationship would indicate that none of the plant residues are entirely indestructible. If there were an indestructible fraction there would not be the equilibrium level that apparently exists in nature.

The microorganisms attack the most easily decomposed materials first, and among the easily decomposed materials are the polysaccharides.   The polysaccharides are by far the most abundant compounds in plant tissue, cellulose alone amounting to almost half the dry weight of most plant tissue.   The next most abundant polysaccharides are the hemicelluloses (including polyuronides, sometimes referred to as sugar acids).

TABLE 15. COMPOSITION OF PLANT TISSUE AND SOIL ORGANIC MATTER

Organic components	Dry mature plant tissue, %	Soil organic matter, %
Cellulose	20–50	2–10
Hemicellulose	10–20	0–2
Lignin	10–30	35–50
Fats, tannins, waxes	1–8	1–8
Protein (or nitrogen equivalent)	1–15	28–35

The lignin fraction of plant residues will range from about 10 to 30 per cent.   As plants mature, lignin is laid down in the cell walls.   Much of the rigidity of mature wheat straw compared to the young succulent stem is due to the lignin content.   Woody plants usually have more lignin than grasses and leguminous field crops.   In any of the plants, however, high lignin content is associated with maturity.

The lignin (or lignin-derived) material makes up about 35 to 50 per cent of the total organic-matter fraction of the soil.   The lignin material is relatively much more resistant to microbial attack than other plant materials and, as a consequence, accumulates in the topsoil[1] to become a higher per cent of the organic-matter fraction than any other major group.

[1] There is evidence that there is considerably less lignin in subsoils than topsoils (6).

Next in abundance are the nitrogenous materials described in the previous section.

The lignin in the soil has many of the characteristics of plant lignin but has undergone some change. One change, in particular, is the increase in carboxyl groups (R—COOH). This feature is of great significance in soils because the hydrogen of the carboxyl group can be exchanged for other cations, thus giving soil organic matter considerable cation-exchange capacity. This is a characteristic not only of the ligninlike material; other organic compounds exist in the soil which have carboxyl groups. Moreover, there are other acidic groups associated with organic molecules which are capable of exchanging hydrogen for other cations.

Organic Carbon Content of Soils. Until recent years, there has not been a satisfactory method for determining organic-matter content of soils. It was assumed that organic matter contained an average of 58 per cent carbon. Since the carbon content of soils is relatively easily determined, the customary practice has been to determine the per cent of carbon and multiply the amount of carbon by 1.724 (a factor obtained by dividing 100 by 58).

With the recent development of more refined methods for determining organic matter and organic carbon separately, it has been learned that soil organic matter rarely has over 52 per cent carbon (6). Broadbent suggests the factor of 1.9 for topsoils and 2.5 for subsoils. The latter is based on the observation that subsoil organic matter contains approximately 40 per cent carbon. The factor of 1.724 has long been used as a factor for calculating the organic-matter content of subsoils, just as for topsoils. One who is interested in reviewing data published on soil organic contents should be aware of the method of determination and calculation. Much of the data on organic-matter content was calculated from carbon data, using the factor 1.724.

Carbon to Nitrogen Ratio of Organic Matter. Soil organic matter contains an average of about 5.0 per cent nitrogen, although the percentage may vary as widely as 4.0 to 6.0 per cent. Organic matter contains about 50 to 54 per cent carbon in topsoils. The average is about 52 per cent. Dividing 52 by 5 one gets 10.4 as a ratio of C to N.[1] The C to N ratio varies between about 10 and 11 to 1. As soils are cultivated, there is some narrowing of the ratio, and although 10.4 represents the ratio of virgin soils 10.0 probably is more nearly representative of cultivated soils.

The carbon content of subsoils varies generally from about 36 to 44 per cent. The average carbon content is estimated to be about 40 per cent.

---

[1] As long as soils were assumed to have 58 per cent carbon, the C to N ratio was considered to average 11.6(58 ÷ 5 = 11.6), and this figure has been widely used in publications.

If one assumes 5.0 per cent nitrogen in subsoil organic matter, the average C to N ratio would be 8 to 1 (obtained by dividing 40 by 5).

The C to N ratio of plant residues varies anywhere from 10 to 1 for young leguminous plant tissue to as high as 200 to 1 for some straw of small grain. Plant materials which are low in nitrogen are generally more resistant to decomposition[1] and the longer the time that is required for the decomposition to reach a stage where nitrogen in the residue becomes available as ammonia or nitrate.

When plant tissue reaches the soil, the microorganisms start decomposing the material (if moisture, temperature, and aeration permit). The organisms increase in number. Among other needs, they require nitrogen for protein of their bodies, carbon for many organic structures of their bodies, and carbon for oxidation as a source of energy. If the ratio of C to N of the plant tissue is wide, the microorganisms have plenty of carbon for synthesis and for energy, but there may not be enough nitrogen for synthesis. As a consequence of a wide C to N ratio the process of decomposition will be slow. By adding available nitrogen the process of decomposition appears to be accelerated. The extra nitrogen is used by the microorganisms, and the population increases. As the population increases, more carbon is assimilated along with the nitrogen and more carbon is oxidized in the respiration process and released as CO_2. As the microorganisms die, their bodies are decomposed (by other organisms). Part of the carbon is reassimilated and part is oxidized as CO_2. The process continues with loss of carbon as CO_2, and the ratio of C to N becomes more narrow. By the time the ratio reaches about 17 to 1 there is more nitrogen than is needed, in relation to carbon needs of the microorganisms, and the nitrogen is released as NH_3. The decomposition does not stop, however. The process continues with the liberation of CO_2 and NH_3.

Table 16 illustrates the relationship of C to N ratio to decomposition and release of carbon and nitrogen.

The material with a high content of nitrogen decomposed at a more rapid rate than did the material of low nitrogen content. This is a well-established principle. Green-manure crops have narrow C to N ratios, decompose much more rapidly, and give up more available nitrogen in a given period of time than the more mature crop residues.

By the time the process approaches an equilibrium, the ratio of C to N of the decomposing mass becomes about 11 to 1. Further decomposition, which is very slow, causes C and N to be released in a ratio of about 11 to 1. Figure 34 illustrates this characteristic of soils.

Fifty soils, half of which were cultivated and half associated unculti-

---

[1] An excellent review article on this subject has been recently published by Bartholomew (1).

vated soils, were moistened and incubated for 25 days at 40°C. The carbon and nitrogen were released in an average ratio of 11 to 1. Most of the plant residues were removed by screening the soils through a 20-mesh sieve before incubation. No energy material or extra nitrogen

TABLE 16. INFLUENCE OF C TO N RATIO OF RYE PLANTS, AS CONTROLLED BY AGE, UPON THEIR DECOMPOSITION DURING A 27-DAY PERIOD (15)

C to N ratio of plants	Relative decomposition C as CO_2 liberated, mg.	N as NH_3 liberated, mg.	N consumed from added nitrogen, mg.
20:1	287	22.2	0
28:1	280	3.0	0
50:1	200	0	7.5
200:1	188	0	8.9

was added. The decomposition represented that which is associated with the equilibrium between carbon and nitrogen existing in the soil at the time of sampling.

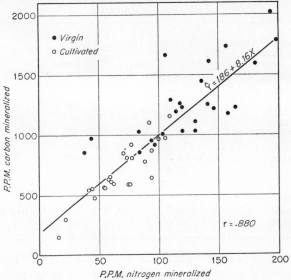

FIG. 34. The relation of mineralization of nitrogen to the mineralization of carbon in 50 soils (11).

It is interesting to speculate on the reason for the existence of an equilibrium C to N ratio of about 10 or 11 to 1. If all of the plant residues were readily consumed by microorganisms, it would be reasonable to assume that the ratio of C to N of the soil organic matter would be the šame as that of microbial tissue, which is estimated to be about 8 to 1 or less. The wider C to N ratio of 10 to 1 in soil organic matter can probably be attributed to the presence of lignin-derived material. Unaltered lignin does not contain nitrogen.

It has already been suggested that the C to N ratio in subsoils is more nearly 8 to 1 than 10 to 1. Some studies have indicated the C to N ratio of subsoils might be as low as 6 to 1 (10,12). Subsoil organic matter contains a lower percentage of lignin and a higher percentage of microbially derived material.

Waksman (14) and others have shown that the C to N ratio is higher in humid-region soils than in arid-region soils. There is also a tendency toward higher ratios in cool climates than in warm climates. There appear to be two "opposing" factors that determine the ratio of carbon to nitrogen in soil organic matter. One is the income of plant residues, and the other is the rate of decomposition. The more thorough the decomposition the more narrow the ratio, as a general rule.

Table 17 shows the carbon and nitrogen relationships in organic materials.

TABLE 17. CARBON AND NITROGEN RELATIONSHIPS IN ORGANIC MATERIALS
Oven-dry weight basis

Composition of tissues and soil	Nitrogen, per cent	Carbon, per cent	Organic matter, per cent	C to N	Organic matter to N
Plant tissue, average:					
Alfalfa hay................	3.0	40	100	13:1	33:1
Oat straw.................	0.5	37	100	80:1	200:1
Microbial tissue, average:					
Bacteria..................	10.0	50	100	5:1	10:1
Actinomycetes............	8.5	50	100	6:1	12:1
Fungi....................	5.0	50	100	10:1	20:1
Average microbe...........	6.25	50	100	8:1	16:1
Soil organic matter:					
Average topsoil............	5.0	52	100	10.4:1	20:1
Average subsoil............	5.0	40	100	8:1	20:1

Bacterial tissue has a C to N ratio of about 5 to 1. If decomposition were to progress in soils without addition of plant tissue for many years, it is believed that the C to N ratio would eventually approach 5 to 1 (10,14). The reason for this belief is that as available energy material of the soil declines, the population of fungi declines markedly. The bacteria consume the fungi. They are much smaller than fungi, and unless fungi produce antibiotics, they may be overwhelmed by bacteria. Broadbent (6) has estimated that a piece of fungal mycelium 1 cm. long and 0.005 mm.

in diameter would be roughly equivalent in weight to a million small bacteria of the type found in soils.   Fungi are prevalent in soils rich in plant residues where competition for food and energy is not so keen, but they decline rapidly in numbers where there is severe competition for food and where environmental conditions are just as favorable for bacteria as for fungi.

The soil is a storehouse of nutrients for microorganisms and higher plants.   They are all feeding out of the same trough.   They compete with each other for nutrients, and the smaller organisms "get there first." The microbial population and higher plants, however, as broad groups, are mutually beneficial.   The higher plants, through photosynthesis, provide energy and metabolic carbon for microorganisms.   The microorganisms decompose the residues of higher plants, thus releasing the nutrients for use by new generations of higher plants.

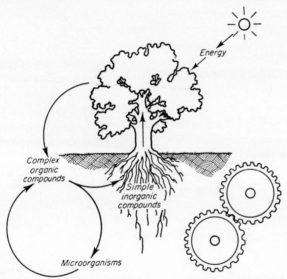

FIG. 35. A diagram showing tne interlocking of the life cycle of higher plants and microorganisms. A vigorous microbial population indicates a productive soil; likewise, a soil producing high yields would be expected to have a large and vigorous microbial population.

Microbial Population.[1]   The microbial population of the soil includes some animal life (such as nematodes and protozoa), but microanimals

---

[1] The term *microorganisms* is used generally in soils literature to include both microflora and any microscopic animal life (the term microfauna is seldom used) that might be present, but it is realized that the microflora are of generally the organisms in mind.   The term *microbe* is sometimes used as a short way of designating microorganisms.

have little effect on the physical properties of soil and the transformations that affect soil fertility. The term microflora is often used to specify the microscopic plant life of the soil. Microflora comprises the various bacteria, actinomycetes, fungi (including yeasts and mushrooms), and algae present in the soil.

Bacteria. Bacteria are the simplest forms of plant life. They are one-celled organisms and are usually round, rod-shaped, or spiral. They occur in fantastic numbers. A soil high in energy material (decomposable plant tissue) may contain a billion or more bacteria in a gram of soil (7). This group is of particular importance, since it includes the nitrogen-fixing organisms and those involved in transforming ammonia nitrogen to nitrate nitrogen. There are two kinds of organisms that fix nitrogen. One is the symbiotic bacteria that fix nitrogen in the nodules on the roots of legumes. The other group is free-living nitrogen-fixing organisms. The free-living (nonsymbiotic) bacteria[1] get their nitrogen from the air and their energy from decomposing dead plant tissue. The symbiotic bacteria get their energy material from the cell sap of the legume and get their nitrogen from the air.

Bacteria are divided into groups called aerobic and anaerobic. The aerobic organisms get their oxygen from the air. The anaerobic organisms do not require (and some may be injured by) the presence of gaseous oxygen. From the standpoint of growth of field crops, the aerobic condition of the soil is better and is necessary for a greater part of the time. Anaerobic conditions result from poor aeration and from the filling of all pore space of the soil with water. Not only do plant roots need oxygen, but the majority of microorganisms concerned with plant nutrient transformations grow best under aerobic conditions.

Heterotrophic organisms get their energy by oxidizing organic materials, while autotrophic organisms get their energy from some other source. The nitrifying organisms which oxidize ammonia to nitrites and nitrites to nitrates are autotrophic.

Bacteria, in general, have a high calcium requirement and do best in neutral soils or in slightly alkaline soils where calcium is high. Bacteria do not thrive in strongly acid conditions.

Actinomycetes. Actinomycetes are intermediate between bacteria and fungi. They are one-celled organisms but are a higher form of plant life than bacteria and are threadlike in shape; the threads may be branched.

[1] There are two well-known nonsymbiotic organisms, Azotobacter, which is an aerobic organism, and Clostridium, which is an anaerobe. The importance of these organisms is still a question. In soils about neutral in reaction, well supplied with calcium and phosphorus and high in available energy material, Azotobacter may fix an appreciable amount of nitrogen but not nearly enough to offset that removed by crops.

They occur in large numbers (in millions per gram of soil), particularly in soils developed under grass where the calcium content is high. The familiar odor of freshly plowed ground is the characteristic odor of actinomycetes.

Fungi. Fungi are quite variable in size. They vary from microscopic (thousands per gram of soil) to the size of mushrooms. They are more numerous in acid forest soils because they can get along on a small amount of calcium and can tolerate the acidity. It is not that they prefer the acid condition but that they are tolerant of acidity and thrive in the absence of competition. Although they are outnumbered by bacteria, as a general rule, they contribute more weight to soil organic matter because of their larger size (7).

Algae. Algae represent a group of organisms which can use energy from the sun. The forms most familiar to us are those that grow in stagnant water or in watering troughs. This group contains species which are able to carry on photosynthesis and transform energy from the sun into energy-bearing organic compounds. They range in size from the one-cell form to long strands that appear somewhat like moss.

In addition to their ability to carry on photosynthesis, some of the blue-green algae are able to fix nitrogen from the air. The importance of nitrogen fixation by algae in well-drained upland soils is still open to question. On the other hand, it is believed that algae have been very important in maintaining the nitrogen levels in soils used for rice production.

Protozoa. Protozoa are the smallest forms of animal life. Their numbers in field soils are not particularly high because of the limited water supply. The group is interesting, however, because it has been observed that when the protozoan population increases, the bacterial population decreases. The Protozoa actually ingest ("swallow") whole bacteria.

Nematodes. Nematodes are known more for their damage to crops than for any particular function in the soil. However, there are many more noninjurious forms than there are injurious forms. They are small animals which live in the soil and may infect the plant roots and live as parasites. Nematodes are particularly bad in orchards in some parts of the country. They are important in areas of the West where they attack the roots of alfalfa, sugar beets, and potatoes. They are also important in the Southern states where they attack corn and tobacco.

Injurious Effect of Microorganisms. An active and thriving microbial population is a good indication of a fertile soil, and the microbial population is necessary for the soil to remain fertile; but unfortunately there are many microbial diseases of plants. While most of the microbial population must wait for the plant to die before getting at the energy supply, some microbes are able to get inside the plant while it is growing. There are ways of treating the soil to combat diseases.   A good example is potato scab, which is caused by an actinomycete.   Liming the soil increases the disease, but making the soil acid might help to control the disease.

Factors Affecting the Growth of Microorganisms.   One factor affecting growth of microorganisms that has already been emphasized and cannot be overemphasized is the energy supply.   Other factors are pH (the degree of acidity or alkalinity); amounts of nitrogen, calcium, phosphorus, potassium, and other nutrients; aeration; moisture; and temperature.

The most favorable temperature for the microbial population as a whole is about 85 to 95°F.   Of course, there are some which prefer a cooler temperature and some which grow best at higher temperatures.

The most favorable moisture level for the population, as a whole, occurs when about half the pore space is filled with water.   This permits aeration as well as a favorable moisture supply.

Exploitation of Soil Organic Matter.   The slow release of carbon and nitrogen through decomposition of the soil organic matter (not the plant residues recently added, but the residual organic matter) accounts for the accumulation of the large reserves we find in uncultivated soils.   Only about 1 to 3 per cent of the nitrogen of soil organic matter of cultivated soil is released in 1 year through decomposition.   This characteristic of soils is more favorable to agriculture than unfavorable.   A more rapid release would mean higher yields but would also mean a more rapid depletion of soil organic matter.   A farmer can supplement the natural release of nitrogen with fertilizer nitrogen to supply needs for higher yields.   The more fortunate farmer, however, is the one whose soil is rich in organic matter and releases a large amount of nitrogen each year.   The soils of the Middle Western part of the United States are particularly high in organic matter.   The release of nitrogen from decomposition of organic matter along with nitrogen supplied by legumes and manure has been great enough to maintain acceptable yields without fertilizer nitrogen in this region until recently.   The higher yields desired have increased the utilization of nitrogen fertilizers.

There are two important concepts to be gained at this moment with regard to release of nitrogen from organic matter.   One is that a higher percentage of the nitrogen of soil organic matter of uncultivated soils will be released in 1 year than from similar soils cropped for many years.   The other is that as organic-matter content declines in a soil under cultivation, there is less organic matter available for decomposition associated with a smaller percentage release each year.   Suppose a farmer had a soil containing 5000 lb. of N (equivalent to 5 per cent organic matter) per acre, releasing 3 per cent per year.   During the first few years he would have in the neighborhood of 150 lb. N available, which is enough to produce 75 to 90 bu. of corn.   But suppose after 25 years the soil contains 3000 lb.

of nitrogen and releases only 2 per cent of nitrogen per year. The soil would give up about 60 lb. of nitrogen, which is enough for only 30 to 35 bu. of corn. It should be obvious, then, why a great interest has developed in fertilizer nitrogen. Scientific improvements in agriculture plus a declining content of organic matter have placed a greater demand on soils for nitrogen than they can deliver through decomposition.

Fresh organic material in the form of plant residues will decompose much more quickly than will the soil organic matter. Broadbent (5) has found that addition of fresh plant residues hastens the decomposition of soil organic matter. He points out that the addition of fresh material is like throwing a bit of kerosene on glowing embers. The kerosene quickly burns and also hastens the burning of the embers.

Factors Affecting the Amount of Organic Matter in Soil. The most important factors affecting the amount of soil organic matter are (a) kind of vegetation, (b) topography, (c) nature of parent material, (d) climate, and (e) time (the same five factors that are important in soil formation).

Vegetation. Organic matter is distributed in the soil in accordance with the distribution of residues turned over to the soil by the plant. The organic matter in grassland soils is derived primarily from the roots of grasses. The organic matter of forest soils is derived primarily from leaf fall. The roots of trees as well as grasses are concentrated in the topsoil and decrease in quantity with depth in the profile. The main difference, however, is the rate at which the roots are turned over to the soil as residues. Many of the grasses are annuals, and even the perennials turn over their root systems periodically, about every 3 years on the average (16). The rate of turnover of tree roots is much slower, but there is some contribution of residues of roots every year. Some cellular tissue is sloughed off, and some roots die for various reasons. In general, the top 4 or 5 in. of forest soils are high in organic matter and the subsurface and subsoils are low in organic matter, as indicated by Fig. 36. The lower part of the litter on the surface of forest soils is classified by forestry students as humus. This finely divided, dark-colored organic matter becomes mixed with the surface few inches by the myriad of insects, worms, and other small animals that live in the soil. The top 4 or 5 in. of soil gain organic matter from decomposing roots as well as the humus from leaf fall. The tree roots of the top 4 or 5 in. also suffer much damage from the macro- and microanimals. The damaged roots contribute to the organic matter, also, along with the remains of these animals. There is very little accumulation of litter on grassland soils. The grass roots account for a high proportion of the soil organic matter in grassland soils. The content of organic matter is highest in the surface and declines gradually with depth as indicated in Fig. 36.

Topography. The effect of topography on soil formation is largely the effect of moisture.   Soils on steep slopes have more runoff and less water available to plants.   The soils are usually more shallow on the slopes for the reason that root development is limited by the water supply.   The soils on the steeper slopes have more aeration, are often warmer (particu-

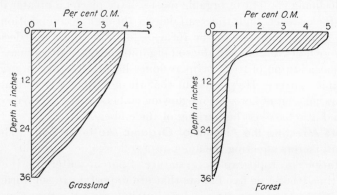

FIG. 36. The distribution of organic matter in typical soil profiles.

larly on southern exposures in the Northern Hemisphere), and the organic matter decomposes more readily.   As a consequence, the organic-matter contents of slopes are less than found on the more level areas, other things being equal.   The organic-matter content of soils is highest in depressed areas that favor large amounts of vegetation and slow rates of decomposition.   Figure 37 shows this topographic relationship.   The sketch is a generalized estimate based on many observations.

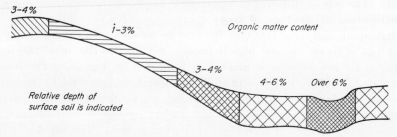

FIG. 37. The effect of topography on accumulation of organic matter under conditions of central Iowa.

The lower slopes receive runoff water from upper slopes, and consequently the lower slopes have deeper solums with more organic matter than found on upper slopes.

Parent Material.   The effect of parent material on soil organic matter is largely through the quantity of vegetation produced.   In this respect, the mineral supply is the main factor.   Thompson (11) found that high phosphorus content in soils was associated with high organic-matter contents in 50 soils collected from several states.

Parent material has a great deal of influence on determining the existence of trees and grasses in climates where either might predominate. Fine-textured soils well supplied with the bases, particularly calcium, are more favorable to grasses than are sandy soils with low base content. Certain trees will usually compete more successfully with grasses on the latter and become the predominant type of vegetation.

As a generalization, one would expect more organic matter in soils of high mineral supply. Under natural conditions the nitrogen supply would not generally be the limiting factor. Nitrogen would be made available by fixation if the fertility would support wild legumes. With higher fertility there would be more plant residues available each year.

The "opposing" factor of organic-matter accumulation, again, is the rate of decomposition. A warmer, better-aerated soil will have more rapid decomposition (other factors being equal) than a cooler, less-aerated soil. Sandy soils are often warmer and better aerated than fine-textured soils and would permit more rapid decomposition of organic matter than finer-textured soils if, again, other things were equal. But of course other things would not be equal. Sandy soils hold less water, and if grasses were the vegetation, there would be less organic residues made available each year. Moreover, sandy soils are inherently less fertile than finer-textured soils and support less plant growth than finer-textured soils. Therefore, whether other factors considered are equal or not, one can generalize and state that there is a correlation of organic-matter content with clay content. Finer textures are associated with more organic matter in a given region. This should be recognized as a generalization, and there are generally exceptions to all rules. A clay soil might have some characteristic that would limit plant growth, and it could have less organic matter than an adjacent coarser-textured soil.

There is another aspect of the relation of clay content to organic-matter content that is receiving considerable attention in research. Clay tends to combine with organic compounds through chemical attraction as indicated in the section on structure in Chap. 2. Proteinaceous compounds with positively charged groups are attracted to negatively charged clays. In a related manner, other electrically charged organic compounds are attracted to clay particles possessing electrical charges, either negative or positive. This is of great significance because the reactive groups on organic compounds are those first attacked by enzymes produced by active microorganisms. Where the reactive group is attracted to an electrically charged clay particle it is less accessible to enzymatic attack. In other words, clay tends to stabilize organic compounds against decomposition. One might expect that there would be a good correlation between clay content and organic-matter content of soils, and there are many examples of data available to support this view.

Influence of Climate.   Climate has marked influence on organic-matter accumulation in two important ways; one is that climate affects the total amount of residues that is turned over to the soil each year, and the other is that climate affects the rate at which the residues decompose.   In the central part of the United States, most of the soils are formed under grass, all the way from Minnesota to Texas.   The Eastern part of the United States is covered by deciduous-coniferous forests all the way from the northern border to the southern border.   The temperature belts cross this region running from east to west.   In the northern part of the region, the soils are frozen during the winter months.   In the southern part of the country the soils are not frozen during the winter, but the vegetation is not abundant during the winter.

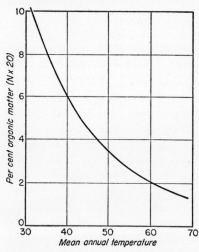

Fig. 38. Relationship of temperature (in degrees Fahrenheit) to organic matter accumulated in humid regions. [*After Jenny* (8).]

The higher temperatures of the southern part of the region are more favorable to decomposition of organic matter than in the northern part. The income of residues versus the decomposition rates is such in the United States that the organic-matter content of the soils decreases from north to south.   Figure 38 was prepared from data of Jenny showing this remarkable relationship.

Conditions in some other countries, particularly in tropical regions, are such that there is less correlation between temperature and organic-matter content of soils.   Again, one must examine the factors affecting income of plant residues in relation to factors affecting the rate of decomposition.

There is a relation between annual precipitation and organic-matter content of soils, but again the relation must be carefully examined in light of associated conditions of fertility level, aeration of the soil, and other factors affecting vegetative production and organic-matter decomposition. In going from the humid prairie region of Central United States westward to the desert region, one finds a decreasing amount of organic matter closely related to the reduction in annual precipitation.   This relation is due primarily to the effect of less water producing less plant residues.

As one goes from the humid prairie region eastward in the United States, it is found that the rainfall increases but that the organic-matter content decreases. The more humid region is more strongly leached and is generally less fertile from a mineral-nutrient point of view. Moreover, the soils are generally covered by forests, and the organic-matter accumulation is shallow. The forest soils of the Eastern United States are generally more strongly differentiated and are more sandy in the surface than the soils developed under grass. The correlation of texture with organic-matter accumulation was emphasized in the previous section.

Time. To understand the time factor in organic-matter accumulation, one may visualize the result of scraping off the top 3 ft. of soil down to the parent material. Such exposures are frequently observed along new highways. During the first few years of exposure there is little vegetative growth, primarily because of lack of nitrogen (which is not present in rocks and minerals except in the rare nitrate deposits). There is a gradual

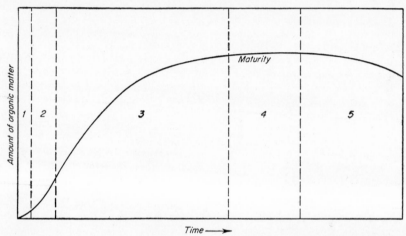

Fig. 39. A schematic diagram showing the rate of accumulation and decline of organic matter in soils.

addition of nitrogen to the soil by rainfall and through fixation of nitrogen by microorganisms, and the growth of plants becomes accelerated by the increase in nitrogen and organic matter. After a period of several decades, possibly several centuries, the accumulation of organic matter begins to slow down and finally levels off to an approximately constant amount of organic matter for the particular set of environmental conditions.

There are probably five phases in the history of organic-matter accumulation. The first phase is the gradual accumulation of enough nitrogen to support a cover of vegetation. The second phase is probably an accelerated rate of organic-matter accumulation because of increased availability of nitrogen and other nutrients. The third phase is the slowing down of the annual rate of organic-matter accumulation. The fourth phase is the equilibrium phase of maturity, where the amount of organic matter remains fairly constant. A fifth phase probably occurs, which is the gradual decrease in organic matter after maturity is reached. Soils of southeastern Illinois probably have less organic matter now than they once had at the time they reached maturity. These soils are very old and strongly differentiated and probably do not support as much cover of grass as they did when they were more fertile.

REFERENCES

1. Bartholomew, W. V., Availability of Organic Nitrogen and Phosphorus from Plant Residues, Manures and Soil Organic Matter, Soil Microbiology Conference, Purdue University, 1954 (mimeo. proc.).
2. Bartholomew, W. V., and C. I. A. Goring, Microbial Products and Soil Organic Matter, Soil Sci. Soc. Amer. Proc., 13:238–241, 1948.
3. Bremner, J. M., and K. Shaw, Studies on the Estimation and Decomposition of Amino Sugars in Soil, J. Agr. Sci., 44:152–159, 1954.
4. Broadbent, F. E., Basic Problems in Organic Matter Transformations, Soil Microbiology Conference, Purdue University, 1954 (mimeo. proc.).
5. Broadbent, F. E., Nitrogen Release and Carbon Loss from Soil Organic Matter during Decomposition of Added Plant Residues, Soil Sci. Soc. Amer. Proc., 12:246–249, 1947.
6. Broadbent, F. E., The Soil Organic Fraction, Advances in Agron., 5:153–183, 1953.
7. Clark, F. E., A Perspective of Soil Microflora, Soil Microbiology Conference, Purdue University, 1954 (mimeo. proc.).
8. Jenny, H., A Study on the Influence of Climate upon the Nitrogen and Organic Matter Content of the Soil, Mo. Agr. Expt. Sta. Res. Bull. 152, 1930.
9. Norman, A. G., Problems in the Chemistry of Soil Organic Matter, Soil. Sci. Soc. Amer. Proc., 7:7–15, 1942.
10. Sievers, F. J., and H. F. Holz, The Significance of Nitrogen in Soil Organic Matter Relationships, Wash. Agr. Expt. Sta. Bull. 206, 1926.
11. Thompson, L. M., C. A. Black, and J. A. Zoellner, Occurrence and Mineralization of Organic Phosphorus in Soils, with Particular Reference to Associations with Nitrogen, Carbon, and pH, Soil Sci., 77:185–196, 1954.
12. Vandecaveye, S. C., and M. C. Allen, Microbial Activities in Soil. II. Activity of Specific Groups of Microbes in Relation to Organic Matter Transformation in Palouse Silt Loam, Soil Sci., 40:331–343, 1935.
13. Waksman, S. A., and K. R. N. Iyer, Contribution to Our Knowledge of the Chemical Nature and Origin of Humus. I. On the Synthesis of the "Humus Nucleus," Soil Sci., 34:43–69, 1932.
14. Waksman, S. A., and I. J. Hutchings, Chemical Nature of Organic Matter in Different Soil Types, Soil Sci., 40:347–363, 1935.
15. Waksman, S. A., The Microbiologist Looks at Soil Organic Matter, Soil Sci. Soc. Amer. Proc., 7:16–21, 1942.
16. Weaver, J. E., and Ellen Zink, Length of Life of Roots of Ten Species of Perennial Range and Pasture Grasses, Plant Physiol., 21:201–217, 1946.

CHAPTER 5

THE CHEMICAL COMPOSITION OF SOILS

There are 19 chemical elements that are of particular importance in soils. These elements with their symbols are listed below. The 15 elements essential to plants are shown in heavy black letters. The 4 elements in italics are listed because of their abundance in soils.

A PARTIAL LIST OF ELEMENTS IMPORTANT IN SOILS

Element	Symbol	Element	Symbol
Aluminum	Al	Molybdenum	Mo
Boron	B	Nitrogen	N
Calcium	Ca	Oxygen	O
Carbon	C	Phosphorus	P
Chlorine	Cl	Potassium	K
Copper	Cu	*Silicon*	Si
Hydrogen	H	*Sodium*	Na
Iron	Fe	Sulfur	S
Magnesium	Mg	Zinc	Zn
Manganese	Mn		

All 19 elements are contained by plants which have been grown in soil. Aluminum, silicon, and sodium are not essential to the growth of plants when grown in culture solutions in the laboratory, but they undoubtedly contribute to plant growth in the field. These elements are important if not essential. Silicon and aluminum as oxides constitute the "skeleton" of the soil. The oxides of these two elements constitute 80 to 85 per cent of most soils. A trace of chlorine in solution cultures was recently found to be essential to the growth of tomatoes. Further studies of additional plants by the refined techniques now employed may cause the addition of chlorine to the list of essential elements. A discussion of chlorine may be found in Chap. 14. Titanium might be listed because of the existence of appreciable quantities in soils, particularly in very old soils. The early analytical work with soils stressed the total chemical composition of soils, and the quantity of titanium oxide was often expressed along with the quantities of silicon dioxide, aluminum oxide, etc. Titanium is not listed since it will be considered only to a limited extent. Sodium and chlorine are among the eight most abundant elements contributed by the soil to plant composition. Sodium and chlorine of plant tissue are the main sources of these elements in animal nutrition. Cobalt might also be added to the list of important elements. Cobalt is essential to animal nutrition, and, as a general rule, animals obtain their cobalt from the soil through plants. In areas known to be deficient in cobalt, the salt provided as a supplement to plant-derived feeds is fortified with cobalt.

There are traces of many other elements contained in plants. These elements are present in plants because they are present in soils. Although selective to a certain extent, plants are unable to control the proportion of the different elements that are absorbed. There is a tendency toward absorbing those elements which are most available. Some of the non-essential trace elements are either toxic to plants or toxic to livestock that eat the plants containing the toxic element. For example, in certain regions of the Western part of the United States selenium may occur abundantly enough (and soluble enough) so that plants take up enough to poison livestock.

Only 19 elements are listed because they are the ones that will be considered many times throughout the book.

From a philosophical point of view it is interesting that these 19 elements are so widely distributed and constitute nearly 98 per cent of the earth's crust. The 19 elements exist in highly variable proportions, but there is hardly a soil anywhere without all 19. The fact that some of them occur in too small amounts and others in excessive amounts contributed to the need for the development of a science of soils. There are some fascinating relations of plants to soils as one considers their chemistry. The evolution of the nutritional requirements of higher plants has been conditioned by the availability of the chemical elements. Plants have developed their characteristics through natural selection. They have adapted themselves, through natural selection, to the conditions that exist in their natural habitat. Certain species of plants thrive on a particular combination of available elements, while other species have adapted themselves to another combination. As one moves a plant from its natural habitat, one often finds it necessary to modify the soil to create a favorable combination of available elements.

Forms in Which the Elements Occur in Soils. There are three forms of plant nutrients which one might recognize as a beginning of the understanding of the chemical composition of soil: (*a*) the *unavailable*, (*b*) the *exchangeable*, which is partly available, (*c*) the *solution* form, which is readily available.

The unavailable form is the form in which the element is combined as a part of a compound and is not accessible to plant absorption until the compound is "decomposed." The term decomposition applies to inorganic compounds like the silicate minerals as well as to organic compounds like proteins.

The exchangeable form is the form in which the element exists as a cation or an anion adsorbed[1] on the surface of organic compounds or clay minerals. The exchangeable ions are available to plants. A very high proportion of the available cations are held in the exchangeable form. The chemical-soil-test data for available potassium, for example, are expressed as exchangeable potassium.

The anions are held as exchangeable ions to a certain extent, but most clays and organic compounds have many more negative than positive positions on their surfaces. Nitrates are quite mobile and are not held "tightly" enough by clays and organic compounds to be considered as exchangeable ions. Sulfates are likewise quite mobile as anions and are not held as exchangeable ions to any appreciable extent. Phosphate ions are less mobile, and appreciable amounts of the available phosphate, particularly that which exists as $H_2PO_4^-$ are held as exchangeable ions in soils. Fortunately, the low anion-exchange capacity of most soils is compensated for by the tendency for the anions to become a part of the organic compounds that exist in the soil.

The solution form is assumed to be the most available form. The water of soils tends to dissolve some of all the ions with which it comes in contact. The solution form is the ionic form with greater mobility. In other words, the cations and anions are rapidly moving about within the solution, while those ions which are adsorbed on the surfaces of clays

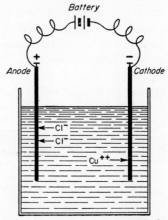

Fig. 40. Cations are positively charged ions, having given up electrons to cause the formation of anions. Cations and anions get their names from the anodes and cathodes to which they are attracted during electrolysis. In this example, copper has given up two electrons to the two chloride atoms, making them each monovalent and leaving the copper with two more protons than electrons.

and organic compounds are oscillating to a lesser extent and limited to an area close to the adsorbing surface. The ions which are moving about in solution exchange places with the ions held on adsorbing surfaces. There tends to be an equilibrium between those ions in solution and those "held" on adsorbing surfaces.

[1] Adsorb is a term which means surface attraction as contrasted with absorption, like absorption of water by a sponge.

Important Cations and Anions in Soils.   The cations for the most part exist as single atoms, the exception being ammonium, since nitrogen must exist in combination with hydrogen or oxygen to be available.   The polyvalent ions like iron and aluminum hold hydroxyl ions firmly enough so that they act much like radicals.[1]   For example, ferric hydroxide may exist as a cation with one positive charge, $Fe(OH)_2{}^+$, which means that two of its positive charges (or protons) are balanced by the two hydroxyl ions.   The third proton or positive charge must be balanced by the attraction of an anion (or an electron).

The anions, which will be considered in this book, are radicals, with the exception of chlorine.   Table 18 lists the more common cations and anions that exist in the soil.   The existence of $H_2PO_4{}^-$, $HPO_4{}^{--}$, or $PO_4{}^{---}$ is associated with the degree of acidity or alkalinity.   The existence of a predominance of $H_2PO_4{}^-$ requires the presence of exchangeable H^+ in excess of OH^-.   An increase in predominance of OH^- increases the proportion of $PO_4{}^{---}$ compared to $HPO_4{}^{--}$.   The same principle applies to $HCO_3{}^-$ and $CO_3{}^{--}$.

TABLE 18. VALENCE NUMBERS OF COMMON ELEMENTS AND RADICALS IN SOILS

Cations			Anions		
+1	+2	+3	−1	−2	−3
H^+	Mg^{++}	Al^{+++}	OH^-	$HPO_4{}^{--}$	$PO_4{}^{---}$
Na^+	Fe^{++}	Fe^{+++}	Cl^-	$CO_3{}^{--}$	
K^+	Zn^{++}			$SO_4{}^{--}$	
$NH_4{}^+$	Ca^{++}		$NO_3{}^-$	$B_4O_7{}^{--}$	
	Cu^{++}		$H_2PO_4{}^-$	$MoO_4{}^{--}$	
	Mn^{++}		$HCO_3{}^-$		

The six macroelements can be conveniently divided into two groups for further understanding of the chemical properties of soils.   Calcium, magnesium, and potassium[2] are the cation-forming elements.   Nitrogen, phosphorus, and sulfur are the anion-forming elements.   The former group does not enter into organic combination to any appreciable extent. The latter elements readily enter into organic combination, and they are stored in the soil in organic matter.   The availability of nitrogen, phosphorus, and sulfur is associated with organic-matter decomposition.   On the other hand, since calcium, magnesium, and potassium are not held as constituents of soil organic matter to any appreciable extent, they would

[1] A radical is a group of atoms that acts as a unit.

[2] Sodium is in this group of cations in terms of the properties being described, and chlorine acts like the group of anions in that it is combined in organic compounds.

soon leach out of the soil if it were not for the cation-exchange capacity of clays and organic compounds. Calcium, magnesium, and potassium are concerned in weathering (or decomposition) of minerals of the soil, particularly the silicate and carbonate minerals.

Acidic Properties of Soils. Clays are very finely divided fragments of minerals. As clay particles become smaller in size they have tremendous surface in proportion to their weight and volume. Their surfaces undergo certain chemical changes whereby one species of an atom might be replaced by another with a different valence,[1] or an atom might be replaced by a *radical* bearing electrical charges. Clay particles may be broken apart so that the broken edges have atoms exposed which have negative or positive charges. These exposed electrical charges on the faces of crystals and on the edges of crystals attract cations and anions. There are many more negative positions, however, than positive positions on most clay particles.

Because of the predominance of negative charges on clay particles or crystals, one might think of them as polyanions; that is, they contain many molecular units and many negative charges. Another way of visualizing clay particles is that they combine with hydrogen to form weak acids.

Hydrogen combines with anions (except the OH^- ion) to form acids, so the saturation of clays with hydrogen forms acids. Hydrogen-saturated clays are too acid for plants to grow in, but they are still very weak, particularly as acids are thought of in chemistry. A weak acid is one with a low degree of ionization. A strong acid has a high degree of ionization; that is, nearly all the hydrogen and the anions separate in solution. For example, hydrochloric acid (HCl) is highly ionized and is a strong acid.

Clays combine with cations to form salts. Cations (except H^+) and anions (except OH^-) form salts. When clays are saturated with cations like Ca^{++} or Na^+ they form alkaline salts. They might be thought of as alkaline salts in the way we visualize sodium bicarbonate. Almost everyone is aware of the alkalizing effect of sodium bicarbonate. It is a salt of a weak acid and a strong base. It hydrolyzes in water to form sodium hydroxide (NaOH), which is a strong base and highly ionized, and carbonic acid (H_2CO_3), which is a weak acid and only slightly ionized. In the solution of sodium bicarbonate there are many more OH^- ions than H^+ ions in solution. Clays which are saturated with a base like sodium or calcium are alkaline in reaction also. Hydrolysis of a sodium-saturated clay forms many more OH^- ions than H^+ ions in solution. The proportion of H^+ ions to bases (Ca^{++}, Mg^{++}, K^+, and Na^+) on the adsorbing surfaces of clays determines whether a soil is acid or alkaline in reaction.

[1] Valence is the expression of electrical charge. For example, the calcium ion (Ca^{++}) has a valence of 2, while the nitrate ion (NO_3^-) has a valence of 1.

When organic matter undergoes decomposition the constituents of plant tissue become finely divided and approach or reach molecular size. Likewise, as microbial tissue undergoes decomposition, its products of decomposition also approach molecular size. One characteristic of organic compounds of particular significance is that molecules may link together to form chainlike compounds or branched compounds of very high molecular weight. Along these large molecules are reactive groups which will exchange cations and anions for those in the surrounding soil solution. Some of the organic compounds of soil organic matter appear to be quite resistant to microbial attack. This is particularly true of lignin-derived material and some of the nitrogenous compounds including microbially derived proteins. These resistant organic compounds develop a high capacity for holding exchangeable cations and anions. But, again, organic matter has many more negative positions than positive positions; that is, soil organic matter has a much higher cation-exchange capacity than anion-exchange capacity. Moreover, a gram of soil organic matter has a higher cation-exchange capacity than a gram of clay.

Among the reactive groups on the organic compounds is the carboxyl group. It is indicated by the symbol R—COOH. The R represents the remainder of the organic compound. The group has the structure:

$$R—C\begin{matrix} \diagup\!\diagup\,O \\ \diagdown\,O—H \end{matrix}$$

The hydrogen of the carboxyl group is exchangeable. The organic compounds with their reactive groups saturated with H^+ ions are referred to as organic acids. These acids are weakly ionized and are similar in this respect to clays.

The degree of acidity or alkalinity of soils is expressed in terms of pH. This subject is dealt with in more detail in Chap. 7. At this point it is well to know that a pH of 7 is neutral. At a pH of 7, OH^- and H^+ ions in solution are equal. The pH values below 7 indicate acidity. The lower the pH the greater the acidity, but a pH of 4 is about the lower limit for soils. Values below pH of 4 are rarely found in soils. The values above 7 indicate alkalinity. High values, those in the range from 8 to 10, are associated with alkali soils. Soils are rarely found with pH values above 10. At about pH of 7.5 one will find that clays and organic matter are base-saturated. As the pH value decreases, the proportion of hydrogen to bases increases. At a pH of 4 the percentage of exchange positions held by H^+ on clays and organic matter is high (in the range of 50 to 100 per cent).

Weathering of Rocks and Minerals in Soils.   Rocks are mixtures of minerals, and as rocks are weathered they tend to break down into the separate minerals of which they are composed. A mineral might be roughly defined as containing molecules all of which are alike.

Rocks are classified as igneous, metamorphic, and sedimentary. Igneous rocks are those which cooled and crystallized from a former molten condition. The crystals of minerals vary greatly in size. In granite, one can easily see the individual crystals of such minerals as quartz, muscovite, biotite, hornblende, and orthoclase, but in basalt the minerals are fine-grained and cannot be recognized by the naked eye.

Sedimentary rocks are those which have formed as sediments in water. They are secondary rocks in that they are composed of materials that suffered weathering at some other location and were transported to their present location and became cemented to form rocks. Examples are shale, sandstone, and limestone.

Metamorphic rocks are those which have had their structure changed by heat or pressure. Materials which are subjected to the weight of thick overdeposits of materials may be greatly changed. Shale may be transformed to slate. Granite may be transformed to gneiss, and sandstone may be fused to form quartzite. Shales which are muds (clays primarily) may be recrystallized to form schists.

Rocks are consolidated materials; that is, they represent a mixture of minerals cemented together. The cementation of materials or crystals of minerals must be gradually broken by weathering so that a mass of friable, unconsolidated material exists from which soil can develop. Much of the fragmentation of rocks and minerals is brought about by physical weathering.

Glaciation and erosion have had tremendous influence on reduction of materials in size. But a great amount of weathering occurs as a combination of chemical and physical weathering. Temperature changes cause some breaking apart of rocks because the different minerals expand to different extents. Where water can get in between crystals and freeze, there is some influence of frost action. But as water and air enter spaces within rocks, chemical weathering takes its toll. Furthermore, weathering is accelerated by the presence of decomposing organic matter. The decomposition of organic matter produces acids which are more effective than water in dissolving minerals. Plant roots hasten decomposition of minerals by exchanging hydrogen for bases. Weathering is most intense where the rocks and minerals are exposed to high-moisture contents, to atmospheric air, to high temperatures, and to biological forces associated with decomposing organic matter. The weathering process in a soil profile is most intense in the surface soil, and the intensity of weathering decreases with depth.

In so far as transported materials are concerned, most of the weathering occurred before deposition in their present location. This is particularly true of the physical weathering which developed the unconsolidated parent material.

When one looks at the C horizon of a soil one is impressed by the absence of organic matter. It must not be overlooked that a high proportion of the parent materials of soils (both unconsolidated materials and sedimentary rocks) were transported to their present position by wind, water, ice, or gravity. Some of the material eroded from soils at some other location at some other time in geological history, and since their deposition, some of the "old" soil organic matter has decomposed. But the lower organic-matter content of the C horizon is largely due to dilution with geological materials not containing organic matter which were deposited along with soils transported from other sites.[1]

Within the over-all process of weathering there are two changes which take place that are of particular significance. One is the reduction in size of the particles of soils which is largely physical weathering (or disintegration), and the other is the chemical decomposition and dissolution that occur. A reduction in size favors the processes through which materials reach the solution state. Moreover, the leaching action of water hastens the weathering process by removal of soluble materials.

Sand weathers into silt, and some dissolution occurs during the process. Likewise, silt weathers into clay, and some solution occurs along with the reduction in size to form clay, but by far most of the reduction in size of sand and silt is a result of fragmentation or breaking apart by physical processes to form many smaller particles. Silt and sand can suffer some weathering without fragmentation; that is, there may be some exchange of atoms on the surfaces of silt and sand or the dissolution of atoms or molecules from their surfaces. But generally speaking, sands and silts are relatively unreactive. The surfaces of sand and silt may be just as reactive as the surfaces of clays, but the surface exposed in a gram of silt or sand is very much lower than the surface exposed by a gram of clay. Therefore the weathering of silt and sand usually represents a low per cent of the total weathering in a soil containing appreciable amounts of clay.

Because of the relatively high surface exposure of clay, this fraction is thought of as the active portion of the mineral component of soils. Clays are tiny fragments of minerals. They are different from their parent minerals, however, in that their chemical structure has been altered. In particular, they gain cation-exchange capacity. If one were to take pieces of minerals and grind them to the size of clay, one would find that the fine material would have a capacity for adsorbing cations and anions.

[1] Personal communication from F. F. Riecken.

Presumably the broken edges of the fragments of clay size have exposed atoms with extra electrons or protons. Yet the finely ground minerals have a relatively small exchange capacity compared to clays of soils.

This may be an oversimplification of clay formation, but it may help in gaining a concept of clay. Silicate minerals, a number of which are listed below, are generally composed of one or more bases (Ca, Mg, K, Na) combined with a skeleton of aluminum oxide and/or silicon dioxide.

Silicate minerals

Muscovite	$H_2KAl_3Si_3O_{12}$
Biotite	$(HK)_2(MgFe)_2(AlFe)_2Si_3O_{12}$
Orthoclase	$KAlSi_3O_8$
Labradorite	$NaCaAl_2Si_6O_{16}$
Albite	$NaAlSi_3O_8$
Anorthite	$CaAl_2Si_2O_8$
Olivine	$MgFeSiO_4$
Talc	$3MgO\cdot4SiO_2\cdot H_2O$
Serpentine	$3MgO\cdot2SiO_2\cdot2H_2O$
Hornblende	$Ca(FeMg)Si_2O_6$

Oxide group

Quartz	SiO_2
Hematite	Fe_2O_3
Magnetite	Fe_3O_4
Limonite	$2Fe_2O_3\cdot3H_2O$
Bauxite	Al_2O_3

Carbonate group

Calcite	$CaCO_3$
Dolomite	$CaCO_3\cdot MgCO_3$
Magnesite	$MgCO_3$

Phosphates

Apatite	$3[Ca_3(PO_4)_2]\cdot CaF_2$

Sulfides and sulfates

Pyrite	FeS
Gypsum	$CaSO_4$

Some of the silicate minerals contain iron. As weathering occurs, the bases are released. Some of the bases leach downward and out of the soil, and some of the bases are held in the soil. The skeleton of aluminum oxide and silicon dioxide remain as the principal constituents of clay; also a part of the skeleton structure is molecules of water (water of hydration, the content of which increases as the weathering progresses). The iron contained in silicate minerals may become a part of the skeleton, but most of it that is released becomes ferric hydroxide if the weathering occurs aerobically. The ferric hydroxide is adsorbed on the surfaces of clay (and to silt and sand to some extent). It stains the soil a yellowish-rusty color. If the clay becomes exposed to long periods of dessication, the iron hydroxide may become dehydrated to form the rusty-red color or even a bright-red color. Some of the aluminum of the skeleton becomes separated as aluminum hydroxide or free alumina (Al_2O_3). Also some of the silicon dioxide becomes separated as silicon dioxide or as silicate ions. But for the most part, the silicon, aluminum, and iron with their oxides and hydroxides remain as the residue of weathering. The bases (Ca, Mg, K, and Na) disappear relatively more rapidly than silicon, aluminum, and iron. Figure 41 illustrates this preferential accumulation of silicon, aluminum, and iron because of the loss of bases.

Relative Rates of Loss of Silicon, Iron, and Aluminum. As clays are formed during the weathering process, the bases are removed by leaching faster than iron, aluminum, and silicon, therefore the latter three increase as percentage of the total chemical components of soils. Yet it should be recognized that clays may gradually weather away entirely. They may break down into their component parts, yielding aluminum hydroxide, iron hydroxide, and silicic acid, and leach from the weathering mass.

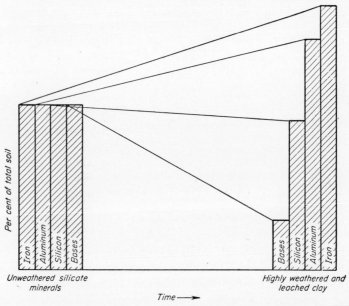

FIG. 41. A schematic diagram showing the differential accumulation of mineral constituents as weathering occurs. The silicon in this example is the silicon contained in silicate minerals and should not be confused with silicon contained in quartz.

The relative rates of loss of silicon, iron, and aluminum are of interest to the soil scientist. They indicate the degree of weathering and the nature of the weathering process and reflect the fertility status. In general, iron and aluminum are removed by leaching more rapidly than silicon under strongly acid conditions. Figure 42 indicates the relation of pH to the relative solubility of silicon, iron, and aluminum. In the humid region of the United States (and other countries of temperate climate) the soils developed under forest cover, especially coniferous types of forest, have developed strongly acid surface layers. The low pH favors the removal of iron and aluminum, and there has been a general preferential loss of iron and aluminum from topsoils and an accumulation of silicon materials, both quartz and colloidal silica, in the topsoils. Most of the iron and aluminum from the topsoils accumulate with the less-acid clay of the subsoils. In the Southeastern part of the United States, the topsoils are light in color and high in quartz sand partly as a result of dissolution of the clay minerals.   Much of the iron and aluminum has accumulated in the subsoils, and the colors due to iron are very outstanding in the subsoils.

Most of the SiO_2 of the topsoil of humid-forest regions of the United States is in the form of quartz sand.   Quartz is one of the most resistant

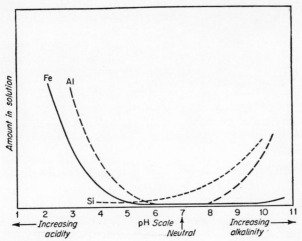

Fig. 42. A schematic diagram showing the relation of acidity or alkalinity to the solubility of silicon, iron, and aluminum.

minerals as long as the particles are larger than silt size.   It is not so resistant, however, in a finely divided condition.   Jackson and Sherman (8) consider quartz to be less resistant to weathering than muscovite if both minerals are of clay size.   It is necessary to keep in mind the difference between quartz and the SiO_2 of silicate minerals as one considers the relative resistance of silicon, aluminum, and iron to weathering (13). The colloidal form of SiO_2 may leach from a soil even under acid conditions.

One way of judging the relative loss of silicon, aluminum, and iron in the weathering process is to examine the ionic content of river water. Table 19 shows the estimated composition of river water from the different continents and the average throughout the world.

These data indicate that the bases are removed much more rapidly than silicon, iron, and aluminum.   The four bases make up only about 11 per cent of the earth's crust, yet they make up over 30 per cent of the material carried in river water.   The ratio of SiO_2 to R_2O_3* is about 3 to 1 in igneous rocks and in the earth's crust.   The ratio of SiO_2 to R_2O_3 in river waters of the world averages about 4 to 1.   In other words, silicon is carried from the land to the oceans faster than iron and aluminum.   If weathering were allowed to continue for a long enough period of time in

* The symbol for Al_2O_3 plus Fe_2O_3.

TABLE 19. AVERAGE COMPOSITION OF RIVER WATER* (5)
Expressed as per cent of the ions in the water

	A	B	C	D	E	F
CO_3	33.40	32.48	39.98	36.61	32.75	35.15
SO_4	15.31	8.04	11.97	13.03	8.67	12.14
Cl	7.44	5.75	3.44	5.30	5.66	5.68
NO_3	1.15	.62	.90	.98	.58	.90
Ca	19.36	18.92	23.19	21.23	19.00	20.39
Mg	4.87	2.59	2.35	3.42	2.68	3.41
Na	7.46	5.03	4.32	5.98	4.90	5.79
K	1.77	1.95	2.75	1.98	2.35	2.12
$(FeAl)_2O_3$	.64	5.74	2.40	1.96	5.52	2.75
SiO_2	8.60	18.88	8.70	9.51	17.89	11.67

*A, North America; B, South America; C, Europe; D, Asia; E Africa; F, average for the five continents.

a given locality, it is expected that iron and aluminum would remain behind to make up the bulk of the soil.

In the tropical regions there are soils with very high contents of iron and aluminum known as Laterite. The term Laterite is derived from the Latin term *later*, which means "brick." The moist soil can be cut out of the profile in the form of bricks, dried in the sun, and used for building purposes. The hydroxides of iron and aluminum dry irreversibly, that is, they do not absorb water readily. Rehydration requires a very long time.

The terms Lateritic and Latosols (preferred) are used for designating soils with a high content of iron and aluminum, while Laterite describes a specific stage of weathering and soil formation. The content of hydrated oxides of iron and aluminum often account for more than 80 per cent of the mineral matter of Laterites. Laterite represents the most advanced stage of weathering. It can hardly be called a soil because it declines in productivity to the extent that it will hardly support vegetation. Where vegetation becomes scant, the material becomes dehydrated through exposure to the sun and wind and forms a hard crust. In this condition it is not really a soil because it will not support plant growth.

The ultimate product of weathering, therefore, is an accumulation of the oxides of iron and aluminum along with titanium oxide. Although aluminum and iron predominate in the most highly weathered deposits, there is a significant quantity of titanium oxide, amounting to several per cent. Jackson and Sherman (8) consider titanium to be more resistant to weathering than either iron or aluminum.

The most highly weathered materials occur in tropical regions. The reason is related to temperature. The soils and soil materials of tropical climates are affected by weathering processes throughout the year, while soils and soil materials of cool temperate climates are frozen during part of the year, during which time chemical decomposition is practically nil. The higher temperatures, associated with the formation of the tropical soils, causes them to weather more rapidly than soils in cooler climates. By translating degree of weathering to terms of time it is estimated that the soils and their underlying materials of the tropics are twenty to thirty times older than the soils and their underlying materials of the North Central part of the United States. One other feature of the soils of the cool temperate regions is that glaciation has exposed fresh material in certain regions several times during the last million years. The recently glaciated materials of the United States and other countries have a relatively high content of easily weathered silicate minerals which are not found in very old soils. Erosion and removal of the highly weathered material keep the soil young in terms of weathering.

In very old and strongly weathered materials, iron and aluminum predominate. Where the soil develops with alternate wetting and drying, iron accumulates to a greater extent than aluminum. On the other hand, if the weathering occurs under permanently moist conditions, aluminum accumulates to a greater extent because the iron is relatively more mobile. The iron may be reduced to the ferrous form and leach from the soil. The more typical situation in soils, however, is the alternate wetting and drying. Under such conditions practically all of the free iron remains in the oxidized form which is very immobile.

Jackson and Sherman (8) rate iron as being more resistant than aluminum. They base their weathering sequence on the content of the various minerals in the clay fraction of soils of different ages. They rate the more resistant materials in the order of $TiO_2 > Fe_2O_3 > Al_2O_3 > SiO_2$, that is, titanium oxide is the most resistant of the major components of soils, followed by iron oxide.

Preferential Loss of the Bases in Weathering. The different minerals vary in the rates at which they weather, and soils vary in their mineral composition. It is possible, however, to generalize on the relative rates at which minerals weather.

It is generally recognized that potassium-bearing minerals weather very slowly (9). Nearly 99 per cent of the total potassium in most soils is in the mineral form. Only about 1 per cent (as a rough idea) of the total potassium in a typical soil is in exchangeable form. There is usually more total potassium than total sodium, calcium, or magnesium in soils. Surface soils often have as much total potassium as is contained by the underlying horizons, on a percentage basis.

It is also generally recognized that calcium-bearing minerals weather more rapidly than the minerals carrying the other bases. Soils usually have less nonexchangeable calcium (mineral form) than nonexchangeable magnesium, sodium, or potassium. Soils often have as much as half their total calcium in the exchangeable form. There probably would not be any argument about whether or not the average of calcium-bearing

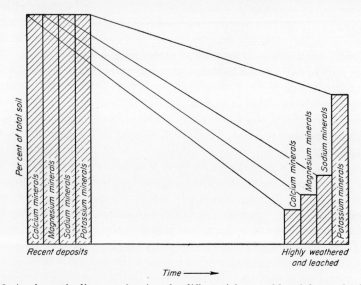

FIG. 43. A schematic diagram showing the differential rate of breakdown of minerals containing bases. The assumption is made that the original contents of bases are the same in this case.

minerals weathers faster than the average of potassium-bearing minerals, but the arrangement of magnesium and sodium minerals in relation to calcium and potassium in terms of rates of weathering is not so simple.

Goldich (7) arranged several minerals in the order of their rates of weathering. His list is reproduced below. The most resistant minerals are at the bottom of the list, and except for quartz (SiO_2), the potassium-bearing minerals are among the more resistant minerals.

MINERAL-STABILITY SERIES IN WEATHERING (7)

Olivine (contains Mg)	Calcic plagioclase
Augite (a complex silicate)	Calcic-alkali plagioclase
Hornblende (contains Ca and Mg)	Alkali-calcic plagioclase
Biotite (contains K)	Alkali plagioclase
	Potash feldspar
	Muscovite (a potassium silicate)
	Quartz

Jackson and Sherman (8) rated 13 mineral groups of the fine clay fraction with a typical mineral for each group. The more easily weathered mineral is listed first: (1) gypsum, (2) calcite, (3) hornblende, (4) biotite,

(5) albite, (6) quartz, (7) muscovite, (8) vermiculite, (9) montmorillonite, (10) kaolinite, (11) gibbsite, (12) hematite, and (13) anatase.

The relative rates of loss of the bases during weathering are shown in Fig. 43. These relative rates of loss were arrived at after the study of a large number of tables of composition contained in the "Atlas of American Agriculture."[1] On the average, it is believed that the rates of weathering are in the order of Ca > Mg > Na > K. The earth's crust contains more calcium than any of the other bases, and the contents of potassium, sodium, and magnesium are not greatly different, yet most topsoils contain the bases (in terms of total quantities of each) in the order of K > Na > Mg or Ca.

From examination of Table 19, it is apparent that sodium exceeds magnesium in the average river water. The four bases are carried in the average river water in the order of Ca > Na > Mg > K. If magnesium minerals weather faster than sodium minerals, one might expect to find more magnesium than sodium in river water. Apparently, the explanation for this relationship is that sodium is quite mobile once it is released in weathering, and it moves into drainage water quite readily. On the other hand, magnesium may be recombined as part of clay crystals in subsoils or precipitated as a slightly soluble magnesium salt in the underlying material of soil rather than leach into the ground waters.

It also follows that the weathering sequence, Ca > Mg > Na > K, should give an indication of the average relative amounts of the bases in the bottom of the B horizon in dry regions. In the subhumid, semiarid, and arid regions of the United States, the C horizon is permanently dry except in river bottoms and in depressed areas. As weathering occurs in the topsoil, the bases move down with percolating water. The bases collect at the bottom of the B horizon as salts of carbonate and sulfates in particular and some chlorides and nitrates.

Retention of Exchangeable Bases by Clays. It should be remembered that each base exists in three main forms: (a) the unavailable, or the mineral, form, (b) the exchangeable form, and (c) the solution form.

As minerals weather, the bases are released as cations, Ca^{++}, Mg^{++}, K^+, and Na^+. Part of the cations are held on the surfaces of the clays and organic compounds as exchangeable ions, and some move down with percolating water to the bottom of the B horizon or to the water table.

The diagram on page 118 is helpful in gaining an understanding of the relative amounts of the different bases that are held as exchangeable cations.

The calcium ion is held with two bonds more closely to the adsorbing surface than magnesium, which also is held with two bonds. Magnesium is more readily displaced than calcium. Sodium and potassium are each

[1] Part III, Soils of the United States, by C. F. Marbut, 1935.

held with one bond, which makes them more easily displaced than the divalent ions, and neither is held in so closely as calcium. Sodium is the one most easily displaced. These four cations are held in the order of Ca > Mg > K > Na, both in terms of quantity and the energy of adsorption.

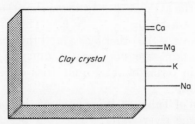

One should not confuse rates of weathering with retention of cations by clays. They are almost the same, however. Their rates of weathering are Ca > Mg ≳ Na > K. Their retention rates are Ca > Mg > K > Na.* The difference is between sodium and potassium. One other point which is often confusing is that the bases calcium, magnesium, and potassium are held by clays in the order of Ca > Mg > K, and yet that is the order in which one finds them in leachates of lysimeter studies. See page 81 for examples of the amounts of the bases contained in drainage water. *The bases are usually lost in drainage water of lysimeters in the same order that they weather from minerals.*

Comparison of Analysis of Earth's Crust with a Representative Humid-region Soil. The data in Table 20 illustrate the effect of weathering on differential loss of mineral constituents. There are many interesting points that may be recognized in this table. The accumulation of iron and aluminum in the B horizon is partially due to movement from the A horizon. The silicon dioxide is more stable than iron and aluminum under acid conditions which prevail in humid-region soils, and the A horizon is more acid than the B horizon.

The stability of potassium-bearing minerals is well illustrated in Table 20. Furthermore, one may readily recognize that sodium minerals are weathered more slowly than calcium and magnesium minerals but more rapidly than potassium minerals.

The difference in amounts of calcium and magnesium cannot be explained on the basis of weathering. Since calcium minerals weather faster than magnesium minerals (on the average), one would expect more magnesium than calcium in the A horizon. There are two important factors which prevent a greater reduction in calcium. One is the fact

* The retention rate here applies to the exchangeable cations. As will be explained in Chap. 11, potassium may also be retained by certain clays in nonexchangeable positions.

that plants, in general, use more calcium than they do magnesium, and therefore more calcium is returned to the surface by plant absorption. The second factor is that calcium ions are held more strongly than magnesium ions by the clay minerals. There is about five times as much cal-

TABLE 20. COMPOSITION OF EARTH'S CRUST COMPARED WITH COMPOSITION OF A REPRESENTATIVE UNITED STATES SOIL (5,10)

Component	Earth's crust, per cent	Humid-region soil horizons, per cent*		
		C	B	A
SiO_2	59.08	66.0	62.0	80.0
Al_2O_3	15.23	15.0	20.0	8.0
Fe_2O_3	3.10	6.0	8.0	3.0
CaO	5.10	3.0	0.8	0.6
MgO	3.45	2.0	1.0	0.5
Na_2O	3.71	1.5	1.3	1.0
K_2O	3.11	2.0	2.0	2.0
Others	1.76	4.5	4.9	4.9

* Estimated from data in reference (10).

cium as magnesium held by clay, on the average. Nearly half the calcium in the surface of humid-region soils is held by clay minerals in exchangeable form. In contrast, about 10 per cent of the magnesium is held in exchangeable form.

Occurrence of Nitrogen, Phosphorus, and Sulfur in Soils. Of the essential elements, we have thus far emphasized calcium, magnesium, and potassium, and iron to a certain extent. These elements exist as cations in solution, or combined with anions to form salts, or held by chemical attraction to humus and clay crystals. Nitrogen, phosphorus, and sulfur exist in the soil in organic combination or (usually) as anions while in the inorganic form.

The occurrence of nitrogen, phosphorus, and sulfur presents a much more complex picture, and each one must be discussed separately. The anion-forming elements are constituents of organic compounds within plants, while the cations (for the most part) remain active and mobile within the plant. When plant residues are returned to the soil, the cations are readily leached from the residues, while the anion-forming elements are released through biological decomposition.

Nitrogen. About 78 per cent of the air is nitrogen, but nitrogen cannot be utilized by plants until it has been chemically combined with hydrogen or oxygen. The combination can be accomplished by certain bacteria living free in the soil or in nodules on roots of legumes, by lightning, or synthetically by man.

About 99 per cent of the nitrogen of the soil exists in organic combination, as in proteins. The distribution of nitrogen in the soil profile follows the same pattern as the distribution of organic matter.

As organic matter decomposes, nitrogen is liberated as ammonia (NH_3). The NH_3 may combine with water to form NH_4OH, which forms NH_4^+ and OH^-. The NH_4^+ does not exist in the soil to any appreciable extent because of the abundance of nitrifying bacteria, which convert the NH_4^+ to nitrate (NO_3^-). The nitrate form is very soluble and leaches from the soil quite readily if it is not taken up by plant absorption or used by microorganisms.

Phosphorus. The phosphorus content of soils is expressed on the basis of phosphorus pentoxide (P_2O_5) rather than elemental phosphorus. The amount of P_2O_5 in soils varies generally from about 1000 to 5000 lb. per acre furrow slice. A representative soil of the humid part of the United States contains about 2500 lb. of P_2O_5 in the surface soil of an acre.

Upland soils of the Corn Belt generally contain more phosphorus than upland soils of the Cotton Belt. On the other hand, some of the river-bottom soils, particularly in the tobacco areas, are rich in phosphorus. The area of soils richest in phosphorus occur in the limestone belt of Kentucky, where soils are known to contain well over 10,000 lb. per acre.

About 25 to 75 per cent of the phosphorus in surface soils is in organic combination. There is some correlation between *total phosphorus* and organic matter in soils; that is, soils high in *total phosphorus* are generally high in organic matter. There is high correlation between *organic phosphorus* and organic nitrogen, but the ratio of organic phosphorus to organic nitrogen varies with climate. The average ratio of organic phosphorus to organic nitrogen in Iowa soils (12) is about 1 to 10, while the ratio for the two components is about 1 to 15 for soils of Oklahoma (6).

There is practically no loss of phosphorus by leaching from soils. The amount of water-soluble phosphorus in an acre furrow slice is very small and may be only 1 or 2 lb. per acre or even less. Because of the low solubility of phosphorus, soils frequently contain a higher percentage of phosphorus in the topsoil than is found in subsoils. The phosphorus is absorbed by plants from subsoils and is left in the surface soil as the plant dies.

Inorganic phosphorus occurs as part of an anion radical in combination with cations such as iron, aluminum, calcium, magnesium, sodium, or potassium. Plants utilize the inorganic form of phosphorus, but organic phosphorus compounds must undergo decomposition before the phosphorus is available to plants.[1]

Sulfur. The sulfur content of soil is expressed on the basis of the tri-

[1] There is evidence from solution culture work that certain forms of organic phosphorus are available to plants (14).

oxide (SO_3).   The amount of sulfur in soils of the humid part of the United States is related to the amount of organic matter, since sulfur is an important constituent of organic compounds.   Most soils contain between 500 and 2500 lb. of SO_3 per acre furrow slice.   Inorganic sulfur compounds are not so resistant to decomposition as phosphate minerals, and leaching removes sulfur rapidly enough so that soils would become exhausted of sulfur if it were not for sulfur added in rainfall (1) and in fertilizers containing ordinary (20 per cent) superphosphate.

Soils of the subhumid and drier regions accumulate considerable amounts of sulfur at the bottom of the B horizon.   Sulfates are sometimes constituents of alkali salts in irrigated soils of dry climates.   On the other hand, sulfur is used extensively in the treatment of alkali soils in which sodium salts have accumulated.   This subject is discussed in Chap. 7.

The use of sulfur as a fertilizer has not been necessary, except in a few isolated areas.   The amounts added by rainfall are almost enough to meet crop needs in most areas, and in some areas the sulfur added by rainfall more than meets crop needs.   Gypsum ($CaSO_4$) makes up nearly half the weight of ordinary superphosphate, so that wherever this phosphate is applied to supply phosphorus, the sulfur needs are also met. Furthermore, farm manure is a good source of sulfur.

While sulfur is generally released from organic matter as hydrogen sulfide (H_2S), the sulfide form does not persist in soils because of the presence of oxidizing bacteria.   The bacteria oxidize the sulfur to the sulfate, and therefore most of the inorganic sulfur occurs in the soil in the anion form (SO_4), in combination with such cations as calcium or magnesium.

The Minor Elements.   The six minor elements are iron, manganese, zinc, copper, molybdenum, and boron.   Chapter 14 is devoted to a discussion of minor elements.

Iron, which has been discussed under rock weathering, is one of the three most abundant mineral elements in soils and rarely becomes deficient except under conditions of alkalinity.

Manganese occurs widely in soils but in highly variable amounts.   Its use as a fertilizer is generally restricted to direct spraying of plants on soils known to be deficient in manganese.   Only a few pounds of available manganese per acre is necessary to support plant growth.   Morris (11) found that 25 naturally acid soils contained from 2.4 to 1276 lb. per acre of exchangeable manganese; that is, the available manganese occurring as a cation on the surfaces of clay crystals and particles of humus.

Zinc occurs in small quantities in soils but is widely distributed and has become deficient only in isolated areas (4).   The citrus-growing areas of California and Florida have soils deficient in zinc, and zinc has been used successfully as a spray directly on the plant.   It is used as a soil amendment only where zinc exhaustion is recognized. Many zinc deficiencies are due to lack of availability of zinc as a result of an unfavorable soil reaction. Zinc is usually added to the soil as zinc sulfate, and the element zinc exists in the soil as a cation or combined with anions or clay crystals.

Copper occurs in the soil as a cation and enters into reactions similar to those of manganese or zinc. Deficiency of copper occurs particularly on peat, in soils with high humus content, and on very sandy soils with low humus content (16).

Molybdenum is the most recent addition to the list of essential elements. Arnon and Stout (3) demonstrated the essentiality of molybdenum in 1939. Soils contain very small amounts of molybdenum, and the addition of as little as 1 lb. per acre of sodium molybdate or ammonium molybdate has been shown to produce satisfactory plant growth on molybdenum-deficient soils (2). Molybdenum occurs as an anion radical similar to phosphorus, and the solubility of the molybdate ion (MoO_4), like that of the phosphate ion (PO_4), is affected by soil reaction, in that liming an acid soil will increase its solubility.

Boron occurs in soils in very small amounts, that is, only a few pounds per acre, but the element is essential to plant growth (15). There are many diseases of plants which are now known to be caused by boron deficiency. Some of the more common deficiency diseases are brown heart of turnips, heart rot of beets, internal brown spot of sweet potatoes, yellow alfalfa, and top sickness of tobacco. Several areas of the United States— the Pacific Coast, Atlantic Coastal Plain, and northern Minnesota, Wisconsin, and Michigan—are known to be deficient in boron, and certain commercial fertilizers in these areas are advertised as including boron. An extensive source of boron occurs in the form of sodium potassium borate (borax) in the California desert area, particularly in Death Valley. Considerable care must be exercised in the use of boron, since too much of the element is toxic. The toxicity limits vary considerably and are affected by the amount of organic matter, amount of clay, and pH of the soil. This subject is discussed further in Chap. 14.

REFERENCES

1. Alway, F. J., A Nutrient Element Slighted in Agricultural Research, *J. Am. Soc. Agron.*, **32**:913–921, 1940.
2. Anderson, A. J., Molybdenum Deficiency on a South Australian Ironstone, *J. Austr. Inst. Agr. Sci.*, **8**:73–75, 1942.
3. Arnon, D. I., and D. R. Stout, Molybdenum as an Essential Element for Higher Plants, *Plant Physiol.*, **14**:599–602, 1939.
4. Camp, A. F., Zinc as a Nutrient in Plant Growth, *Soil Sci.*, **60**:157–164, 1945.
5. Clarke, F. W., The Data of Geochemistry, *U.S. Geol. Survey Bull.* 770, 1924.
6. Garman, William L., Organic Phosphorus in Oklahoma Soils, *Okla. Acad. Sci. Proc.*, **28**:89–100, 1948.

7. Goldich, S. S., A Study in Rock-weathering, *J. Geol.*, **46**:17–58, 1938.
8. Jackson, M. L., and G. Ronald Sherman, Chemical Weathering of Minerals in Soils, *Advances in Agron*, **5**:221–318, 1953.
9. Jeffries, C. D., and J. W. White, Some Mineralogical and Chemical Characteristics of a Hagerstown Soil Profile, *Soil Sci. Soc. Amer. Proc.*, **2**:133–141, 1937.
10. Marbut, C. F., Soils of the United States, in "Atlas of American Agriculture," Part III, Washington, D.C., 1935.
11. Morris, H. D., Soluble Manganese Content of Acid Soils and Its Relation to the Growth and Manganese Content of Sweet Clover and Lespedeza, *Soil Sci. Soc. Amer. Proc.*, **13**:362–371, 1948.
12. Pearson, R. W., and Roy W. Simonson, Organic Phosphorus in Seven Iowa Soil Profiles: Distribution and Amounts as Compared to Organic Carbon and Nitrogen, *Soil Sci. Soc. Amer. Proc.*, **4**:162–167, 1939.
13. Reiche, Parry, A Survey of Weathering Processes and Products, *N. Mex. Univ. Pub. Geol.* 1, 1945.
14. Rogers, H. T., R. W. Pearson, and W. H. Pierre, Absorption of Organic Phosphorus by Corn and Tomato Plants and the Mineralizing Action of Exo-enzyme Systems of Growing Roots, *Soil Sci. Soc. Amer. Proc.*, **5**:285–291, 1940.
15. Shive, J. M., Boron in Plant Life: A Brief Historical Survey, *Soil Sci.*, **60**:41–51, 1945.
16. Sommer, A. L., Copper and Plant Growth, *Soil Sci.*, **60**:71–79, 1945.

CHAPTER 6

SOIL FORMATION AND CLASSIFICATION

A scheme of soil classification is necessary for the extension of the knowledge gained in research. There are experiment stations located in many sections of the United States, and the reason for so many different stations is the fact that so many different soil conditions exist which need special attention. In order to know how to apply information gained at each station, there must be available a description of the soils at the station, so that farmers can compare the soils at the experiment station with their own soils and decide whether the information gained is applicable to their conditions.

The soil on an experiment station may have one name and the soil on John Doe's farm a different name, yet the fertilizer and cropping practices for the two soils may be similar. If a soil map is available, it is quite convenient to determine whether or not the soil names agree; or with study, one can determine whether or not the descriptions agree. It is not always possible to get an up-to-date soils map of a county. Some of the old surveys include names no longer used, and a farmer is not likely to go to the trouble to try to find out the new name of the soil. The natural tendency is for the farmer to think of his land as "black loam," or "heavy blackland," or "light-colored sandy land," or some other simple description and then relate such description to experiment-station soils or demonstration-farm land.

A farmer can learn the different soil conditions on his farm by acquiring some knowledge of the development and differentiation of the A and B horizons. An understanding of how soils are developed can prove helpful in managing soils.

Soil Profile. Before beginning a discussion of the formation of soils and their classification, a few general remarks regarding their nature are necessary.

It must be emphasized that soil develops from parent material by processes of soil formation that differ from processes of rock weathering, which produce parent material. In the development of parent material the rocks and minerals are broken down to an unconsolidated mass largely by physical weathering. As a soil is developed from the parent material, certain changes take place which differentiate the various horizons to give soils their distinct layering. These changes are brought about largely by shifting of materials either mechanically or in solution to various layers within the horizons or completely out of the soil. The introduction of organic matter greatly facilitates the shifting of these materials. The acids produced as a result of decomposition of organic matter hasten the dissolution of minerals. Some of the organic acids form complexes with the relatively insoluble compounds of iron and aluminum and cause them to move downward in the profile in strongly acid soils. Moreover, the anions produced by organic-matter decomposition are, for the most part, mobile in soils, and as they leach from the profile they carry with them an equivalence in cations, most of which are bases. The term eluviation has been adopted to designate this movement of materials either mechanically or chemically.

As a vertical section of a well-developed soil is opened from the surface downward and into the parent material, it is possible to recognize a certain degree of differentiation into layers brought about by soil-forming processes. This vertical section is known as the soil profile. Three distinct horizons are distinguishable in a well-developed profile. These horizons vary tremendously in different soils. In some soils the horizons appear quite distinct, while in other soils the horizons are only weakly developed.

Fig. 44. This profile shows a bleached layer in the A horizon which is characteristic of strongly differentiated soils, particularly where the soil was developed in a cool climate under coniferous forest. This soil is a Podzol and is described on page 154. (*Courtesy of Charles E. Kellogg.*)

Figure 45 shows a hypothetical profile. It is not to be inferred that all profiles will have all the distinguishable layers shown in the figure. In

order to be recognized as a soil, however, the A and B horizons must be
at least faintly developed.   The A_{00} is the layer of undecomposed organic
matter, ordinarily called litter, such as loose leaves and other organic
debris.   The A_0 is the layer of partially decomposed organic matter
resting on the surface of the A horizon.   In cultivated soils the A_{00} and
A_0 layers are not present, and soils developed under grass usually do not
have these layers.   The A horizon is known as the zone of *eluviation*,

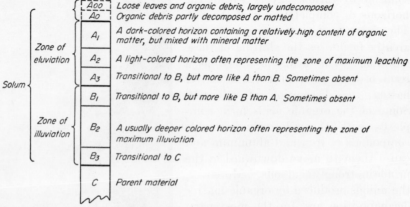

FIG. 45. A hypothetical soil profile.

while the B horizon is recognized as the zone of *illuviation*.   Collectively
these two horizons make up the solum, or true soil.   In soils developed
where leaching has been intense, the A horizon is impoverished of bases
and clay by eluviation.

   The A_1 layer of the A horizon is usually darker in color, containing more
organic matter.   The A_2 is the layer from which there has been maximum
eluviation.   In some forest soils this layer is often bleached to an ashy-
gray color.   The A_3 may or may not be present in a well-developed soil.
If the A horizon grades into the B horizon, the A_3 may be distinguishable.
On the other hand, the A_2 layer may rest directly on the B horizon.
B_2 designates the zone of maximum illuviation.   The B_1 and B_3 are
designated only in cases where there are definite transitional layers.

   The C horizon is the parent material of the soil.   In describing a profile,
the C horizon is also described.   In order to avoid confusion here, the
reader is reminded that the A and B horizons constitute the solum, or
true soil, while the C horizon is the parent material from which the soil
is developed.   All three horizons, A, B, and C, constitute the soil profile;
and soil classification is essentially that of classifying soil profiles.

   The C horizon is usually unconsolidated, and in the case of transported
parent material—marine, alluvial, etc.—it does exist as unconsolidated
material.   In the development of residual soils, however, soil formation

may keep pace with rock weathering, so that the B horizon rests directly on the parent rock. It is usually where the parent rock is extremely resistant to weathering that it appears just beneath the B horizon. The recent trend is to describe the consolidated parent material below the C horizon (or immediately beneath the B horizon) as the D$_r$ horizon. The solum may be formed from a material that differs from the underlying formation. For example, there are loess deposits in several sections of the United States that are only about 30 in. deep. The A and B horizons have developed from the loess. The underlying material is not the parent material, nor is it the C horizon. The unrelated formation just beneath the B horizon is referred to as the D horizon.

Classification of Parent Materials. It has long been the custom of agronomists to refer to the origin of the parent material when indicating the nature of the soil. An understanding of the origin and classification of parent materials is desirable before we go into origin and classification of soils.

Soil parent materials are undifferentiated, while soils are differentiated into horizons. The undifferentiated parent material is referred to as a geological formation and is a layer of material over other geological formations. The parent material varies from a few feet in thickness to many feet. Wherever a geological formation is exposed at the earth's surface, either there is soil formation taking place or a soil has already developed from the exposed material.

The parent material may be classified as to its geological origin as follows:

Parent material	Transporting agency	Origin	Classification
Consolidated.................	Weathered in place	Residual	Residual
Unconsolidated..............	Water	Marine	Marine
		Lacustrine	Lacustrine
		Alluvial	Alluvial fan
			Delta
			Flood plain
			Terrace
	Ice	Glacial	Ground moraine
			Terminal moraine
			Outwash plain
	Wind	Aeolian	Loess
			Volcanic ash
			Dune sand
	Gravity	Colluvial	Colluvial

Residual Materials. *Residual* materials are those which have weathered from the underlying rocks and minerals. Most rock formations at the earth's surface are sedimentary, and sedimentary materials have accumulated as erosional debris from other locations and have become cemented, or *consolidated*. So in reality, many residual materials have weathered from rocks which were consolidated from transported materials. To avoid any confusion as to what is *residual* and what is *transported*, it is well to keep in mind the following description. Transported parent materials are those which are unconsolidated and which have not been consolidated since being transported to their present location. Residual materials have weathered from *consolidated materials*.

Examples of residual materials are those which have weathered from limestone, sandstones, shales and slates, and many crystalline rocks such as granites and basalts. Important areas of residual materials are the limestone and sandstone areas of Central United States, the Piedmont area near the Atlantic Coast, and the mountainous areas of the Western part of the country.

Transported Materials. *Marine* materials are those which have eroded from continental areas, washed into seas or oceans (salt water), and later lifted above sea level. Most of the area in the Cotton Belt of the United States was at one time under the water of the Gulf. As the Gulf of Mexico gradually receded, layer after layer of sediments was exposed to soil-forming processes. The layers of materials vary all the way from practically pure quartz sand (probably old beach sand) to highly calcareous clays. In regions of marine materials one can often find the poorest and the richest soils of the country within a few miles of each other. The layers of marine materials are exposed as bands of material a few yards to many miles in width, approximately parallel to the original shore line of the Gulf.

Wherever the marine material accumulated *slowly* as erosional debris from continental areas and included a large amount of skeletal material of aquatic animals, the material became high in lime. Furthermore, since the lime owes its origin to skeletons, one would expect the same material to contain a large amount of phosphorus, of which bones are a good source. The calcareous marine materials of the Cotton Belt have developed into the richest upland soils of the region.

The topography near the Gulf is young and, away from rivers, is quite level for many miles. Near river outlets there is much swampy land. The farther the material from the Gulf, the older it is, the stronger the relief, and the more rolling is the topography.

Lacustrine materials are those which have eroded into lakes from surrounding uplands. The nature of the material is determined largely by the nature of the surrounding upland material. If the upland material is calcareous, the lacustrine material will likewise be high in lime. Since the water table in old lakes is usually high, there is not much leaching or much differentiation of the A and B horizons in soil development. The materials frequently require drainage before cultivation, but the topography is very smooth and favorable to reclamation. Soils developed under conditions of poor drainage are often high in organic matter.

The lacustrine soils are most important in the glaciated sections of the North Central United States.

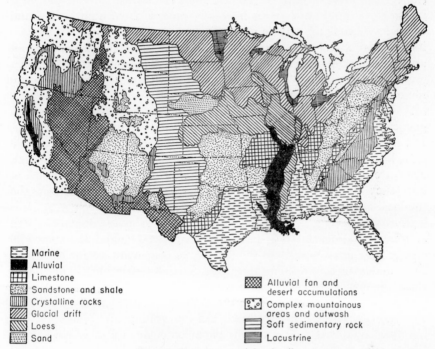

Marine
Alluvial
Limestone
Sandstone and shale
Crystalline rocks
Glacial drift
Loess
Sand

Alluvial fan and desert accumulations
Complex mountainous areas and outwash
Soft sedimentary rock
Lacustrine

FIG. 46. Parent materials of soils.

Alluvial materials are those which have been transported by streams. *Alluvial fans* are accumulated on land. In mountainous areas of the arid regions, streams carry materials down during floods and deposit them in fan-shaped deposits at the foot of the mountains. The alluvial-fan material is quite extensive along valleys between mountains in the desert region of the United States. When traveling west through Death Valley in an automobile, one drives up a smooth incline for about 8 miles on an old alluvial fan. From an airplane, it appears that alluvial fans occur at the base of mountains wherever streams flow down between two peaks of mountains. The alluvial-fan material develops into soils which are somewhat coarse but are productive under irrigation.

A *flood plain* is that part of the river valley which is subject to overflow. Flood-plain material is still being deposited and, though cultivated as a soil, is in reality a parent material. The oldest civilizations of the world developed on alluvial materials, and particularly on flood plains. Because of constant renewal of fertility by accumulation of soil during floods, flood plains such as the valley of the Nile River in Egypt have remained fertile for thousands of years.

A *terrace* is an alluvial deposit along a stream valley which is no longer subject to overflow. As the upland rises, the stream cuts deeper, or in young topography, the stream may cut deeper without uplift of the land. In either case, as the stream gradually cuts deeper, it leaves remnants of its old flood plain above overflows. Soils developed from stream terraces are generally very desirable for cultivation. The soils are often high in organic matter, usually quite well supplied with mineral nutrients, and removed from the hazards of floods.

A *delta* is a fan-shaped alluvial deposit at the mouth of a stream. It gets its name from the Greek letter Δ because of its triangular shape. Delta materials are like flood-plain materials in that they are used as soils, but as long as they are still being deposited, they are not true soils. They are parent materials which, when left above overflow, will develop into true soils of the region when time has permitted the manifestation of the local climate and vegetation.

Glacial Materials. When the climate becomes so cold that the winter accumulation of snow fails to melt during the summer, the snow piles deeper year after year. As the snow gets deeper its weight causes the snow underneath to become somewhat like ice. To visualize glacial ice, think of snow squeezed in the preparation of a snowball. The pressure on the snow causes apparent melting followed by recrystallization of ice. The snowball after being squeezed has less volume and is less likely to fall apart and at the same time is plastic enough to fit the curvature of the palm of the hand.

Glaciers which formed during the great glacial periods of Pleistocene time[1] came as far south as southern Illinois (see parent-materials map of the United States on page 129). The effect of glaciation was that of wearing down hills and filling valleys. Rocks were ground up like flour in some cases, and in others, the rocks were carried along and worn to somewhat rounded shapes. Glacial material, called *till*, is characterized by having all sizes of material—clay, silt, sand, gravel, cobbles, and even boulders several feet in diameter.

When a glacier front was somewhat stationary for a very long period, there was an accumulation of unstratified materials of all sizes in somewhat rough topography along the front of the glacier. During the sum-

[1] The Pleistocene period in geological history includes several hundred thousand years up until recent time. Recent time geologically goes back to the last glacial period, about 10,000 years ago.

mer, the glacier front would melt back, but the next winter the glacier would move forward again with another load of till. After many years of advance and retreat in the same area, the glacier front became marked by the greater accumulation of soil material. The southernmost extent of each of the great ice sheets is marked by the hilly topography called *terminal moraine*. Where the glacier melted back rather rapidly for several years in succession, the topography was left relatively smooth. A large amount of material was mixed in with the ice, and as the ice melted, the material was dropped in place. The relatively smooth topography left in this manner is called *ground moraine*. As the glaciers retreated they left wide bands of ground moraine between more narrow bands of terminal moraine, indicating cycles of weather causing a series of more or less stationary fronts of the glacier.

At the southern edge of glaciers (in the Northern Hemisphere) there was continuous melting in the summer. Great torrents of water poured out with such velocity that large rocks were carried for many miles. Much material, including sand, silt, clay, and rocks, was deposited below the glacier front. Because of the sorting action of water, the deposited material was stratified. This material is called *outwash*.

Loess. Loess is a silty material deposited by wind. Although not all loess is of glacial origin, most of the loess of Central United States was ground to the silt size by glaciation and then picked up by the wind and carried for great distances. Important loess deposits in this country are along the east side of the Mississippi and Missouri River Valleys. The loess deposits are most striking on the east side of the Mississippi River near Vicksburg. The deposits are over 100 ft. thick in places. Roads have been cut through the deposits, and the vertical banks have stood for more than a half century in many places. If the banks are sloped, erosion is severe along roads unless they are protected by sod or vines. The banks cause less trouble if left vertical. Gullying is hazardous in thick loess deposits. Frequently the material is eroded so that the gully extends to the full depth of the loess, and the banks of the gully remain vertical.

Loess is characterized by its high proportion of silt. It is believed that most loess was blown out of river valleys. This is particularly true of the loess on the east side of the Mississippi and Missouri Rivers. In both areas it is found that the loess is deeper and coarser near the river and shallower and finer farther from the river.

Aeolian Material. *Volcanic ash* is fine material which is carried by wind from active volcanoes. The material is not important in this country but is an important source of soil material in Mexico, South America, and islands of the Pacific.

Dune sands are extensively accumulated along the eastern fringe of the desert region of the United States. There is a very large region in Nebraska referred to as the Sand Hills of Nebraska. Some vegetation is supported on the sand, and in Nebraska this region is well known for its large ranches.

Colluvial material is transported by gravity. It is not important as a source of soil-parent material. It is found in mountainous areas where cliffs slough off or where landslides occur.

The term colluvium has been used to describe local alluvium. Colluvium is also recognized as alluvium which has washed to the bottom of hills or has accumulated in upland drainageways from local slopes.

Factors in Soil Formation.[1] It has been mentioned in foregoing paragraphs that soil-profile characteristics vary tremendously from place to place. Yet it is found that soils developed under similar environmental conditions tend to develop similarities in the profiles to the extent that parent materials are similar. With a general understanding of the influence of the various factors in soil formation, the student is better prepared for distinguishing soils or for the mapping of soils in the field. It is sometimes necessary to look further than just the color, texture, structure, etc., of the various layers in the profile in order to determine the series or type name. A consideration of the factors that tend to develop the particular soil in question will often lead to a more logical conclusion in regard to its classification, particularly in determining soil-type boundaries.

As we consider the soil as a natural body associated with its geographic location, we may readily list some of the major factors contributing to its characteristics. These factors are climate, vegetation, topography, parent material, and time. Probably climate, vegetation, and time have the greatest influence on the classification of soils on a regional basis. In a given locality, however, where climate and vegetation are similar, the influence of topography, parent material, and time often receive greater attention in classifying soils.

Climate. Climate has tremendous influence on soil formation. The steps in soil development from rock weathering to the formation of a well-developed soil are largely the result of climatic forces as they are related to other factors in soil formation. Climate determines to a great extent the kind of vegetation predominating in any region. The development of relief is greatly influenced by climatic agencies. The wide variation in topographical features in any area is largely the result of some climatic agency, such as glaciers, large amount of rainfall, or strong winds. And topography influences soil formation largely by influencing moisture, temperature, and aeration relations within the soil profile.

---

[1] The discussion of the five factors in soil formation was developed after reference (3). A detailed discussion of these factors is contained in "Factors of Soil Formation" by Hans Jenny, McGraw-Hill, New York, 1941.

Since some weathering continues with soil development from parent material, the relationship of rainfall and temperature to the chemical processes of weathering is of considerable importance in the study of the processes of soil formation.   Where high rainfall is coupled with high temperature, chemical weathering is extremely drastic.   Most of the silicate minerals may have decomposed, and the products of decomposition

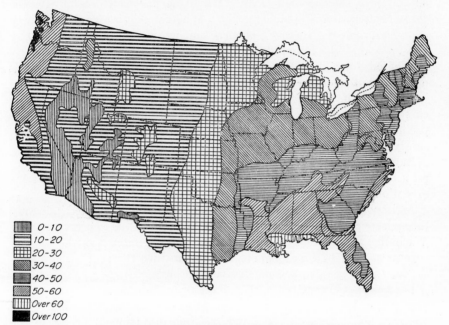

0-10
10-20
20-30
30-40
40-50
50-60
Over 60
Over 100

Fig. 47. Generalized map of annual precipitation.

have been removed in drainage or left to recombine to form new compounds.   The result is that a soil is formed which differs greatly from its parent material.

In areas of cold temperatures and/or low rainfall, chemical weathering is relatively slow.   The effect of temperature is great, however, because there is the usual effect of temperature changes, resulting in disintegration.

The amount of water percolating through the soil body affects the kind and degree of eluviation.   The amount of percolation is, in turn, influenced by the amount of precipitation, relative humidity, temperature, and length of the frost-free period.   Where the greatest amount of precipitation is coupled with the lowest temperature above freezing, the amount of leaching is greatest because of low evaporation; likewise, with a given rainfall, the amount of leaching is increased with an increase in relative humidity.

If the greatest amount of the annual rainfall comes during the period of highest temperatures, the evaporation is high and the amount of water left to percolate through the soil is reduced to a minimum. Movement of materials in solution may then be generally toward the surface, as in the case of arid soils.

The temperature factor has already been stressed in Chap. 5 in the discussion of weathering. An increase in temperature has the effect of speeding up chemical reactions. The higher temperatures also hasten the decomposition of organic matter. Where parent materials have been exposed for about the same geological time in different parts of the world, one finds that the materials in the warmer climates are more strongly weathered than those in cooler climates. The base content of soils decreases with weathering, while the content of silica, iron, and aluminum increases. The organic-matter content of soils is usually higher in cooler climates because of the higher base status contributing to more vegetative production, and particularly because the organic matter decomposes more slowly in a cooler climate.

In general, the boundaries of climatic types roughly parallel the boundaries of the great soil groups of the world. There are, however, some exceptions to this statement.

An important influence of climate on soil formation is exerted indirectly through its partial determination of the predominating vegetation under which the soil develops. The soil itself greatly influences the kind of vegetation that becomes established, and in turn the vegetation affects the formative process, so they evolve together.

Vegetation. Vegetation is the source of organic matter in soils. We may regard the introduction of organic matter as the beginning of the *constructional* process of soil building. Soil development occurs in the portion of the soil profile in which there is a noticeable influence of organic materials on the changes in physical and chemical properties of the mineral constituents. The layers beneath the soil layers, or solum, may be suffering changes, both physical and chemical; but the result is development of parent material by the destructive processes of weathering.

We very often hear it said that the soil is the weathered portion of the profile, or that as one studies the profile from the surface downward, one encounters the C horizon when the unweathered material below is reached. Statements of this nature should be avoided, since the parent material is usually unconsolidated and a result of the process of weathering. Probably the best thing to remember is that the association of living matter helps to differentiate the solum from the layers beneath, and that the parent material, or the C horizon, is below the direct influence of the biological forces involved in the formation of the soil.

There are two general groups of living matter which are involved in soil formation: first, those organisms which tend to destroy or decompose other materials, both organic and inorganic, for their own food and energy; second, those organisms which tend to build up organic matter from the more simple compounds of decomposition. There are two most important general groups of organisms or plants which synthesize organic matter—grasses and trees. These two groups vary considerably in their feeding habits and in the amount of the various elements taken up by their roots and deposited in or on top of the solum.[1]

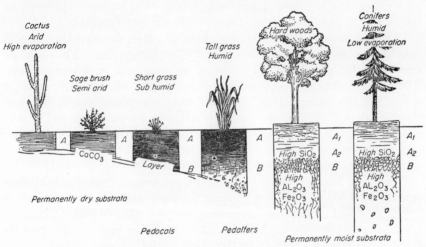

FIG. 48. Schematic diagram showing relation of climate and vegetation to soil development. See page 151 for discussion of Pedocals and Pedalfers.

In general, climate determines whether or not a forest growth will survive in any region. Forests in turn exert a tremendous influence on the kind of soil developed. Coniferous trees are light feeders on bases, and leaf fall of these plants results in an accumulation of acid residues. Moreover, because members of this group of plants are light feeders on such bases as calcium and magnesium, the solum is likely to become impoverished of bases as leaching occurs. Trees vary, though, in their demand for basic elements; a beech-maple forest will have an accumulation of organic matter with a higher content of bases than a pine forest. In general, deciduous forests are heavier feeders on bases than coniferous forests, but forests as a whole are lighter feeders on bases than grasses. It may be stated that the amount and kind of bases found in the residues of leaf fall depend on the feeding habits of the plants and on the amounts of bases available to them.

Grasses, in general, have a higher requirement for bases than do forest species. The return of the bases to the surface by plant absorption keeps

[1] An excellent review of the differences in soils of the forest-grassland transition is provided in reference (9).

the soil from becoming strongly acid and slows down the aging process. The various species of grasses vary in the amounts of bases they absorb and in the proportionate amount of the various bases. If the plants are heavy feeders on calcium, the soil is likely to be high in calcium, and in turn the clay fraction of the soil will have high proportion of exchangeable calcium. On the other hand, if the parent materials are high in sodium, one would expect to find sodium-tolerant plants, and the soil developed under them will be likely to have a high content of exchangeable sodium, which will in turn cause easy dispersion of the clay fraction.

Of the organisms that decompose organic matter, there are three important groups: (a) bacteria, (b) fungi, and (c) actinomycetes. The optimum conditions for growth of these groups of organisms vary considerably. The actual end products of decomposition by the different organisms are essentially the same; that is, carbon dioxide, water, and simple inorganic compounds. However, the products actually found in the soil at any moment are largely intermediate organic compounds of decomposition, and these products vary according to the soil conditions and the kind of organism responsible for the decomposition.

In general, bacteria and actinomycetes are less tolerant of acidity than fungi. It is found that fungi usually predominate in forest soils, which are usually acid in reaction. Actinomycetes are quite important in grassland soils and other soils high in calcium. Since bacteria are directly involved in nitrogen transformations and since they are favored by soils high in lime, the soils developed under grass in cool and temperate regions are more favorable for the accumulation of organic matter if other conditions are equal. In forest soils there are less favorable conditions for most nitrogen-fixing organisms, but because of the large amount of organic matter added to the soil each year by leaf fall, the soils have a rather large amount of residues on the surface.

The organic matter developed under forests is usually acid and somewhat more soluble than organic matter developed under grass. Organic matter developed under grass, through the influence of bacteria and actinomycetes, is, in general, less acid and less soluble than organic matter developed under forest cover, where fungi are most important in decomposition.

Soils developed under forests, then, differ greatly in their fertility potentialities from soils developed under grass. Such subgroups of bacteria as the nitrogen-fixing organisms are favored by soils high in bases. This means that soils which are acid in reaction will require liming in order to stimulate nitrogen fixation, even though the soils are inoculated with the organisms.

It is also known that the bacteria which bring about the change from ammonia nitrogen to nitrate nitrogen thrive best in soils which are about neutral in reaction.

The organic matter of soils from forest cover is derived primarily from leaf fall, and the organic matter is concentrated in the immediate surface.

The roots of forest species are more concentrated in the surface soil than in lower depths, just as is true of grasses, but tree roots are usually more deeply distributed than grass roots. There is more annual turnover of grass roots to the soil organic matter than from tree roots. A new root system of perennial grasses is produced about every 3 years or less (11). Within a mixture of grasses there are also many annuals that produce a new root system every year. On the other hand, tree roots live much longer, and the annual contribution of root tissue to soil organic matter is relatively low compared to grasses.

On poor, sandy soils of the forest-grassland transition zone of the United States there will usually be a predominance of trees. The soils are considered droughty, and judging from Fig. 48, one would expect trees to have a higher water requirement than grasses. The existence of trees on sandy soils is due to a combination of requirements for bases and water. The base content of the surface soil does not favor grasses. The water-holding capacity of the sandy soil is low for the shallow roots of grasses. Trees survive on sandy soils because of their lower requirement for bases and deeper roots of longer life. Moreover, the water that does fall on sandy soils percolates to lower depths with a minimum of runoff and

Fig. 49. A Red Podzolic soil, a member of the Ruston series. The topsoil has a low content of organic matter and is somewhat typical of the sandy soils of Southeastern United States. (*Courtesy of Roy W. Simonson.*)

evaporation. The amount of water left for transpiration is actually greater on the sandy soils than on neighboring fine-textured soils. Once trees become established, they further protect their water supply in another way. The shade under trees causes the soil to have a lower tem-

perature by as much as 15°F. or more.   The lower temperature reduces
evaporation.   Furthermore, the lower temperature lowers the decomposition rate of the litter on top of the soil.   The litter serves as a mulch
in reducing runoff and evaporation.

Grasses will grow on fine-textured soils in forest-grassland transition
zones better than trees in temperate climates.   The finer-textured soils
are usually higher in bases and provide a favorable nutrient supply for
grasses.   Rain water may not penetrate very deep, but the wetting of
the surface soil supplies the needs of the grasses where trees would not
survive.   Grasses have the capacity to become somewhat dormant during
droughty periods provided there is adequate moisture in the topsoil
periodically.

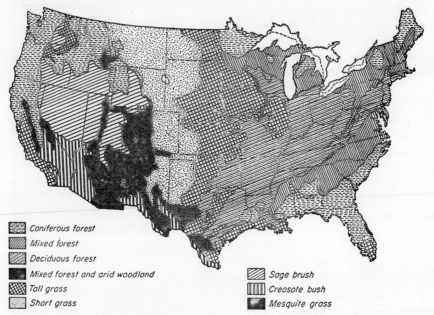

Coniferous forest
Mixed forest
Deciduous forest
Mixed forest and arid woodland
Tall grass
Short grass
Sage brush
Creosote bush
Mesquite grass

Fig. 50. Generalized map of natural vegetation.

Figure 48 shows hardwoods between conifers and tall grasses in the
bioclimatic sequence.   This sequence has been questioned by Dr. Paul
Kramer of Duke University (personal communication), and rightly so.
They are placed in the sequence shown in Fig. 48 because hardwoods
occur as a wide band between the tall grasses and the mixed deciduous-
coniferous forests of the United States.   To say that one group, conifers
or deciduous (hardwoods), requires more water than another is probably
not advisable.   Both groups have wide ranges of adaptability to moisture
conditions, and both groups have representatives throughout the range of
moisture conditions favorable to trees.   The fact that deciduous trees

shed their leaves permits certain species to grow in relatively dry climates. They do not draw on the moisture supply that is being stored in the soil during the dormant periods.   On the other hand, conifers transpire during the winter months.

Conifers are found to predominate on very sandy soils in mixed deciduous-coniferous forests.   The conifers appear to tolerate the physical conditions and fertility status of sandy soils more than deciduous (hardwood) trees.   But in the forest-grassland transitions, deciduous trees compete more successfully than grasses on the sandy soils.

Influence of Topography.   Topography influences soil in many ways. The variations in topography affect moisture and temperature relations to such an extent that one might describe topography in terms of microclimate.

Steep slopes have more runoff and less water percolating through the soil than occur on more gentle slopes.   With less water percolating in the soil on steep slopes there may be shallow rooting of plants; particularly is this true in climates associated with grasslands.   Furthermore, less vegetation is supported on the steeper slope because of the limitations of water.   Steeper slopes also suffer more geological erosion, and the more strongly weathered material is gradually eroded away, exposing fresh or less-weathered materials.   Steeper slopes have better aeration as a result of less water held in pore spaces; and as a consequence of better aeration, organic matter decomposes more rapidly on steeper slopes.   There is more desiccation on steeper slopes and more dehydration of iron hydroxide, resulting in redder colors (or browner colors if the organic-matter content is relatively high).

Slopes facing the sun are much warmer than their opposite slopes and have a greater degree of weathering and more decomposition of organic matter.   The cooler slopes, facing away from the sun most of the day, have less evaporation of water than the warmer slopes, which may cause more vegetation to be produced and a greater accumulation of soil organic matter.

Figure 51 shows the relative thickness of soil occurring on different degrees of slope.   Gentle slopes have more water available to plants than the steeper slopes because of less runoff.   With more water, there is more vegetation and more residues for organic matter.   Also with more water there may be less aeration, and with less aeration there is slower decomposition of organic matter and greater accumulation of organic matter. With more water there is more leaching, and the possibility exists that there will be greater acidity.   With more water and less desiccation on the gentle slopes, the iron compounds are more likely to be hydrated, and with alternate wetting and drying the color of the iron staining will likely be yellow or rusty, whereas red colors might prevail on the steeper slopes.

On gentle slopes below steeper slopes there may be some accumulation of soil that erodes from the higher places. This causes a thicker topsoil to occur than might be found on gentle slopes above steep slopes. Moreover, the lower slopes have more water percolating into the soil than the upper slopes. Some of the water that runs off the upper slope is retained on the lower slope.

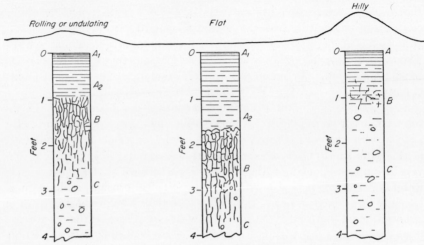

FIG. 51. A schematic diagram showing the effect of slope on the depth and degree of horizon differentiation of soils developed from similar parent materials.

The relation of topography to organic matter has been described on page 98. The greater accumulation of organic matter is associated with more plant growth where the soil supplies more water and where cooler temperature and lower aeration favor accumulation of more slowly decomposing residues.

Where parent materials are similar from the top of a hill to the lower slopes and on to the lower depressed or flat areas, one finds a sequence of soil-profile conditions giving rise to several soil series. Each similar combination of slope conditions on the same parent material gives rise to a similar sequence of profile conditions. This topo-sequence is referred to as a *catena*, from the Latin term meaning chain. A catena is defined as a group of soil series within a particular climatic zone developed under similar vegetation from similar parent material but differing in characteristics of the solum owing to differences in relief or drainage.

Within a catena one may find great differences in degree of profile differentiation. As a general rule, the soils on the upper drier slopes have suffered less weathering and have less profile differentiation than is found on lower, more moist slopes. The soils occurring on flat stream *divides* (ridges) may develop profiles with stronger differentiation than on other topographic conditions within the topo-sequence. Erosion may gradually lower the drainage ways and remove the more strongly weathered topsoil, so that the flat areas adjacent to stream bottoms may be more fertile than flat areas on stream divides. As a consequence of geological erosion that removes the more strongly weathered surface, one finds less profile differentiation than occurs where there is no erosion.

Figure 52 shows two different catenas developed from loess in Iowa. One catena is developed under grass. It includes the Sperry, Taintor, Mahaska, and Otley series. These four series differ greatly as a result of differences in relief. The most strongly differentiated soil is the Sperry, which occupies the depressed areas on the stream divides. The least differentiation occurs in the Otley series. It is well drained and has less organic matter accumulated than is found in other members of the catena. The Otley has a lighter brown color than its associate, the Mahaska series. And while the Mahaska is darker than the Otley, it is not as dark as the Taintor. The Taintor soil is almost black because of the high humus content associated with a gray color due to the iron being predominately in the reduced form. The Otley is brown because of less organic matter and more oxidized iron, much of which is dehydrated and reddish in color.

Another catena in Fig. 52 is developed under deciduous forest. It includes the Clinton and the Givin series. The Givin series, which occupies the more gentle slope, has a more strongly differentiated profile than the Clinton series, which occupies the steeper slope.

In catenas developed in the Southwestern part of the United States one finds the redder member of the catena on the upper slope, the yellow member on the lower slope, and the gray member on the flats. Yellow and gray mottling indicates imperfect drainage, while red and yellow or red and gray mottling indicates better drainage than is evidenced in a yellow and gray soil profile.

The position of the water table has a major influence on profile differentiation on flat topography. This relationship is shown schematically in Fig. 53. If the water table is very near the surface, there is a minimum of percolation of water through the solum to cause differentiation. It is expected that the most strongly differentiated profile will occur in humid regions where the water table is low enough to cause more downward movement of soil water, other conditions being equal with respect to parent material, relief, rainfall, etc.

In warm dry climates, a high water table may increase the rate of weathering compared to soils with no water table near the surface. The higher moisture content resulting from capillary rise from the water table favors chemical decomposition of minerals of the soil. Furthermore, the

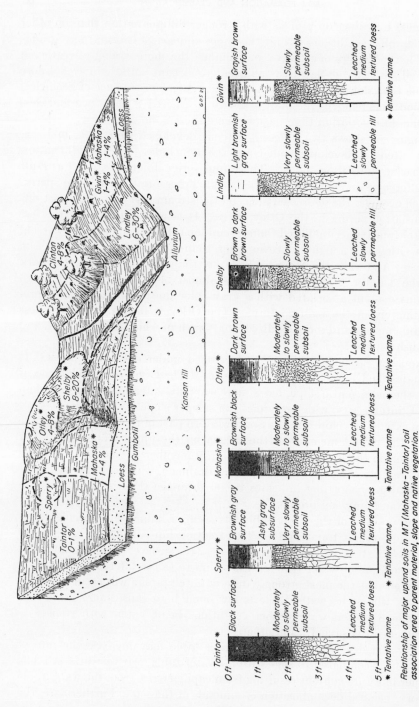

Relationship of major upland soils in MT (Mahaska–Taintor) soil
association area to parent material, slope and native vegetation.

FIG. 52. Principal soil series in the Mahaska–Taintor soil-association area of Iowa (8).

142

organic-matter content of the soil may be higher in the soil with a high water table. Nevertheless, there is little likelihood of downward movement of clay from the A to the B horizon under such conditions. The B horizon with higher clay content than the A horizon in an arid soil with a high water table might be explained by greater weathering in the B horizon, which would be more moist than the A horizon most of the time.

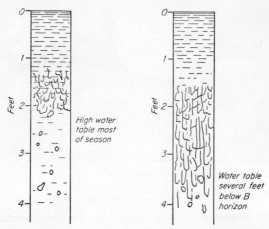

FIG. 53. The influence of a high water table on profile development.

Influence of Parent Material. As a general rule, one can use a map of parent materials (perhaps a geology map) as a foundation for preparation of a soil survey. Within an area of a particular kind of parent material one will find one or more catenas. The members of the catena, that is, the several series within the catena, will often occur only within the boundaries of the particular kind of parent material. Figure 54 shows the distribution of parent materials in Iowa. Figure 55 shows the boundaries of the soil associations (frequently soil association is the same as catena). It is apparent that each soil association (or each catena) is developed from a particular kind of parent material.

The principal characteristics of parent materials that affect soil development are texture and mineralogical composition.

Texture. The texture of the parent material determines the water and aeration relations of the developing soil and may determine the type of vegetation that will occupy the soil. Sandy parent materials often favor conifers rather than hardwoods in the humid regions and favor hardwoods rather than grasses in the transition between the humid and subhumid regions.

Deeper solums are associated with coarse-textured materials low in clay content, while shallow solums develop from materials with a high proportion of clay, other things being equal.

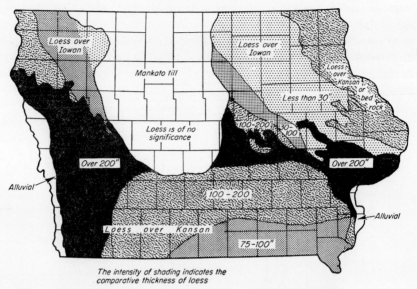

The intensity of shading indicates the
comparative thickness of loess

FIG. 54. Principal soil-parent materials in Iowa.

PRINCIPAL SOIL ASSOCIATIONS

CC: Carrington and Clyde
CKC: Cresco*, Kasson*, Clyde
CL: Clinton and Lindley
CW: Clarion and Webster
F: Fayette
FDS: Fayette, Dubuque, and Stony Land
GH: Grundy and Haig*
GPS: Galva*, Primghar*, and Sac*
M: Marshall
MIH: Monona*, Ida*, and Hamburg*

Mo: Moody*
MPS: Marcus, Primghar*, and Sac*
MT: Mahaska*, and Taintor*
SCW: Storden*, Clarion, and Webster
SGH: Shelby, Grundy, and Haig*
SSE: Shelby, Seymour*, and Edina
SSW: Shelby, Sharpsburg*, and Winterset*
TD: Tama and Downs*
TM: Tama and Muscatine
WL: Weller and Lindley

x New names not on county soil maps
B: Soils of bottomlands

——— Abrupt boundary
---- Tentative boundary
llllll Gradational boundary

Iowa Agric. Expt. Sta. in
Cooperation with Div.of
Soils Survey, U.S. Dept.of
Agric. 1952
F.F.R. and G.D.S. 1952

FIG. 55. Principal soil-association areas in Iowa.

There are many areas in the Coastal Plains of the Cotton Belt where the soil is quite sandy to depths of 20 ft. or more. The conclusion one might draw from examination of the deep sandy soils like the Norfolk sands is that there is no profile differentiation. Dr. Guy Smith[1] of the U.S. Department of Agriculture, Soil Survey Division, points out that if one

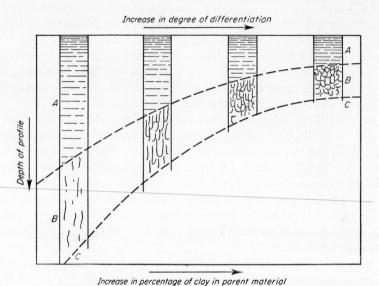

Increase in degree of differentiation

Depth of profile

Increase in percentage of clay in parent material

FIG. 56. The effect of texture of parent material on profile development. [*After Smith, Allaway, and Riecken* (9).]

looks deep enough in the sands one will see that the B horizon is differentiated. The diagram in Fig. 56 shows schematically the relation of texture of parent material to profile development.

Sands are usually high in quartz although they do contain other minerals, such as the feldspars. They usually represent resistant minerals, and their rates of weathering are also slow because of the low surface area in relation to their weight and volume. Consequently, sands are poor sources of nutrients. They do not hold much water. Organic matter does not accumulate as much in sandy soils compared to fine-textured soils.

The texture of the sand in the parent material is reflected by the texture of the topsoil. Where no sand occurs in the parent material (as in some loess) one should not expect to find sand in the A or B horizon. The trend in weathering is to reduce the size of sand and silt particles rather than increase their size.

The occurrence of rocks or gravel in the topsoil is usually a charac-

[1] Personal communication.

teristic inherited from the parent material. Erosion and leaching of weathered material gradually remove the finer material, leaving the coarse material behind to make up the resulting soil. In the regions where the soil is frozen much of the time, frost heaving causes some movement of rocks to the surface from lower depths.

In the loess-derived soils along the east side of major streams of the United States, one finds that profile differentiation increases with distance from the origin of the loess, the origin being the river valley. The coarse material is dropped by the wind close to the river, while the finer material is carried farther away. The finer material weathers into clay more readily than the coarser material, and this factor, among others, affects the degree of horizon differentiation.

The correlation between texture and organic-matter accumulation has already been discussed on page 99. As a general rule, the finer the texture, the greater the percentage of organic matter in the surface soil.

The mineralogical content of parent materials is of particular significance in determining the fertility level of the soil. The presence of a high proportion of calcium-magnesium minerals and a high content of total phosphorus is associated with a youthful and fertile material. As materials undergo long periods of weathering there is a decrease in calcium-magnesium minerals; and the easily weathered potassium minerals also disappear. The older and more strongly weathered materials are a poor source of plant nutrients, and they support only those species of plants having the lowest annual requirement for bases. In forested areas, the conifers are found to predominate on the more strongly weathered materials while the hardwoods occupy the more fertile materials. But in the forest-grassland transition, the grasses generally occupy the soils with the higher base status while forests generally occupy the soils with the lower base status.

Where one particular type of vegetation, grasses, for example, exists on several associated soil series, one will find that the organic-matter content of the soil is positively correlated with the fertility level. The higher organic-matter content is associated with higher fertility level.

Influence of Time. As soon as a material has become unconsolidated enough to be a source of water and oxygen for plant roots and contains enough available nutrients to support plant growth, it can be thought of as a soil. In terms of geologic time, this amount of soil formation would require a very short time.

Our interest in time, however, is primarily in terms of profile differentiation and the degree of weathering. We are interested in profile differentiation largely because of its relation to physical properties, and we are interested in degree of weathering largely because of its relation to rate of release of plant nutrients.

For many years it has been the custom to use the terms *young, mature,* and *old* to describe the degree of profile differentiation. A young soil is one with little or no horizon differentiation. A mature soil has been defined[1] as "a soil in which the profile shows full development of the A and B horizons in equilibrium with the prevailing weathering forces." At one time, a popular concept was that within a particular climatic zone a soil on gently rolling topography finally reached equilibrium at maturity and maintained its characteristics as long as the factors of soil formation remained unchanged. It was believed that natural geologic erosion would be balanced by incorporation of parent material with the solum. It was also believed that, without geological erosion, soils would eventually become *degraded*; that is, the fully matured profile would become more strongly weathered, more strongly differentiated, and less fertile after a long period of time without some erosion. Such soils were referred to as old soils.

There is a trend away from the concept of *equilibrium* in profile development. Soils probably never reach equilibrium in horizon differentiation. They do get older, however; that is, all soils are suffering a certain amount of weathering all the time. Some "age" faster than others. Some soils are destroyed by erosion, and the process of soil formation starts over from a freshly exposed material. Some soils have been exposed without erosion for hundreds of thousands of years. There is great variation in soil-profile development, and some means of designating the degree of development is desirable.

If one were to examine the soils from northern Iowa to southeast Texas one would find forest-grassland-transition soils all the way. Yet, from north to south through this region, one finds two very important differences in soils and in factors of soil formation.

1. The soils of northern Iowa are developed from late Pleistocene materials, some of which were exposed only about 10,000 years ago. Some soils of southern Iowa and northern Missouri are developed from materials deposited in and weathered since early Pleistocene time. Soils of southern Missouri, Oklahoma, and the northeastern part of Texas were exposed prior to Pleistocene time. It is only logical to expect to find more weathering with longer time of exposure to soil-forming processes as one goes from late Pleistocene to pre-Pleistocene time.

2. As one goes from Iowa to Texas one finds increasing mean annual temperature and increasing number of frost-free days during the year. The effect of temperature alone on the degree of weathering is enough to cause weathering to be several times more effective in southeast Texas compared to northern Iowa.

This general relationship holds for comparing soils of the Northern

[1] Report of the seventh annual meeting of the American Soil Survey Association.

part of the United States with those of the Southern part. Glaciation has affected parent materials generally north of the Ohio and Missouri Rivers (see Fig. 46). The soils of the Southern states have developed from older materials (which means more weathered materials) in a climate favoring more rapid weathering. There are some exceptions to this generalization, and the most notable exception is the exposed calcareous deposits of the Cretaceous period. While these Cretaceous deposits were laid down long ago, in geologic time, they have the chemical characteristics which are associated with youth. But generally speaking, the parent materials and the soils of Southern United States are quite old compared to soils of the Northern states along any north-south line.

The very sandy topsoils over clay subsoils of the Southern states east of the 30-in. rainfall line represent an aging process associated with destructive weathering of the clays of the surface soil. Some of the clay moved from the A to the B horizon by mechanical eluviation, but for the most part the very sandy topsoils represent a residue of long and continuous chemical decomposition of the minerals of the topsoil.

Within any zone (associated with similarities of climate and vegetation) one will find soils which are slightly differentiated, some strongly differentiated, and some only moderately differentiated. They may all be relatively old or relatively young in terms of the degree to which the minerals have weathered. To distinguish between differentiation and severity of weathering, Thorp and Smith have proposed the terms *minimal*, for slight differentiation, *maximal* for strong differentiation, and *medial* for the well-developed profile (10). The medial soil would be with the "modal," or "normal," soil of the zone. The gently or moderately rolling topography would generally favor the development of the medial soil. Allowed enough time, however, all soils of the zone would develop a maximal profile. It is proposed that soils of each zonal group be divided into minimal, medial, and maximal subgroups. Figure 57 shows the general distribution of the subgroups of the Prairie soils of the upper Mississippi Valley of the United States.

In degree of weathering, all of the Prairie[1] soils are much younger than the forest soils of the Southeastern United States. Moreover, some soils of the tropics are much older in terms of weathering than the soils of the Southeastern United States. It is highly desirable to distinguish between degree of profile differentiation and degree of weathering. Within each weathering sequence one may expect different degrees of profile differentiation. Five stages of weathering are described below. With such a scheme one has to be arbitrary in choosing the number of stages. As was pointed out on page 116 Jackson and his associates in Wisconsin have

[1] Prairie soils have been recently named Brunizems.

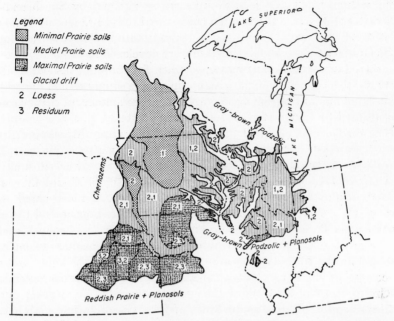

FIG. 57. Distribution of minimal, medial, and maximal Prairie soils and dominant parent materials in the upper Mississippi Valley (9).

described 13 stages (2). For advanced study the greater number of stages is to be commended.

A Grouping of Soils in Terms of Weathering

I   *Young.* High content of easily weathered calcium and magnesium minerals. High per cent of base saturation of clays of 2:1 crystal lattice.[1]

II   Low content of easily weathered calcium and magnesium minerals. High content of slowly decomposing sodium and potassium minerals. Medium per cent of base saturation. Mixed clays of 2:1 and 1:1 crystal lattice with dominance of the 2:1 type.

III   Some slowly weathering sodium and potassium minerals. Very little unweathered calcium and magnesium minerals. Predominance of clays of 1:1 crystal lattice, but some clay of 2:1 crystal lattice. Low per cent of base saturation.

IV   High content of quartz sand and little or no silt-size fraction in the topsoil. Clays of subsoil of 1:1 crystal lattice with high per cent of hydrogen saturation. Large amount of free alumina and iron oxide either hydrated or dehydrated. Little if any unweathered silicate minerals.

V   *Old.* Some quartz sand and a high proportion of free alumina and iron oxide. Some clay of 1:1 crystal lattice. Forms hard crust on desiccation.

The highly fertile soils developed from recently deposited loess and glacial till of the northern part of Iowa belong to Group I of the weath-

[1] See page 166.

ering sequence. These soils were shown as minimal by Smith and his associates (Fig. 57). It has often been stated that Iowa has about 25 per cent of all the Grade A land in the United States. Those soils thought of as Grade A by the laymen in Iowa were developed from young, slightly weathered materials. The materials when first brought into cultivation were weathering fast enough to maintain a large supply of plant nutrients for a large amount of plant growth. The large amount of plant growth contributed to a large store of soil organic matter.

The medial and maximal Prairie soils of the upper Mississippi River Valley are most nearly like Group II of the weathering sequence. The forest soils of the cool temperate part of the United States are most nearly like Group III. Of course they overlap into Groups II and IV. The forest soils of the Southeastern United States are most nearly like Group IV. The blackland Prairie soils of the Southeastern states from central Texas to Alabama are much like Group I. Group V occurs to the greatest extent in the tropical regions. The nearest we have to Group V in the United States are the Cecil soils of the Piedmont and the Nacogdoches soils of east Texas. These materials have the characteristics of Group V except for forming the crust on drying.

Classification of Soils on the Basis of Their Characteristics. The soil type is the principal unit of classification.[1] A simple definition of *a type* is *a group of soils that are similar in all their profile characteristics.* Soil types are further grouped into *series: a group of soils that are similar in all their profile characteristics except the texture of the A horizon.* Further grouping of soils into higher categories makes it necessary to consider only those characteristics which will include a greater number of series. A soils map of a county with a scale of 1 or 2 in. to 1 mile can usually show the mappable soil units. As the scale is decreased, however, the individual delineated area may become so small as to make it necessary to group the similar units into higher categories in order to have a map that clearly expresses regional differences.

The next higher category is the family. Our system of classifying soils is yet incomplete, and all series are not grouped into families. A family is composed of one or more series with similar characteristics yet differing enough to allow consistent separation in field mapping. The family name is the same as one series member of the family at the present time; for example, the Muscatine family includes the following series: Muscatine, Mahaska, and Brenton.

---

[1] A phase of soil type is frequently mapped. According to Riecken and Smith (7), "Phases are separated within a soil type on the basis of characteristics which, although significant to use of the soil by man, have little or no significance in the genesis of the soil." Such variations as stoniness, degree of slope, or degree of erosion have been indicated by a phase name, for example, *Houston clay, stony phase.*

The category above families is the great soil group. Several of the great soil groups of the United States include over one hundred series. The grouping is based on similarities of profile characteristics, but the groups differ from one another in important ways such as parent material, relief, and age.

Marbut (5) recognized that well-developed soils on gently rolling or undulating topography of the drier climates of Western United States usually contain accumulations of calcium carbonate in the profile. On the other hand, the well-developed soils on similar topography of the Eastern United States do not contain accumulations of calcium carbonate but usually contain greater proportions of iron and aluminum in the B horizon than in the A or C horizons. He referred to the well-developed soils on gently rolling or undulating topography as *normal* soils and grouped them under two headings, Pedocals ("pedo" from pedology and "cal" from calcium) and Pedalfers ("ped" from pedology, "al" from aluminum, and "fer" from iron). Marbut considered soils which were developed under poor drainage, or with excessive geological erosion, or with unusual characteristics due to parent material (such as a calcareous soil in a humid region) as abnormal and did not separate the abnormal soils into Pedocals and Pedalfers. Figure 48 indicates the difference between Pedalfers and Pedocals. This concept has not proved useful in the more recent efforts to group great soil groups into higher categories.

Great Soil Groups. The great soil groups of the world are listed on pages 157 to 160 along with a brief description of each one. The most extensive great soil groups of the United States are shown in Fig. 58.

For the beginning student the long list of great soil groups has little meaning unless they are associated with some scheme that will help in remembering them. Figure 59 is a schematic diagram that will help the student associate the principal groups in the United States with factors of their formation.

Starting with Chernozems (a Russian term for black earth) one finds that the solums get shallower and lighter in color as one proceeds to the desert soils of the United States. There is an accumulation of calcium carbonate in the bottom of the B horizon of the *Chernozems, Chestnuts, Browns,* and *Desert* soils. Since the solums become shallower with drier climate, the accumulation of calcium carbonate gets shallower as the desert condition is approached.

The Deserts, Browns, Chestnuts, and Chernozems represent very early stages of weathering, mostly Group I of the weathering sequence. There is some movement of clay from the A to the B horizon in these groups but not nearly so much as found in the Prairie soils. These soils have more organic matter than their southern "equivalents."

The *Reddish Chestnut, Reddish Brown,* and *Red Desert* soils have

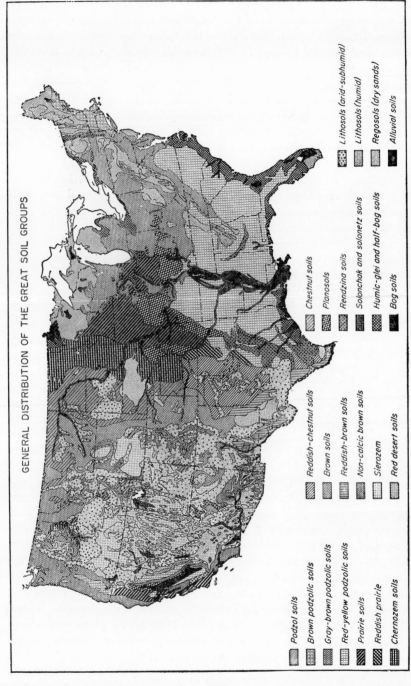

GENERAL DISTRIBUTION OF THE GREAT SOIL GROUPS

Podzol soils
Brown podzolic soils
Gray-brown podzolic soils
Red-yellow podzolic soils
Prairie soils
Reddish prairie
Chernozem soils

Reddish-chestnut soils
Brown soils
Reddish-brown soils
Non-calcic brown soils
Sierozem
Red desert soils

Chestnut soils
Planosols
Rendzina soils
Solonchak and solonetz soils
Humic-glei and half-bog soils
Bog soils

Lithosols (arid-subhumid)
Lithosols (humid)
Regosols (dry sands)
Alluvial soils

FIG. 58. The great soil groups of the United States. (U.S. Department of Agriculture, Soil Survey Division.)

less organic matter and brighter colors because of the dehydration of the free iron oxides. These soils have developed from a more weathered material than occurs under the soils to the North, but much of the reddish color is inherited from previous cycles of weathering and due to a high degree of desiccation of a relatively small amount of free iron. Generally speaking, the soils of this region are well supplied with bases, including available potassium. They have not been impoverished by leaching. As the bases were released in weathering, some of the excess (above the

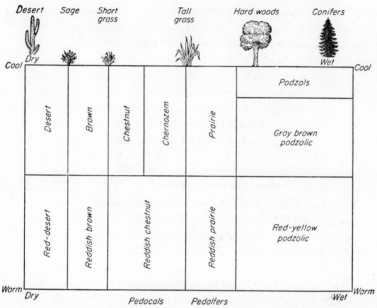

FIG. 59. Schematic diagram showing relative position of several great soil groups with respect to climate and vegetation.

exchange capacity of the soil) moved to the bottom of the B horizon, and some of the excess bases were precipitated as carbonates in the topsoil. Calcareous soils are common throughout the region west of the Prairies to the desert of the United States.

The *Prairie (Brunizem)* soils are similar to the Chernozems. There is considerable accumulation of calcium carbonate at the bottom of the B horizon of the Chernozem while the calcium carbonates have generally leached to a greater depth in the Prairies. Both of these groups developed under tall grass, but the Prairie soils developed under a little more rainfall and have suffered more weathering and more leaching. They are generally more like Group II, with some of their members in Group I of the weathering sequence. The Prairies have more highly differentiated profiles than are found among the Chernozems (except where forests have encroached on the Chernozems).

The Chernozems are the important soils for wheat production, while the Prairies are the important soils in corn production. Rainfall limits crop production on the Chernozems. When water is available in adequate quantities, the Chernozems are among the most productive soils of the world. Because of the more favorable rainfall, the Prairies are the most productive of the extensive upland great soil groups in the United States.

The Prairies generally require lime, and they also respond, for the most part, to additions of nitrogen, phosphorus, and potassium fertilizers, the most notable exceptions being the minimal Prairies which are sometimes rich in bases. Yields of 100 to 125 bu. of corn per acre are common under favorable rainfall on well-managed Prairie soils.

The *Reddish Prairie* soils occur to a limited extent in north Texas, Oklahoma, and southern Kansas. These soils are similar to the Prairies except for less organic matter and redder color. They have suffered more weathering than the Prairie soils but are not generally as strongly differentiated as the maximal Prairies. They are less productive than the Prairies because of the unfavorable high rate of evaporation characteristic of their climate.

The *Rendzina* soils shown in Fig. 58 are not included in the schematic diagram of Fig. 59. They have developed under prairie vegetation from cretaceous chalks and marls and have retained the characteristics of slightly weathered materials described in Group I of the weathering sequence. They are the blacklands of Texas, Alabama, and Mississippi. Generally speaking, they are the most productive upland soils in these three states. Because of high temperatures and the high rate of evaporation, the same amount of rainfall received at Temple, Texas, as received in Ames, Iowa, will produce about half as much corn in Temple as produced in Ames, assuming adequate fertilization at both places. The use of supplemental irrigation at Temple has increased the yield of corn from about 50 bu. per acre to about 90 bu. per acre on well-fertilized plots.[1]

The forest soils shown in the schematic diagram, Fig. 59, are *Podzols*, *Gray-Brown Podzolic* and *Red-Yellow Podzolic*. The term Podzol comes from a Russian term meaning "ash." The A_2 layer of a typical Podzol profile is an ashy-gray color. The ashy gray is due to the removal of iron and aluminum and an accumulation of silica, mostly in the form of quartz.

The Podzols are typically developed under a predominance of conifers. They are also more typically developed from a soil material with a high proportion of sand. The climate most favorable to their development is cool and humid. This combination of factors favors an accumulation of

[1] Personal communication from Dr. R. M. Smith, see page 71.

an acid litter, strong leaching, and a movement of the iron and aluminum from the A to the B horizon. The stage of weathering of the true Podzol is much like Groups III and IV. The A_1 layer of the Podzol is high in organic matter, partly because of the mixing of the decomposing litter with the surface 4 or 5 in. by earthworms, ants, and other macroorganisms of forest soils. As the organic matter of the A_1 decomposes to form organic acids, some of the material combines with iron and aluminum and moves out of the A horizon. The upper B horizon (B_1 layer) accumulates some of the organic residues to form a dark-colored layer above a somewhat more reddish or yellowish B_2 layer.

A low pH and high per cent of saturation of clays and humus with hydrogen are characteristic of Podzols. They require much lime and moderately large applications of fertilizers in order to make them productive. They do respond favorably to good management, however, and are important agricultural soils.

The *Gray-Brown Podzolic* soils are somewhat transitional between Prairies and Podzols in terms of weathering. The Gray-Brown Podzolic soils are generally more like Group II, although some of them are more like Group III of the weathering sequence. They have generally formed under deciduous forest. They have usually suffered more weathering than the Prairies, and they generally have more strongly differentiated profiles than the Prairies as a group. They do not have the ashy-gray A_2 layer characteristic of the Podzols, but have a gray-brown A_2 instead. They do have many characteristics of the Podzols, however, in that the topsoil becomes quite acid, frequently below pH of 5, and iron and aluminum move to the B horizon to some extent leaving an A horizon high in silicon dioxide. The Gray-Brown Podzolic soils are important agricultural soils and form the dominant group in the eastern part of the Corn Belt of the United States. They are less productive than the Prairie soils without fertilizer, but because of their favorable climate the Gray-Brown Podzolic soils can be made just as productive as the Prairies with good fertility management.

The Red-Yellow Podzolic soils really include two associated great soil groups, the *Red Podzolic* and the *Yellow Podzolic*. The recent trend is to call them one group since it is impossible to separate them on a small-scale map.

In general, the *Red-Yellow Podzolic* soils are strongly weathered and are similar to Group IV of the weathering sequence. Because of the warm climate in which they have developed, there is little accumulation of organic matter as litter or within the A_1 layer. The surface soil does not become strongly acid as is found in the Podzol, but the per cent base saturation is low. The exchange capacity of the typical topsoil is low, meaning that the topsoil is a "poor storehouse" for available calcium, magnesium, and potassium. The low content of organic matter in the profile and the high degree of weathering and release of free iron cause the colors to be relatively bright. Where the topsoil is sandy, the color due to iron is usually associated with the subsoil. The Red-Yellow Podzolic soils were settled early in the history of the United States, and they have suffered much accelerated erosion. A large proportion of the cultivated Red-Yellow Podzolic soils has eroded to the extent that some of the B horizon has been mixed with the plowed layer. Some of these soils have a moderately favorable climate and respond markedly to good management. Krantz (4) has reported many yields of more than 100 bu. of corn in some favorable years in North Carolina with heavy fertilization.

The *Planosols* are not shown in the schematic diagram on page 153, but their principal area of occurrence is indicated in Fig. 58. Planosols are soils with sharply contrasting horizons. An important feature is the presence of a claypan upper B horizon. Smith *et al.* considered a true Planosol to be a soil in which an intermittent water table formed above the B horizon which caused a bleached A_2 horizon with a base saturation below 50 per cent (9). They recognized that Planosols with claypan B horizons were similar to maximal Prairie soils and that these soils are an important part of the landscape in the area designated as maximal Prairie soils shown in Fig. 57. Earlier, as is shown in Fig. 58, Planosols were indicated to occur quite extensively in the Middle Western part of the United States. But while Planosols are important in the area, they are less dominant than other soils.

The Planosols as we now recognize them offer one of the greatest challenges to soil management. Research has not yet provided a practical way to maintain good drainage and good aeration in the subsoils of the Planosols.

Higher Categories of Soil Classification. The great soil groups are fairly well defined by soil scientists, and there has been general acceptance of the names and their definitions.

Marbut developed a system of grouping the great soil groups into fewer and higher categories. His system is contained in the "Atlas of American Agriculture," Part III, Soils of the United States, 1935. Kellogg, who succeeded Marbut as Chief of the Soil Survey Division of the U.S. Department of Agriculture, made some improvements in the system. The U.S. Department of Agriculture Yearbook "Soils and Men," 1938, contains the concept developed at that time by Kellogg and his associates. A special issue of *Soil Science*, Vol. 67, 1949, is devoted to some newer concepts of soil classification. The description of the great soil groups shown on pages 157 to 160 were taken from the 1938 Yearbook of Agriculture and modified in accordance with Vol. 67 of *Soil Science*.

No attempt is made in this book, however, to describe the higher cate-

GENERAL CHARACTERISTICS OF THE GREAT SOIL GROUPS (1,10)

Great soil group	Profile	Native vegetation	Climate	Natural drainage
Tundra	Dark-brown peaty layers over grayish horizons mottled with rust; substrata of ever-frozen material	Lichens, moss, flowering plants, shrubs	Frigid humid	Poor
Desert	Light gray or light brownish gray, low in organic matter, closely underlain by calcareous material	Scattered shrubby desert plants	Temperate to cool; arid	Good to imperfect
Red Desert	Light reddish-brown surface soil, brownish-red or red heavier subsoil closely underlain by calcareous material	Desert plants, mostly shrubs	Warm temperate to hot; arid	Good to imperfect
Sierozem	Pale-grayish soil grading into calcareous material at a depth of 1 ft. or less	Desert plants, scattered short grass, and scattered brush	Temperate to cool; arid	Good to imperfect
Brown	Brown soil grading into a whitish calcareous horizon 1 to 3 ft. from surface	Short-grass and bunch grass prairie	Temperate to cool; arid to semiarid	Good
Reddish Brown	Reddish-brown soil grading into red or dull-red heavier subsoil and then into whitish calcareous horizon, either cemented or soft	Tall bunch grass and shrub growth	Temperate to hot; arid to semiarid	Good
Chestnut	Dark-brown friable and platy soil over brown prismatic soil with lime accumulation at a depth of 1½ to 4½ ft.	Mixed tall- and short-grass prairie	Temperate to cool; semiarid	Good
Reddish Chestnut	Dark reddish-brown cast in surface soil, heavier and reddish-brown or red sandy clay below; lime accumulation at a depth of 2 ft. or more	Mixed grasses and shrubs	Warm temperate to hot; semiarid	Good
Chernozem	Black or very dark grayish-brown friable soil to a depth ranging up to 3 or 4 ft., grading through lighter color to whitish lime accumulation	Tall- and mixed-grass prairie	Temperate to cool; subhumid	Good
Prairie (Brunizem)	Very dark brown or grayish-brown soil grading through brown to lighter-colored parent material at a depth of 2 to 5 ft.	Tall-grass prairie	Temperate to cool temperate; humid	Good
Reddish Prairie	Dark-brown or reddish-brown soil grading through reddish-brown heavier subsoil to parent material; moderately acid	Tall- and mixed-grass prairie	Warm temperate; humid to subhumid; possibly some tropical conditions	Good
Degraded Chernozem	Nearly black A₁, somewhat bleached grayish A₂, incipient heavy B, and vestiges of lime accumulation in deep layers	Forest encroaching on tall-grass prairie	Temperate and cool; subhumid to humid	Good
Noncalcic Brown (Shantung Brown)	Brown or light-brown friable soil over pale reddish-brown or dull-red B horizon	Mostly deciduous forest of thin stand with brush and grasses	Temperate or warm temperate; wet to dry; subhumid to semiarid	Good

GENERAL CHARACTERISTICS OF THE GREAT SOIL GROUPS (1,10) (*Continued*)

Great soil group	Profile	Native vegetation	Climate	Natural drainage
Podzol	A few inches of leaf mat and acid humus, a very thin dark-gray A_1 horizon, a whitish-gray A_2 a few inches thick, a dark- or coffee-brown B_1 horizon, and a yellowish-brown B_2; strongly acid	Coniferous or mixed coniferous and deciduous forest	Cool temperate, except in certain places where the climate is temperate; humid	Good
Gray Podzolic (Gray Wooded)	Moderately thin A_0 and thin organic-mineral A_1, over a light-colored bleached A_2, over a brown, more clayey, blocky, or nuciform B_2, grading into a lighter-colored, more friable B_3 or C horizon; moderately acid	Coniferous or deciduous or mixed forest	Subhumid to semiarid; cool	Good
Brown Podzolic	Leaf mat and acid humus over thin dark-gray A_1 and thin gray-brown or yellowish-brown A_2, over brown B horizon which is only slightly heavier than surface soil; solum seldom more than 24 in. thick	Deciduous or mixed deciduous and coniferous forest	Cool temperate; humid; effective moisture slightly less than in Podzol	Good
Gray-Brown Podzolic	Thin leaf litter, over more mild humus, over dark-colored surface soil 2 to 4 in. thick, over grayish-brown leached horizon, over brown heavy B horizon; less acid than Podzols	Mostly deciduous forest with mixture of conifers in places	Temperate; humid	Good
Red-Yellow Podzolic	Thin organic A_0 and organic-mineral A_1 over a light-colored bleached A_2, over a red, yellowish-red, or yellow, more clayey B horizon, grading into a siliceous parent material	Coniferous or mixed coniferous and deciduous forest	Warm temperate to tropical humid	Good
Reddish Brown and Yellowish Brown Lateritic	Brown or reddish-brown friable clayey soil over yellowish-brown or red friable or granular clay; acid to neutral; deep substrata reticulately mottled in places	Tropical rain forest, evergreen and deciduous	Tropical wet to dry; high to moderate rainfall	Good
Latosol (Chromosol)	Red-brown surface soil, red deep B horizon, red or reticulately mottled parent material; very deeply weathered	Tropical selva and savannah vegetation (some cogonales)	Tropical; wet to dry; high to moderate rainfall	Good

gories. It is believed that the beginning student can benefit most by devoting his time on soil classification above the *series* level to gaining an appreciation for the great soil groups. Advanced students will find it to their advantage to refer to the references described above.

Soil Association. The most important grouping of series, in so far as the farmer is concerned, is that of the soil association. A soil association includes series which are geographically associated and which may not

GENERAL CHARACTERISTICS OF THE GREAT SOIL GROUPS (1, 10) (*Continued*)

Great soil group	Profile	Native vegetation	Climate	Factors responsible for development	Natural drainage
Solonchak	Gray, thin, salty crust on surface, fine granular mulch just below, and grayish, friable, salty soil below; salts may be concentrated above or below	Sparse growth of halophytic grasses, shrubs, and some trees	Usually sub-humid to arid; may be hot or cool	Poor drainage with evaporation of capillary water; salty accumulations	Poor or imperfect
Solonetz	Very thin to a few inches of friable surface soil underlain by dark, hard, columnar layer, usually highly alkaline	Halophytic plants and thin stand of others	Usually sub-humid to arid; may be hot or cool	Improved drainage of a sodium Solonchak	Imperfect
Soloth	Thin grayish-brown horizon of friable soil over whitish leached horizon, underlain by dark-brown heavy horizon	Mixed prairie or shrub	Usually sub-humid to semiarid; may be hot or cold	Improved drainage and leaching of Solonetz	Imperfect to good
Humic Glei (includes Weisenboden)	Dark-colored organic-mineral horizons of moderate thickness underlain by mineral-glei horizons	Swamp forest or herbaceous marsh	Cool or warm; humid to sub-humid	Poor drainage	Poor
Alpine Meadow	Dark-brown soil grading, at a depth of 1 or 2 ft., into grayish and rust-colored soil, streaked and mottled	Grasses, sedges, and flowering plants	Cool temperate to frigid (alpine)	Poor drainage and cold climate	Poor
Bog	Brown, dark-brown, or black peat or muck over brown peaty material	Swamp forest or sedges and grasses	Cool to tropical; generally humid	Poor drainage; water-covered much of the time	Very poor
Half-bog	Dark-brown or black peaty material over grayish and rust-mottled mineral soil	Swamp forest or sedges and grasses	Cool to tropical; generally humid	Poor drainage; water-covered much of the time	Very poor
Low Humic Glei	Thin surface horizon moderately high in organic matter over mottled gray and brown Gleilike mineral horizon	Swamp forest or marsh	Humid, warm	Poor drainage	Poor
Planosols	Strongly leached surface soils over compact or cemented claypan or hardpan; some have normal A and B horizons above the claypan or hardpan— a secondary profile	Grass or forest	Cool to tropical; humid to sub-humid	Flat relief, imperfect drainage, and great age	Imperfect or poor

GENERAL CHARACTERISTICS OF THE GREAT SOIL GROUPS (1,10) (*Continued*)

Great soil group	Profile	Native vegetation	Climate	Factors responsible for development	Natural drainage
Ground-water Podzols	Organic mat over very thin acid humus, over whitish-gray leached layer up to 2 or 3 ft. thick, over brown or very dark brown cemented hardpan or ortstein; grayish deep substrata	Forest of various types	Cool to tropical; humid	Imperfect drainage and usually sandy material	Imperfect or poor
Ground-water Laterites	Gray or gray-brown surface layer over leached yellowish-gray A_2, over thick, reticulately mottled cemented hardpan at a depth of 1 ft. or more; hardpan up to several feet thick; laterite parent material; concretions throughout	Tropical forest	Hot and humid; wet and dry seasons	Poor drainage and considerable or great age	Imperfect or poor
Brown Forest (Braunerde)	Very dark brown friable surface soil grading through lighter-colored soil to parent material; little illuviation; high adsorbed calcium	Forest, usually broad-leaved	Cool temperate to warm temperate; humid	High calcium colloids and youth	Good
Rendzina	Dark grayish-brown to black granular soil underlain by gray or yellowish, usually soft, calcareous material	Usually grass; some broad-leaved forest	Cool to hot; humid to semiarid	High content of available lime carbonate in parent material	Good
Lithosols	Incomplete solum or no clearly expressed morphology, consisting of a freshly and imperfectly weathered mass of hard rock	Depends on climate	All climates; most characteristic of deserts, least so of humid tropics	Steep topography, parent material usually consolidated	Good to excessive
Regosols (includes Dry Sands)	Essentially no development in sands, deep loess, or glacial drift	Scanty grass or scrubby forest; much of land has no vegetation	Humid to arid, temperate to hot	Steep topography	Excessive
Alluvial	Little profile development; some organic matter accumulated; stratified	Scanty grass or scrubby forest; much of land has no vegetation	All climates except extremely frigid ones	Deposition by stream action	A wide range, mostly poor to good

be similar to all; for example, the Clarion and Webster association in north central Iowa includes different great soil groups, but they are members of the same catena.   Figure 55 shows a soil-association map of Iowa. In the preparation of a soil-association map, the separation of groups is

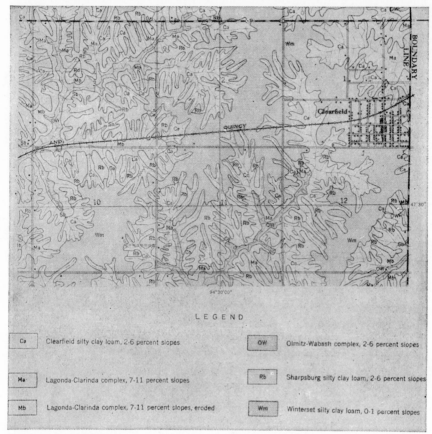

FIG. 60. A portion of the soil-survey map of Taylor County, Iowa, published in 1954. The scale of the published map is 2 in. equals 1 mile.   There are six sections (each 1 sq. mile) shown in this figure.

closely related to parent material and the association is often a catena. The map in Fig. 54 shows parent materials of the soils of Iowa.   The similarity of the two maps in Figs. 54 and 55 is striking.   The difference in parent material, of course, is not necessarily the criterion for separation of groups; neither is the association always the same as a catena.   Other factors such as relief or vegetation may provide criteria for separation of groups.

The separation of associations on a map as in Fig. 55 is a guide only to the nature of the soils within the delineated area of the association. The area of the Mahaska-Taintor association, for example, includes several series, as shown in Fig. 52. Each series is associated with particular factors of formation such as topographic position or natural vegetation. The most important soils of the Mahaska-Taintor association are shown in Fig. 52. Diagrams for each of the soil-association areas of Iowa are published in "Understanding Iowa Soils" by Simonson, Riecken, and Smith (8), and the diagrams have been very helpful to farmers who live in counties where the survey maps are old and the series names out of date. Farmers like to know the names of soils on their farms, since many management recommendations are made on the soil-series basis.

County Soil Surveys. Soil surveys are made by state-college personnel in cooperation with the Soil Survey Division of the U.S. Department of Agriculture. Each survey is published by the Soil Survey Division as a bulletin accompanied by a map. The scale of the map is usually 1 to 2 in. to the mile. The bulletin includes a description of the agriculture of the county, a description of each type or phase, and management recommendations. Concepts of mapping units change through the years, and while all counties have not yet been mapped, some counties need to be remapped in order to show more useful detail and to bring the names up to date. A portion of a county map is presented in Fig. 60. It is a recent survey and illustrates the way in which soil types are separated on a map.

A recent trend is to prepare shorter reports with the soil-survey map. For example, several states have recently published surveys which included a map on one side of a sheet and the descriptive data and agronomic recommendations on the reverse side. The sheet is folded to look like a brochure or pamphlet.

REFERENCES

1. Baldwin, Mark, Charles E. Kellogg, and James Thorp, Soil Classification, *U.S. Dept. Agr. Yearbook*, pp. 979–1001, 1938.
2. Jackson, M. L., and G. Donald Sherman, Chemical Weathering of Minerals in Soils, *Advances in Agron.*, 5:221–318, 1953.
3. Kellogg, C. E., The Development and Significance of the Great Soil Groups of the United States, *U.S. Dept. Agr. Misc. Pub.* 229, 1936.
4. Krantz, B. A., Fertilize Corn for Higher Yields, *N.C. Agr. Expt. Sta. Bull.* 366, 1949.
5. Marbut, C. F., The Soils of the United States, in "Atlas of American Agriculture," Part III, Washington, D.C., 1935.
6. Riecken, F. F., and Guy D. Smith, Principal Upland Soils of Iowa, *Iowa State Coll. Agron. Bull.* 49, 1949.
7. Riecken, F. F., and Guy D. Smith, Lower Categories of Soil Classification: Family, Series, Type, and Phase, *Soil Sci.*, 67:107–115, 1949.
8. Simonson, Roy W., F. F. Riecken, and Guy D. Smith, "Understanding Iowa Soils," Wm. C. Brown Co., Dubuque, Iowa.

9. Smith, Guy D., W. H. Allaway, and F. F. Riecken, Prairie Soils of the Upper Mississippi Valley, *Advances in Agron.*, **2**:157–205, 1950.
10. Thorp, James, and Guy D. Smith, Higher Categories of Soil Classification: Order, Suborder, and Great Soil Group, *Soil Sci.*, **67**:117–126, 1949.
11. Weaver, J. E., and Ellen Zink, Length of Life of Roots of Ten Species of Perennial Range and Pasture Grasses, *Plant Physiol.*, **21**:201–217, 1946.

CHAPTER 7

CLAY MINERALS, ACIDITY, AND ALKALINITY

The clay fraction of the soil includes all mineral matter smaller than 2 microns (0.002 mm.) in diameter. In temperate and cool climates, the silicate clays known as clay minerals make up the bulk of the clay fraction. In tropical climates, iron and aluminum hydroxides (or hydrated oxides of iron and aluminum) make up an appreciable amount, sometimes the greater part, of the clay fraction. Because of the low amounts of iron and aluminum hydroxides in most of the soils of the United States, this chapter will be built around the clay minerals.

Composition and Classification of Clay Minerals. We think of clay as a sticky plastic substance that can be molded into almost any shape, yet clay is made up of very small crystals. The tiny crystals have a definite arrangement of the silicon, aluminum, hydrogen, oxygen, and other elements, just as do crystals of orthoclase, or hornblende, or any other mineral. There are different kinds of clay crystals, depending on the proportion and arrangement of the different elements, but the most abundant are montmorillonite, kaolinite, illite, and vermiculite.

The diagrams in Fig. 61 illustrate the chemical structure of the important clay minerals.

The diagrams show only silicon, aluminum, hydrogen, oxygen, and potassium. These are idealized structures, and it is realized that iron makes up an appreciable percentage of the clay fraction. Furthermore, other elements such as magnesium may occur as part of the crystal structure, and attracted to the clay crystal are various cations like Ca^{++}, K^+, Mg^{++}, Na^+, Fe^{++}, Mn^{++}, Cu^{++}, and Zn^{++}, which are not part of the crystal structure but are part of the clay fraction of the soil.

The illite crystal can be thought of as a layer of hydrated aluminum oxide sandwiched between two layers of silicon dioxide. Potassium ions occur between adjacent silica layers, and its chemical bond is such that it may hold two silica layers together.

The diagrams in Fig. 62 indicate an illite crystal two units in thickness, but there may be many units of thickness. Likewise the lateral extension

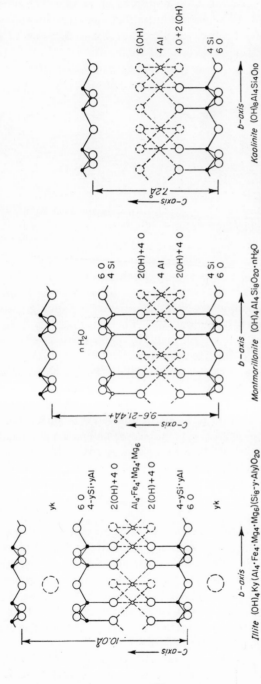

FIG. 61. Diagrams representing the structure of the principal clay minerals. The *C*-axis (vertical-axis) dimensions are expressed in angstrom units. One angstrom unit is equal to 0.000,000,1 mm. In the illite clay there is indication that Al may be substituted for Si and that Fe or Mg may be substituted for Al. Similar substitution may occur in montmorillonite. [*From various sources cited by Grim* (14).]

Illite $(OH)_4 K_y (Al_4 \cdot Fe_4 \cdot Mg_4 \cdot Mg_6)(Si_{8-y} \cdot Al_y)O_{20}$ *Montmorillonite* $(OH)_4 Al_4 Si_8 O_{20} \cdot nH_2O$ *Kaolinite* $(OH)_8 Al_4 Si_4 O_{10}$

of one clay crystal may include hundreds of units. The effect of the potassium is to bind the sandwich units together strongly enough to prevent water molecules from expanding the units. Samples of illite clay expand little on wetting and shrink little on drying. Illite is frequently described as having a 2 *to* 1 *nonexpanding crystal lattice,* while montmorillonite has a 2 *to* 1 *expanding crystal lattice.*

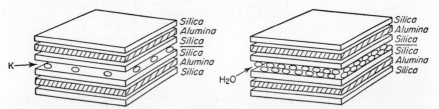

FIG. 62. Diagram illustrating the arrangement of the silica and alumina sheets of the illite crystal.

Diagram illustrating where water molecules cause expansion of the crystal lattice of montmorillonite.

Montmorillonite has a chemical structure similar to illite with the exception of the potassium linkage. There is no chemical bond between adjacent silica layers to prevent water molecules from expanding the crystal lattice. Consequently, montmorillonite expands greatly on wetting and shrinks greatly on drying. The interfacial surface is much greater in montmorillonite than in illite. The vertical extension of the units is less in montmorillonite than in illite. In the absence of chemical bonding forces, it is possible for montmorillonite to be only one unit thick. Its lateral extension, of course, may approach 2 microns. The expansion of montmorillonite in the presence of water has the effect of increasing the interfacial surface in so far as mobility of cations is concerned. Cations may move into the expanded crystal between silica layers. This type of clay is very sticky and plastic when wet. A soil containing a high percentage of montmorillonite clay swells when wet and permits only a very slow penetration of water. When the swollen soil dries out, large cracks form; the cracks may be 6 in. wide and extend to a depth of many feet in some cases.

Kaolinite is more common in soils of the Southeastern states and in soils developed in a warm humid climate. Kaolinite is described as having a 1 *to* 1 *nonexpanding lattice.* The 1 to 1 means one layer of silica to one of alumina. The nonexpanding lattice means that water molecules cannot cause swelling of the crystal. Soils high in kaolinitic clay do not shrink much on drying and swell very little on wetting. Since the clay does not swell appreciably on wetting, soils high in kaolinitic clay have a rapid rate of water intake if the surface is granular. Contrasted with this condition, the montmorillonite clay swells on wetting. The surface of montmorillonitic soils tends to seal over owing to swelling and breaking apart of the aggregates and the filling of pore spaces with clay at the immediate surface. The stability of an aggregate of montmorillonite is much less than that of an aggregate of kaolinite from the standpoint of erosion.

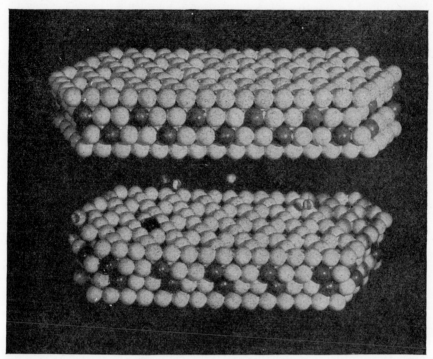

FIG. 63. Arrangement of the ions in two adjoining units of a montmorillonite clay mineral crystal. The white spheres represent oxygen ions. The dark-colored spheres represent hydroxyl ions. The small spheres between the units represent exchangeable ions. Small silicon ions reside in the spaces between the oxygen ions in the top and bottom layers of each unit. Small aluminum ions occupy spaces between oxygen and hydroxyl ions of the center layer of each unit. (*Courtesy of C. E. Marshall.*)

Vermiculite[1] is described as having a 2 *to* 1 *partially expanded crystal lattice*. Instead of having potassium between adjacent silica layers, as found in illite, this mineral has been somewhat expanded and is hydrated,

[1] Associated with vermiculite and illite are the interstratified minerals (12,16). A crystal of mica may lose K by weathering from between alternate units rather than between all units. That is, K may be removed from between adjacent silica layers of every other unit to give a crystal with alternate 10 and 14 Å (or wider) spacings for the C axis rather than a uniform spacing as found in illite and the micas. Where Mg replaces K between alternate units, the illite-vermiculite intermediate is found. Where K is removed from alternate units of illite, the clay would be referred to as an intermediate between illite and montmorillonite, or it might be referred to as an interstratified mineral.

and the spaces between adjacent silica layers are occupied by magnesium or magnesium and calcium. The calcium and magnesium are exchangeable with other ions. Figure 61 shows the C axis of illite to be about 10 Å (angstrom units). The figure also shows that the C axis of montmorillonite might be 9.6 to 21.4 Å or greater. Vermiculite has a spacing of about 14 to 15 Å, which places it in an intermediate position between illite and montmorillonite in this respect. But oddly enough, it is not intermediate in terms of exchange capacity. As will be indicated later, vermiculite has an exchange capacity much greater than montmorillonite. This mineral is not as abundant in soils as the three minerals previously described, but is of great significance where it occurs because of its high exchange capacity and its capacity to fix ammonium ions in positions somewhat inaccessible to nitrifying organisms (3,4,8).

Origin of Clay Minerals. All clay minerals are derived from the weathering of primary silicate minerals such as orthoclase, muscovite, biotite, and hornblende. The occurrence of montmorillonite, vermiculite, illite, or kaolinite is related to the degree of weathering and the chemical nature of the weathering complex.

Muscovite tends to produce illite, while biotite tends to produce vermiculite. Both illite and vermiculite are associated with slightly weathered materials. Vermiculite requires the presence of a large amount of magnesium during the clay formation, which would most likely occur in neutral or slightly alkaline soils. Illite occurs to a greater extent than vermiculite in soils of moderate acidity.

There is some evidence that illite forms montmorillonite as potassium is removed in weathering, but the exact origin of montmorillonite is still open to question. One important difference that exists between illite and montmorillonite must be considered, that is, montmorillonite appears to have more substitution of magnesium for aluminum in the alumina layer while illite has more substitution of aluminum for silicon in the silica layer.

Montmorillonite is an important component of slightly to moderately weathered soils which have relatively high pH values and in soils containing large amounts of organic matter (12). In forest-grassland transition areas one usually finds a higher proportion of montmorillonite in relation to kaolinite on the grassland soil.

Kaolinite minerals are predominant in highly weathered, strongly leached, acidic soils. Some kaolinite occurs in most clays, but kaolinite would not be expected to occur in large amounts in slightly weathered materials. It is generally believed that the 2 to 1 layer minerals eventually weather into kaolinite under acid conditions and as they gradually lose silica. However, it is logical to assume that silica and alumina may accumulate in a particular soil material in a ratio favorable to kaolinite formation (5). Likewise, it is possible for other clay minerals to be synthesized by having the source materials accumulating in proper ratio. It should not be assumed that kaolinite forms only from montmorillonite. Neither should it be assumed that montmorillonite forms only from illite or vermiculite. A primary mineral like muscovite or biotite may weather to form montmorillonite rather than either illite or vermiculite, and furthermore, a primary mineral like orthoclase may weather to form kaolinite. The sequence of formation (that is, illite → montmorillonite → kaolinite) may be an important stepwise process, but the more important concept is that of association of the clay mineral with the stage of weathering.

Vermiculite and illite are associated with youthful materials of stages I and II (see page 149). Montmorillonite is important in stages I and II and decreases successively with stages III and IV, with none expected in stage V. Kaolinite increases with the later stages of weathering so that it is the only important silicate mineral of stage V. Montmorillonite and kaolinite are gradually weathered to produce silica and alumina separately, and in very old soils, the silica is removed by leaching more rapidly than alumina. It is recognized that silica is more susceptible to *removal* by leaching than either iron or aluminum except under strongly acid conditions. Old soils of the tropics have a high percentage of aluminum and iron. Soils of the warm temperate regions have a high percentage of kaolinite in the clay fraction. Clays of cooler climates have a high proportion of illite and montmorillonite because of their youthfulness.

As one associates the different clay minerals with stages of weathering, it becomes apparent that kaolinite predominates in old soils because of its resistance to weathering. The 2 to 1 layer minerals gradually disappear because they are more easily weathered. This concept is in keeping with the expression, used many times in this book, that the more resistant materials remain behind to make up the soil.

As progress is made from cool to warmer climate, the effect of temperature is to speed up chemical and biological reactions. Clays of warmer climates have suffered greater losses of silica than clays of cooler climates. Consequently one would expect more kaolinite in soils of the Southeastern United States than in soils of the Northern part of the country, a condition that is well illustrated in Table 21. The clay fractions of the Corn Belt soils are generally high in montmorillonite and illite but low in kaolinite. The Reddish Prairie soil in Table 21 was collected in Oklahoma by Wilkinson and Gray. Although collected in a warm temperate climate, the soil was developed from a calcareous material. Table 21 shows a gradual decrease in kaolinite and an increase in montmorillonite. These soils are arranged in order of weathering, the youngest materials at the bottom of the table.

TABLE 21. ESTIMATED MINERAL COMPONENTS OF CLAY FRACTION FROM
REPRESENTATIVE SOILS (1,32,35)

Great soil group and soil series	Mineral component, per cent				
	Kaolinite	Illite	Montmo-rillonite	Free Fe oxides	Calcite
Red Podzolic, Cecil..............	80	0	0	15	0
Gray-Brown Podzolic, Hagerstown	70	20	0	9	0
Prairie, Carrington..............	50	30	10	10	0
Chernozem, Barnes..............	30	40	20	0	6
Prairie, Clarion.................	15	25	60	*	*
Prairie, Tama..................	15	30	55	*	*
Reddish Prairie, Dennis..........	*	25	50	*	*
Gray-Brown Podzolic, Weller......	20	35	45	*	*
Planosol (grass), Grundy..........	5	30	65	*	*
Wiesenboden, Webster...........	0	15	85	*	*

* Not determined.

Vermiculite was not determined in the analysis above, and if vermiculite occurs in these soils it may have been overlooked and grouped with one or more of the other minerals.

Since the existence of vermiculite with high exchange capacity has been recognized (since about 1948), several studies have shown the presence of vermiculite in soils (4). Coleman et al. (10) reported the presence of vermiculite in all of the seven North Carolina soils investigated. The vermiculite content was higher in the coarse-clay fraction (0.2 to 2 microns) than in the fine-clay fraction, which indicates the low tolerance of vermiculite to weathering.

Existing as a part of a clay fraction are quartz and the free oxides of iron and aluminum. According to Jackson and Sherman (16), quartz is an important part of the coarse-clay fraction of soils (0.2 to 2 microns) but disappears very early in weathering from the fine-clay fraction (<0.2 micron). Quartz is very resistant to weathering if it occurs in particles larger than 2 microns, but its resistance to weathering decreases rapidly as its particle size is reduced below 2 microns.

As weathering progresses in soils, the content of each of the clay minerals increases up to a certain age, then decreases thereafter. The content of quartz in the clay fraction is relatively important in young soils but gradually decreases with weathering (time). The content of free oxides of iron and aluminum is low in young soils but increases gradually as the soil ages. In very old soils, kaolinite and the hydrated oxides of iron and aluminum constitute nearly all of the clay fraction, and as aging continues, the kaolinite decreases in content as the iron and aluminum oxides increase. Figure 64 is a schematic diagram to indicate these relations.

Chemical Nature of Clay. The many diagrams of clay crystals in this book give the impression of a three-dimensional figure, the shape of a book, or some similar object: Perhaps a better way of visualizing clay

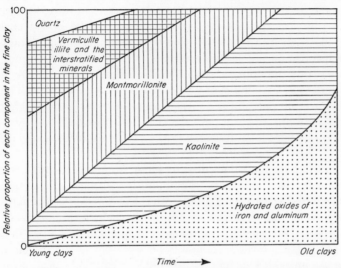

FIG. 64. The relative proportion of the principal clay components in the fine-clay (0.2-micron) fraction of soils of different ages. [*Based on work of M. L. Jackson and his associates* (10,16).] See page 167 for a discussion of interstratified minerals.

is to think in terms of sheets of frayed and torn paper with holes of indiscriminate size and shape (12). Clay crystals are secondary minerals, having been developed as a result of weathering of primary minerals or having been synthesized from silica and hydrated alumina and atoms of various kinds. They have many imperfections due to weathering, and at different points atoms are missing in the structure which might have given rise to a continuous uniform arrangement of the crystal. Atoms of one kind may be substituted for atoms of another kind and sometimes without materially changing the structure. For example, aluminum may replace silicon in the silica layer. Ordinarily, silicon exists in the space formed where four oxygen atoms fit together to form a tetrahedron. Where aluminum (*with three positive charges*) replaces silicon (*with four positive charges*) within the tetrahedral arrangement, a negative bond of one of the oxygen atoms is left unsatisfied. The negative bond will attract a cation, which will be held as a replaceable ion. The replacement of silicon by aluminum in the silica tetrahedral layer is called *isomorphous* replacement because the structure or configuration remains unchanged (21). Another example of isomorphous replacement is the replacement of aluminum (*with three positive charges*) by magnesium (*with two positive charges*) in the alumina layer. The alumina layer includes oxygen and hydroxyl ions arranged in an octahedral pattern with aluminum fitting in the interstitial spaces between the oxygen atoms and the hydroxyl ions. This layer is sometimes referred to as the alumina octahedral layer. The isomorphous replacement of aluminum by magnesium causes a negative charge to be left unsatisfied. In other words, the crystal gains one negative position by the substitution of magnesium for aluminum.

Illite has isomorphous replacement of silicon by aluminum in the silica layer, but the potassium ions which are held between the adjacent silica layers tend to balance any unsatisfied negative bonds. The potassium held in such position is nonexchangeable. As the nonexchangeable potassium is removed from between the silica layers of illite by weathering, however, there is an increase in the cation exchange capacity of the clay.

Montmorillonite and vermiculite have isomorphous replacement of magnesium for aluminum, and aluminum for silicon; and the unsatisfied negative charges thus resulting between the layers of these minerals cause them to have a high capacity for adsorbing exchangeable cations.

Isomorphous replacement in kaolinite is uncommon if such does occur (22). The lattice is nonexpanding because of the hydrogen bonding between the units. This feature accounts for at least a part of the resistance of kaolinite to weathering. Close and regular packing of atoms in a crystal increases resistance to weathering. The fact that kaolinite may not have isomorphous replacement in the silica and alumina layers means that potassium cannot be fixed in nonexchangeable positions within the interior of the clay crystals as might occur in illite and vermiculite.

Some exchange capacity (both cation- and anion-exchange capacity) occurs on the edges of all clay crystals. The relative proportion of this particular exchange capacity is small for vermiculite, montmorillonite, and illite, but probably accounts for most or all of the exchange capacity for kaolinite. It is believed that hydrogen is dissociated from exposed SiOH groups to cause negative charges on edges of clay crystals and that the dissociation of the hydroxyl ion from exposed AlOH groups causes a positive charge on the clay crystal. According to Marshall (22), the number of positive positions should be equal to the number of negative positions on the edges of kaolinite crystals. Experimental evidence for this belief has been obtained by Dean and Rubins (11), who found anion-exchange capacity to be equal to the cation-exchange capacity of kaolinite.

Figure 65 is a schematic diagram relating degree of weathering (time) to the relative proportions of cation-exchange capacity to anion-exchange capacity.   It has already been emphasized that young clays have a high proportion of the 2 to 1 layer silicate minerals, including montmorillonite, vermiculite, and illite.   The exchange capacities for these clays are relatively high.   Older clays have a high proportion of kaolinite (1 to 1 layer silicate) minerals.   Also, as soils weather and become old, they have a higher proportion of free iron and aluminum in the clay fraction.   The

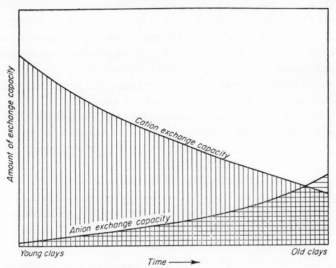

Fig. 65. The relation of age of clays to their capacities for adsorbing cations and anions. The younger clays contain a high proportion of the 2 to 1 layer silicates.   The older clays contain a high proportion of kaolinite and hydrated oxides of iron and aluminum.

free iron and aluminum exist as hydrated oxides or as hydroxides.   Kaolinite has a low cation-exchange capacity which is probably balanced by an equivalent amount of anion-exchange capacity.   The free iron and aluminum compounds (probably mostly hydroxides) are positively charged; that is, hydroxyl ions are dissociated, thus leaving a positively charged compound of iron or aluminum.   Figure 65 indicates that the cation-exchange capacity declines as clays become older, while the anion-exchange capacity increases with age.   Where anion-exchange capacity predominates over cation-exchange capacity one would expect the clay to be a composite of kaolinite and hydroxides of iron and aluminum. Evidence of greater anion-exchange capacity than cation-exchange capacity was recently published by Miller and Coleman (26) following a study of several soils from Western Equatorial South America.

The exchange capacity of a mixture of clays is most difficult to determine and subject to serious errors.   One problem in particular is that mixtures of silicate clays are predominately negatively charged, yet iron and aluminum hydroxides are positively charged.   Consequently, these two oppositely charged materials are attracted to each other to a certain extent. In other words, the iron and aluminum compounds combine with the silicate clays to form rather stable arrangements. Toth (33) found that if he removed free iron and aluminum from clays he increased the cation-exchange capacity.

Another problem in estimating exchange capacity is that a divalent cation like Ca^{++} may hold on to clay with one bond and hold on to $H_2PO_4^-$ or OH^- with the other bond. If very much "bridging" occurs in a soil, then the determination of total bases could be off as much as 10 or 15 per cent or more. Such a condition has been demonstrated by Bower and Truog (9). It is generally assumed that both bonds of Ca^{++} and Mg^{++} are attached to the clay (or organic anion) in exchange-capacity determinations, but this may not be true at all.

Clays and organic ions are extremely complex, and little is known yet about their anion-exchange properties. It is generally assumed that the OH^- and $H_2PO_4^-$ ions are the principal anions involved in anion-exchange reactions. The other important anions in terms of quantity are Cl^-, NO_3^-, HCO_3^-, and SO_4^{--}, all of which are so active that they do not compete for anion-exchange positions to any appreciable extent.

Older clays, those high in kaolinite and hydroxides of iron and aluminum, have a high capacity for adsorbing $H_2PO_4^-$. Presumably, an OH^- ion is exchanged for an ion of $H_2PO_4^-$, as follows:

$$\boxed{\text{Clay}}-OH + H_2PO_4^- \rightleftharpoons \boxed{\text{Clay}}-H_2PO_4 + OH^-$$

The anion-exchange capacity can be estimated by determining the amount of $H_2PO_4^-$ adsorbed, but the real question is whether or not we should refer to this anion-exchange capacity in the same way as we refer to the cation-exchange capacity. The problem is that only a small fraction of the $H_2PO_4^-$ ions (of an $H_2PO_4^-$ saturated clay) appears to be readily exchangeable. The reaction pictured above is reversible, but slowly reversible.

Cation exchange is relatively more rapid than anion exchange, although there is considerable variation in the ease with which the different cations are exchangeable, a subject to be discussed later. Cation exchange is illustrated as follows:

$$\boxed{\text{Clay}}-K + H^+ \rightleftharpoons \boxed{\text{Clay}}-H + K^+$$

The exchangeable cations are those which are attracted to the "surface"-negative positions of the clay crystal structure. The nonexchangeable cations are those which occur as part of the crystal structure or are held in positions inaccessible to the entry of other exchangeable ions which might effect ready displacement.

Cation-exchange Capacity of Clays and Humus. The cation-exchange capacity is expressed as milliequivalents per 100 g. of the material. A milliequivalent is 0.001 g. of hydrogen or its equivalent in 100 g. of material. The abbreviation meq. will be used for milliequivalent in this book. Grim (15) estimated the cation-exchange capacity of several clays as follows:

	Exchange capacity.
Clay	*meq./100 g.*
Montmorillonite	60–100
Illite	20–40
Kaolinite	3–15

Barshad (4) has reported that vermiculite has about 50 per cent greater cation-exchange capacity than montmorillonite. Numerous investigations of the cation-exchange capacity of humus show a range of 100 to 300 meq. exchange capacity per 100 g. of the material. The following capacities are suggested for humus and the more important clay minerals.

	Cation-exchange capacity,
	meq./100 g.
Humus	200
Vermiculite	150
Montmorillonite	100
Illite	30
Kaolinite	10

Cation-exchange Capacity of Soils. Soils contain sand and silt in addition to clay and organic matter, and the clay may contain any combination of the different clay minerals. The percentage of organic matter varies with different soils, therefore cation-exchange capacity of soils varies with (*a*) the kind of clay, (*b*) the per cent of clay, and (*c*) the per cent of organic matter.

The cation-exchange capacity is usually determined in the laboratory by leaching a sample of soil with ammonium acetate. The bases are collected in the leachate, which is evaporated and ashed. The base content (in the ash) is determined by titration with a standard acid. The milliequivalents of hydrogen of the acid neutralized (per 100 g. of soil) expresses the milliequivalents of total bases. This may not be the cation-exchange capacity, however, since hydrogen may have constituted a part of the exchangeable cation content. The leached sample of soil is ammonium-saturated; that is, all of the cation-exchange positions are occupied by ammonium ions, but the sample must be leached with alcohol to wash out any excess ammonium acetate. The sample is then placed in a Kjeldahl flask to which water and magnesium oxide are added. The

Kjeldahl flask is then heated and the ammonium ion is displaced by magnesium. The ammonium ion volatilizes as ammonia, which is collected in a standard acid. Titration against a standard base then provides the data for calculating the milliequivalents of hydrogen (per 100 g. of soil) neutralized by the ammonia. This value is the cation-exchange capacity of the soil. It is generally determined by undergraduate students in the laboratory for a soil-fertility course. With the beginning student this may not be done, but it is desirable to develop an appreciation for the variation in exchange capacity of different soils.

An average sample of montmorillonite will have about 100 meq. per 100 g. of the clay. A soil with 20 per cent clay, all of which is montmorillonite, would have only 20 meq. due to clay. Soil organic matter (or humus) has about 200 meq. exchange capacity per 100 g. of the material. If the above soil had 4 per cent organic matter, then it would have 8 meq. due to organic matter. The soil would have a total cation exchange capacity of 28 meq.

Soils may contain some of each of the clay minerals as well as organic matter. The data for the capacities of the different exchange materials per 1 per cent of the materials are as follows:

CATION-EXCHANGE CAPACITY

Meq.	*Per 1% of:*
2	Humus
1.5	Vermiculite
1.0	Montmorillonite
0.3	Illite
0.1	Kaolinite

A soil with 20 per cent clay (of which 30 per cent is montmorillonite and 70 per cent is kaolinite) and 3 per cent organic matter would have the following exchange capacity:

$$20\% \text{ clay} \times 70\% \text{ kaolinite} \times 0.1 \qquad = \quad 1.4 \text{ meq.}$$
$$20\% \text{ clay} \times 30\% \text{ montmorillonite} \times 1.0 = \quad 6.0 \text{ meq.}$$
$$3\% \text{ organic matter} \times 2 \qquad\qquad\quad = \quad \underline{6.0} \text{ meq.}$$
$$\text{Total} \qquad\qquad\qquad\qquad\qquad\quad = 13.4 \text{ meq.}$$

Clays of soils represent mixtures of different minerals, and it is not feasible to suggest an average exchange capacity to represent all soils. For purposes of estimating exchange capacities of various soils of the United States, however, the following values are recommended:

Per 1% clay

Soils of the United States except for the Red-Yellow Podzolic
soils.. 0.6 meq.
Red-Yellow Podzolic soils except in the Piedmont area...... 0.4 meq.
Soils of the Piedmont and others known to be high in kaolinite 0.2 meq.

A typical Corn Belt soil has about 20 per cent clay and 4 per cent organic matter. The exchange capacity would be roughly

20% clay $\times$ 0.6 = 12 meq.

4% organic matter $\times$ 2 =   8 meq., or a total of 20 meq./100 g. of soil

Relation of Age of Clay to Particle-size Distribution. As clays weather they tend to be reduced in size. One would expect slightly weathered clays to have a small proportion of fine clay ($<$0.2 micron) in relation to coarse clay. Likewise, one would expect to find a high proportion of fine clay in relation to coarse clay in the more strongly weathered soils.

The following data illustrate the relation of weathering to the content of fine clay in three soil profiles. The A and B horizons of the soils have suffered much more weathering than the C horizons and have higher proportions of fine clay in relation to total clay contents.

TABLE 22. RELATION OF PARTICLE SIZE OF CLAY TO DEPTH IN THE PROFILE AND TO EXCHANGE CAPACITY (20)

Particle-size distribution			Cation-exchange capacity, meq. per 100 g.	
Depth, in.	Total clay, %	Fine clay, % below 0.2 micron	Coarse clay, 0.2 to 2 microns	Fine clay, below 0.2 micron
Holdredge silt loam				
0–7	20.8	16.1	16.1	55.3
17–24	28.1	21.6	60.4	88.8
36–48	12.1	2.0	47.5	69.9
Keith silt loam				
0–4	16.8	11.2	64.9	107.4
8–13	19.7	13.5	52.4	89.1
36–48	8.4	.9	40.6	81.7
Dawes silt loam				
0–5	16.0	11.2	31.6	60.2
5–9	19.2	15.1	31.6	86.6
12–18	32.5	24.6	55.0	89.2
28–38	10.8	4.2	49.4	76.3

Table 22 also illustrates one other important characteristic of clays. The fine-clay fraction usually has a higher exchange capacity because of the tendency for montmorillonite to readily break down to fine-clay size.

Larson and his associates (20) found that illite and montmorillonite were the principal clay minerals in the three Nebraska soils described in Table 22.

Wilkinson and Gray (35) found that montmorillonite predominated in the fine-clay fraction of the horizons of three Oklahoma soils and that other minerals were dominant in the coarse-clay fraction. Illite was the only other mineral identified.

The kaolinite minerals do not break down to fine clay as much as montmorillonite. Very old clays containing kaolinite and the hydrous oxides of iron and aluminum may have as much coarse clay (>0.2 micron) as fine clay (<0.2 micron).

Distribution of Cation-exchange Capacity in the Soil Profile. Tables 23 and 24 show the exchange capacity for different layers of soil profiles.

TABLE 23. EXCHANGE CAPACITY, EXCHANGEABLE BASES, AND EXCHANGEABLE HYDROGEN IN TAMA SILT LOAM, A PRAIRIE SOIL

Horizon	Depth, in.	Exchangeable cations*				Cation-exchange capacity
		Ca	Mg	K	H	
A_1	0–1½	26.24	4.51	1.19	1.35	33.29
	1½–3	17.83	3.99	0.77	1.61	24.20
	6–9	13.07	3.86	0.38	4.44	21.75
A_3	15–18	10.05	4.06	0.28	5.21	19.60
B_2	24–27	12.09	6.35	0.42	3.38	22.24
B_3	33–36	12.07	5.18	0.36	3.94	21.55
C_1	42–45	12.24	5.57	0.40	0.93	19.32

* Values are in milliequivalents per 100 g. oven-dry soil.　R. W. Simonson, unpublished data.

The Tama profile shows a reduction in exchange capacity from the top of the A horizon to the bottom of the B horizon, a change which is due largely to decrease in organic matter from the A to the B horizon. At the same time, any horizon differentiation has the effect of decreasing the clay content of the A horizon and increasing the clay content of the B horizon; therefore, if the organic matter were removed from the Tama profile, one would expect a higher exchange capacity in the B horizon than in the A horizon.

The Fayette soil is a strongly differentiated forest soil with an accumulation of organic matter in the A_1 horizon and a strongly leached A_2 horizon which is fairly low in organic matter. The A_1 horizon is also relatively low in clay, so that the exchange capacity of the A_1 is due largely to organic matter.

TABLE 24. EXCHANGE CAPACITY, EXCHANGEABLE BASES, AND EXCHANGEABLE HYDROGEN IN FAYETTE SILT LOAM, A GRAY-BROWN PODZOLIC SOIL

Horizon	Depth, in.	Exchangeable cations*				Cation-exchange capacity
		Ca	Mg	K	H	
A₁	0–2	22.89	3.72	0.72	0	25.49
	2–4	9.35	2.55	0.29	1.92	14.11
A₂	4–7	7.47	2.35	0.25	1.20	11.29
	7–9	7.99	2.92	0.36	1.41	12.68
B₁	12–15	10.60	4.09	0.46	0.82	15.97
	18–21	14.02	5.68	....	....	20.39
B₂	24–27	14.41	6.85	0.43	0.23	21.92
	30–33	15.48	7.18	0.49	0.26	23.41
B₃	36–39	15.45	7.18	0.52	0	23.08
	42–45	14.84	7.08	0.42	0	21.53
C	48–51	15.30	7.54	0.39	0	23.09

* Values are in milliequivalents per 100 g. oven-dry soil. R. W. Simonson, unpublished data.

Figure 66 illustrates the exchange-capacity relationships of an undifferentiated prairie soil and a strongly differentiated forest soil.

Data in Table 25 illustrate the wide variation in exchange capacity of soils from different parts of the country. The higher exchange capacitieᵣ

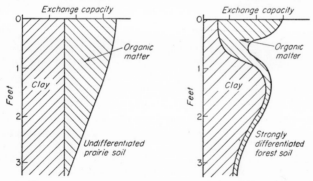

FIG. 66. A schematic diagram showing the relative proportions of exchange capacity contributed by clay and organic matter under different soil conditions.

are to be found in heavy black soils of the Corn Belt. These soils are high in both humus and montmorillonitic clay. The soils of the Southeastern states are characterized by sandy A horizons containing a small percentage of clay, which is largely kaolinitic, and a small amount of humus.

TABLE 25. PERCENTAGE BASE SATURATION OF DIFFERENT SOILS AT LIKE
pH VALUES (31)

Great soil group	Soil type	Location	Total exchange capacity, meq./100 g.	Percentage base saturation at pH values of:				
				4.8	5.0	5.5	6.0	6.5
Yellow Podzolic..	Norfolk sandy loam	Alabama	1.83	9	16	32	44	60
Red Podzolic.....	Cecil clay loam	Alabama	4.85	6	23	41	58	74
Gray-Brown Podzolic.......	Miami silt loam	Wisconsin	9.79	43	50	63	72	82
Planosol (grass)..	Grundy silt loam	Illinois	26.33	57	60	69	80	91

Percentage Base Saturation. If a soil has an exchange capacity of 20 meq. and has 15 meq. of bases, the soil is 75 per cent base-saturated. A soil that is 100 per cent base-saturated would be alkaline in reaction. A soil becomes acid enough to require lime for the production of field crops as the base saturation decreases below about 80 to 90 per cent.

Proportion of the Different Exchangeable Bases. The proportionate amounts of the different cations that accumulate in dry climates are deter-

TABLE 26. EXCHANGEABLE BASES IN STRONGLY ALKALINE SOILS (17)

Soil type	Location	Total exchangeable bases, meq./100 g.	100 meq. of exchangeable bases contain			
			Ca	Mg	K	Na
Fresno fine sandy loam........	California	6.0	0	0	35.0	65.0
Jordan fine sandy loam........	Utah	9.5	0	0	39.6	60.4
Jordan silt loam..............	Arizona	9.4	0	0	19.1	80.9
Hanford silt loam............	California	12.2	0	54.1	12.3	33.6
Lahontan clay...............	Nevada	25.6	0	0	3.1	96.9
Average...................	....	....	0	10.8	21.8	67.4

mined by the rate of release of the different bases. There are practically no losses by leaching in dry climate, and the base saturation is near 100 per cent. The usual rate of release from silicate minerals is in the order of $Ca > Mg > Na > K$, and the exchangeable bases usually occur in this order in soils of dry regions.

If a water table is near enough to the surface to allow capillary movement of water to the surface, soluble salts accumulate in the topsoil. The sodium ions are more soluble than other bases and may rise to the surface and dominate the exchange complex. Such a condition is referred to as *alkali*. Sodium ions cause dispersion of clays and cause soils to become puddled and slowly permeable.

Alkali soils may have little or no exchangeable calcium, as illustrated by Table 26. The high activity of the sodium causes displacement of the calcium, which in turn is precipitated as calcium carbonate.

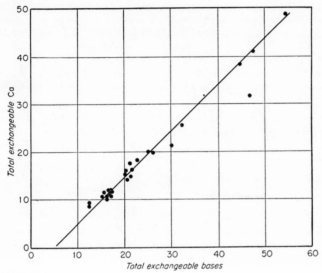

FIG. 67. The relation of exchangeable Ca to total exchangeable bases. Ca is an average of 83 per cent of total bases. (*Unpublished data by students in Agronomy 354, Iowa State College, 1947.*)

The amount of exchangeable sodium in humid-region soils is usually very low—as a rule, lower than potassium. Sodium is held with less force than calcium, magnesium, or potassium and is quite readily removed by leaching. The chemical force with which the bases are held is in the order of Ca > Mg > K > Na, and therefore they tend to accumulate in this same order in soils subject to leaching losses. W. H. Pierre[1] suggests that Ca will constitute about 80 to 85 per cent of the total bases in most soils of the humid region of the United States. This estimate is confirmed by data presented in Fig. 67. A very high correlation exists between the content of calcium and the content of total bases in this particular illustration. The average per cent of calcium (expressed as per cent of total bases) was 83.

Table 27 shows the approximate relative proportions of the different

[1] Personal communication.

exchangeable bases in soils of the humid region of the United States. Ammonium is shown as one of the bases in this table, but soils carry only a trace of ammonium most of the time. As was pointed out in earlier chapters, ammonium is readily oxidized to nitrate by nitrifying bacteria of the soil. In soils quite high in kaolinite one might find a higher proportion of potassium than is indicated in Table 27, but probably not over 5 per cent for a typical kaolinitic soil.

TABLE 27. PROPORTION OF BASES IN A REPRESENTATIVE HUMID-REGION SOIL

Bases.....................	Ca	Mg	K	Na	NH₄
Percentage of total exchangeable bases...............	80–85	15–20	Less than 1	Less than 1	Less than 1

As the per cent of base saturation decreases, the per cent of hydrogen saturation increases. The relative proportion of the bases is changed very little, however. The significance of this statement at this point is that calcium or hydrogen, or calcium plus hydrogen, nearly always makes up over 80 per cent of the exchangeable cations in humid-region soils. This is important, and fortunate, because clays tend to remain flocculated in the presence of hydrogen or calcium, or both. A high proportion of sodium, on the other hand, causes deflocculation (or dispersion). Flocculation is necessary in order to have aggregation and pore space.

There are several reasons why calcium predominates over other bases in the exchange complex:

1. The release of bases during weathering is generally in the order of $Ca > Mg > Na > K$.

2. The energy of adsorption of bases by clay and humus is in the order of $Ca > Mg > K > Na$.

3. Plants in general use more calcium than magnesium. Under natural conditions the plant residues are returned to the topsoil, and therefore there is greater opportunity for calcium to be held against leaching losses.

Other Exchangeable Cations. It is generally assumed that the six cations H^+, Mg^{++}, Ca^{++}, K^+, Na^+, and NH_4^+ constitute about 99 per cent of the exchangeable cations in soils. According to Black (7) a considerable part of the exchangeable-cation content may be aluminum rather than hydrogen in acid soils. There is no doubt that aluminum does exist as exchangeable aluminum, and it is recognized that its solubility and mobility increase with hydrogen saturation. Iron also exists as exchangeable iron in the form of Fe^{++} and $Fe(OH)_2^+$ and in other combinations as well. Cu^{++}, Mn^{++}, and Zn^{++} also exist in trace amounts as exchangeable ions. As will be emphasized later, all of the ions of the minor elements mentioned above exist in more available forms as acidity increases.   It is conceivable that the amounts of these ions in exchangeable form increase likewise as acidity increases.

Calculations with Exchangeable Ions.   An *equivalent* of hydrogen is one gram of hydrogen or its equivalent in chemical reactions.   One gram of hydrogen is equivalent to the atomic weight of monovalent elements like sodium or potassium (23* and 39 g., respectively).   One gram of hydrogen is equivalent to the atomic weight of other elements divided by their valence.   For example, calcium has an atomic weight of 40, but a valence of 2, therefore the equivalent weight of calcium would be 20. Furthermore, one gram of hydrogen is equivalent to the weight of an anion divided by its valence.   The equivalent weight of any element, ion, or compound, is its weight divided by its valence or hydrogen equivalent.   Calcium carbonate has a molecular weight of 100, and in a chemical reaction $(2HCl + CaCO_3 \rightarrow CaCl_2 + CO_2 + H_2O)$ calcium carbonate is equal to two hydrogens.   Its weight must be divided by 2 in order to arrive at the equivalent weight, the equivalent weight being 50.

A milliequivalent is an equivalent weight divided by 1000.   In exchange-capacity studies, the milliequivalent values are based on 100 g. of soil.   One milliequivalent per 100 g. of soil is the same as 0.001 g. of hydrogen or its equivalent in 100 g. of soil.   This is expressed as a fraction as follows:

$$\frac{0.001 \text{ g. of hydrogen (or its equivalent)}}{100 \text{ g. of soil}}$$

This is equal to

$$\frac{1 \text{ g. of hydrogen}}{100,000 \text{ g. of soil}}$$

The numerator and denominator were multiplied by 1000.   By multiplying both by 20 one gets

$$\frac{20}{2,000,000}$$

By using pounds rather than grams we find that 1 milliequivalent of hydrogen in 100 g. of soil is equal to 20 lb. of hydrogen in 2 million lb. (the acre furrow slice).

This is a figure that should be committed to memory.   One milliequivalent of hydrogen is equal to 20 lb. per acre.   The figure is used in the following manner.

Calcium carbonate has an equivalent weight of 50, and 50 lb. of $CaCO_3$ equals 1 lb. of H.   Therefore, in terms of $CaCO_3$, 1 meq. of H is

* Approximate weights are used in this chapter.

equal to 1000 lb. of $CaCO_3$ per acre, obtained as follows:

$$meq. \times 20 \times equivalent\ weight = lb./acre$$

One more example: 0.2 meq. of K in a soil would be

$$0.2 \times 20 \times 39 = 156\ lb./acre$$

Soil Reaction. It has already been pointed out that if the clay is holding appreciable amounts of hydrogen the soil will be acid, and it will be alkaline if there is a high amount of basic cations (those cations that combine with OH^- ions to form bases or hydroxides).

Example:
$$Na^+ + OH^- \rightarrow NaOH\ (sodium\ hydroxide)$$

Soil reaction may be described as neutral, acid, or alkaline. The degree of alkalinity or acidity may be expressed as slight, medium, or strong and can be measured. In measuring the degree of acidity and alkalinity, an instrument is used that indicates the proportion of H^+ to OH^- ions in solution. At neutrality the H^+ ions equal the OH^- ions in solution.

A liter of distilled water is neutral and contains 0.000,000,1 g. of active hydrogen. A liter of 1 N hydrochloric acid (HCl) contains 1 g. of hydrogen. A liter of 1 N *any acid* contains 1 g. of hydrogen. A 0.01 N acid contains 0.01 g. of hydrogen per liter. In doing analytical work in the laboratory one refers to the normality of solutions, because the normalities will usually be little more than 1 or little less than 1. Since soils vary around neutrality, the normality would have to be expressed as a very small fraction. A neutral soil is 0.000,000,1 N. Rather than use the very small fractions, it is customary to express the normality as the *logarithm of the reciprocal of the hydrogen-ion concentration.* The reciprocal of any fraction is the inverted fraction. The reciprocal of 0.000,000,1 is 10,000,000, and the logarithm of 10 million is 7. Ten multiplied by itself 7 times equals 10 million. The term pH is used to express the hydrogen-ion concentration, and the pH value is the logarithm of the reciprocal of the hydrogen-ion concentration. A strong acid solution, 0.01 N with respect to the H ion, has a pH of 2, since 2 is the logarithm of 100 (10^2). The following table shows the relationship of the normality to pH and pOH (pOH is the log of the reciprocal of the OH concentration).

The pH Scale. Soils vary in pH from about 4 to 10. Soils of the humid regions are generally acid and have a pH below 7. Soils developed from high-lime deposits will often be alkaline in reaction. Soils high in calcium seldom have pH values above 7.5, but the presence of high amounts of calcium carbonate may run the pH up to as high as 8.5.   The presence of sodium causes very high pH values.   Where the pH is found to be above

TABLE 28. RELATION OF pH AND pOH TO NORMALITIES OF ACID AND ALKALINE SOLUTIONS

pH	Acid (normality of H)	Alkaline (normality of OH)	pOH
0	1.0	0.000,000,000,000,01	14
1	0.1	0.000,000,000,000,1	13
2	0.01	0.000,000,000,001	12
3	0.001	0.000,000,000,01	11
4	0.0001	0.000,000,000,1	10
5	0.00001	0.000,000,001	9
6	0.000001	0.000,000,01	8
7	0.000,000,1	0.000,000,1	7
8	0.000,000,01	0.000001	6
9	0.000,000,001	0.00001	5
10	0.000,000,000,1	0.0001	4
11	0.000,000,000,01	0.001	3
12	0.000,000,000,001	0.01	2
13	0.000,000,000,000,1	0.1	1
14	0.000,000,000,000,01	1.0	0

8.5 there is high probability of an excess of sodium.   The smaller the amount of calcium, the lower the pH, generally, and to correct an acid condition necessitates the addition of calcium in the form of limestone. The following pH scale is very important as a reference in study of soil management.   It should be committed to memory.

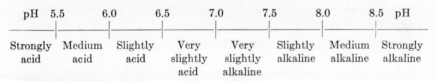

pH   5.5   6.0   6.5   7.0   7.5   8.0   8.5   pH

Strongly   Medium   Slightly   Very   Very   Slightly   Medium   Strongly
acid   acid   acid   slightly slightly alkaline   alkaline alkaline
                               acid   alkaline

Relation of Base Saturation to pH in Soils.   The pH of a soil can be measured quite easily in a very short time, and the pH of soils is usually determined in order to estimate the need for lime.

The pH indicates the relative amounts of H^+ and OH^- ions in solution, and it also reflects the percentage of base saturation.

When one estimates the lime requirement of a soil one is primarily interested in the amount of $CaCO_3$ needed to neutralize exchangeable H^+ rather than H^+ ions in solution.   The reason is obvious after the following illustration.

Assume a soil to have a pH of 5 with 22 per cent moisture.   This amount of moisture would represent 440,000 lb. of water per acre furrow slice. With 2.2 lb. per liter, this would represent 200,000 liters, of water. At a pH of 5 there is 0.00001 g. of H^+ per liter, or 1 g. in 100,000 liters. Therefore, in 200,000 liters one would have 2 g. of active H^+ ions in solution. This would be equivalent to 100 g. of $CaCO_3$. In other words, less than ¼ lb. of $CaCO_3$ would be required to neutralize the H^+ ions in solution in 1 acre at a pH of 5. As the H^+ ions in solution are neutralized, more H^+ ions leave the surface of clays and organic matter to enter the soil solution. The soil system is highly buffered against a change in pH.

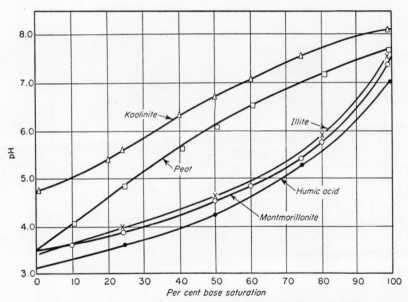

FIG. 68. pH–base-saturation curves for different colloids (24,25).

It is necessary to add enough $CaCO_3$ to neutralize most of the exchangeable H^+ ions held by the clay crystals and organic compounds. An estimate of the amount of $CaCO_3$ required is based on the exchange capacity of the soil and the per cent base saturation at various pH levels.

It is not practical to determine the exchange capacity and per cent base saturation for all soils sent in to soil-testing laboratories. The usual procedure is to prepare pH and base-saturation curves as illustrated in Fig. 68. These curves were prepared by Mehlich (24,25) of North Carolina. It has been learned that Iowa soils fit the curve for montmorillonite fairly closely. Iowa soils have a base saturation of about 90 per cent at a pH of 6.5, and it is desirable to lime Iowa soils to a base saturation of 90 per cent.   In other states, the soils may differ significantly in their pH–base-saturation relationships because of the presence of high amounts of kaolinite.   For example, soils are limed to 80 per cent base saturation in New Jersey.

The following data illustrate the way in which one might calculate the need for $CaCO_3$ from knowledge of the cation-exchange capacity:

Assume the soil to be montmorillonitic with a pH of 5 and cation-exchange capacity of 20.   From Fig. 68 the per cent base saturation would be 65, and it is desirable to lime to 90 per cent base saturation.

$$\begin{aligned}
\text{pH } 6.5 \ (90\% \text{ of } 20) &= 18 \text{ meq.} \\
\text{pH } 5.0 \ (65\% \text{ of } 20) &= 13 \text{ meq.} \\
\text{Difference} &= \overline{5} \text{ meq.}
\end{aligned}$$

In other words, 5 meq. of H^+ must be neutralized, which would require $2\frac{1}{2}$ tons of finely ground limestone with 100 per cent $CaCO_3$.

Soil-testing laboratories prepare tables from pH–base-saturation curves so that by determining pH one may quickly refer to the table for the amount of lime to apply.   The table should indicate the lime needed for soils of different textures and different organic-matter contents at various pH levels.

Activity of Calcium in Relation to Clay Minerals.   Hydrogen ions are held more strongly than Ca^{++} ions by kaolinite.   The activity of Ca^{++} being greater than H^+ causes a pH of 7 to occur at about 60 per cent base saturation in kaolinite.   In contrast to kaolinite, Fig. 68 indicates a base saturation of about 95 per cent at a pH of 7 for montmorillonite.   In the case of montmorillonite, Ca^{++} is held more strongly than H^+, and a high Ca^{++} saturation is necessary to provide adequate available calcium (21).

An H^+-saturated montmorillonite has a pH of about 3.5, while an H^+-saturated kaolinite has a pH of almost 5.   This means that H^+ ions are more readily dissociated from montmorillonite than from kaolinite in the presence of water.   In other words, H^+-saturated montmorillonite is a stronger acid than H^+-saturated kaolinite.

A kaolinite with 60 per cent Ca^{++} saturation and 40 per cent H^+ saturation has a pH of 7 because at that point Ca^{++} in solution causes the appearance of enough OH^- ions to balance H^+ ions in solution.

A montmorillonite with 60 per cent Ca^{++} saturation and 40 per cent H^+ saturation has a pH below 5.   In contrast with kaolinite, the Ca^{++} ions are held much more strongly by montmorillonite, while the H^+ ions are readily dissociated, causing a greater acidity.

A possible explanation of this behavior is presented with the following diagrams.

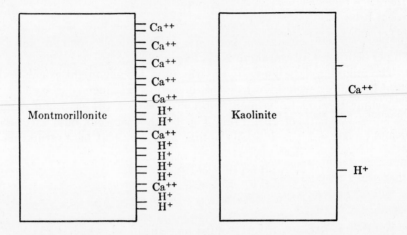

In kaolinite there are fewer exchange positions with greater distance between them than occur in montmorillonite. A divalent ion like calcium will be relatively weakly adsorbed by kaolinite, since the ion cannot be held close to both exchange positions at once and a monovalent ion might compete more successfully for a single exchange position. The exchange positions on montmorillonite are more numerous and closer-spaced. A divalent ion is adsorbed relatively strongly since it can be close to two exchange positions at the same time. This causes divalent ions to be more successful than monovalent ions in competing for the exchange positions on montmorillonite.

This difference in the way H^+ and Ca^{++} are held by kaolinite and montmorillonite not only affects the base saturation to which soils should be limed but also affects the potassium relationships, a subject to be treated in Chap. 11.

Causes of Acidity and Alkalinity. In the briefest expression, acidity is caused by removal of bases and the substitution of hydrogen; and alkalinity is caused by the accumulation of bases. In humid regions under natural conditions the removal of bases is brought about largely by leaching. In arid regions there is lack of leaching and the bases accumulate as rocks and minerals are weathered. If for any reason the water table comes near the surface in arid regions, the rising capillary water brings salts to the surface which accumulate in the surface soil as evaporation occurs. The accumulation of salts results in an alkaline condition.

Effect of Vegetation on Soil Reaction. In humid climates where leaching occurs during all or part of the year, there is a tendency for soils to become more acid all the time, owing to removal of bases, particularly calcium. The natural vegetation has a marked influence on the rate of removal of bases by leaching. If the plant is a heavy feeder on calcium, there is a replenishment of the calcium supply in the surface soil as plant roots bring the bases back to the surface from lower depths.   On the other hand, if the plant is a light feeder on calcium, the rate of removal by leaching is more rapid.

Trees, in general, are light feeders on bases, while grasses, in general, are heavy feeders on bases.   In the first place, trees are more likely to survive on a soil low in bases, and second, the trees permit the soil to become more acid.   In humid regions where the soil is high in bases, the grasses may compete successfully with trees, and if so, the grasses help to keep the soil from becoming strongly acid.   Where both forests and prairies are common, one will usually find the forest soils are more acid than the grassland soils.

The Prairie soils are generally acid and require lime in order to grow legumes successfully.   These soils are acid because of leaching and *because of accumulation of organic matter*.   The addition of organic matter to a soil causes an increase in exchange capacity but does not include enough bases to balance the increase in exchange capacity.   The accumulation of organic matter decreases the percentage of base saturation.   Furthermore, the organic matter contains more acid-forming material than base-forming material; therefore added organic matter produces acids directly on decomposition and produces humus, which increases the exchange capacity and consequently reduces the percentage of base saturation.

Relation of Crop Production to pH.   The effect of pH on plant growth is largely nutritional.   Alfalfa, for example, is a plant known to require a pH of 6.5 or above for successful production.   Alfalfa has a high requirement for calcium, which is most abundant and most available in the pH range from about 7 to 8.   Some plants, like azaleas, have a preference for soils in a lower pH range, not because of a preference for hydrogen, but because of a high requirement for iron which is more available in the low pH range.   This subject will be expanded in the next chapter.

Effect of pH on the Availability of Plant Nutrients.   The solubility of inorganic *nitrogenous* salts is high for the entire pH range in soils.   The amount of mineralization of nitrogen from organic matter is greatest in the range from 6 to 8.

Phosphorus solubility decreases with a decrease in pH below 6.5.   On the other hand, phosphorus solubility decreases as the pH rises above 7.5. The problem in soils is that more iron and aluminum occur in solution in soils with low pH values, and phosphorus is precipitated readily by either of these constituents.   At a pH of 6.5 there is less iron and aluminum in solution to precipitate phosphorus.   A pH between 6.5 and 7.5 is about optimum for phosphorus solubility in soils.   In soils above pH 7.5, phosphorus may be precipitated by calcium.   The solubility of phosphorus is very low in the range from pH 7.5 to 8.5.   In this range the alkalinity is due to excess calcium carbonate. Phosphorus is usually more soluble at pH values above 8.5 because of the presence of sodium, which, when combined with phosphorus, is relatively soluble.

Potassium availability is sometimes suppressed by addition of lime to an acid soil. It is generally true that the more strongly acid soils have been leached and the more acid the soils, the greater is their need for potassium. In contrast to this, soils which have not been leached are high in bases and are generally high in available potassium. In high-lime soils, potassium may occur in amounts of around 200 lb. of exchangeable potassium per acre furrow slice (which is medium to high for most soils) and still be deficient for corn production. *Excess* calcium carbonate suppresses the activity of potassium, and an unfavorably high calcium to potassium ratio exists in the soil solution. Therefore the pH range from 7.5 to 8.5 is unfavorable for potassium availability. In soils with pH values above 8.5 there is usually plenty of available potassium.

The solubility of inorganic *sulfur* compounds is high enough to supply crop needs in the whole pH range for soils. The sulfur problem, however, is like the nitrogen problem, since sulfur is combined in organic form, and the mineralization of sulfur is favored by higher pH values. The quantity of sulfur is usually lower in soils with lower pH values because of leaching losses.

Iron, manganese, copper, and *zinc* are all metallic cations that are more soluble in moderately acid conditions. In soils below pH of 5, iron is more soluble, while the availability of copper, zinc, and manganese may be depressed. Any one or all of these heavy metals may limit plant growth in high-lime or alkaline soils. Soybeans growing on high-lime soils frequently show chlorosis, which has recently been shown to be due to iron deficiency (28).

Calcium and *magnesium* are more available at higher pH values except under strongly alkaline conditions. An acid condition in the soil is usually the result of leaching of bases, particularly calcium and magnesium. It is only logical, then, that as the pH of a soil increases, the availability of calcium and magnesium also increases, because it is generally through an increase in calcium and magnesium that the pH is increased. If the pH is increased above 8.5 there is a reduction in availability of calcium and magnesium. This reduction is due to the fact that sodium and potassium replace calcium and magnesium on the clay crystals, and the calcium and magnesium are precipitated as carbonates.

Boron is most available in the pH range from 5 to 7. Figure 69 indicates that the solubility of boron is low above 8.5. Recent work of Olson and Berger (29) indicates that sodium as well as calcium will depress the solubility of boron at high pH values. However, Truog (34) points out that boron is plentiful in alkali soils because of lack of leaching losses.

The solubility of *molybdenum* is increased by liming. At low pH values, molybdenum is precipitated by iron or aluminum.

Injurious Effects of Strong Acidity. There is no evidence that the high concentrations of hydrogen ions in acid soils are directly the cause of depressed crop growth. The effect of acidity is indirect, in that availability of nutrients is affected and strong acidity increases the aluminum

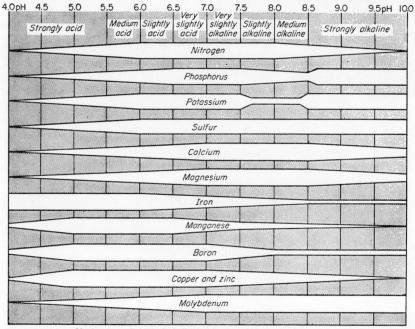

Maximum availability is indicated by the widest part of the bar

FIG. 69. Soil-reaction influence on availability of plant nutrients. [*After Truog* (34).]

and manganese in solution to such extent that plants may be injured. Pierre and his associates (30) found a high correlation between acidity and amounts of soluble aluminum in the soil solution; that is, the lower the pH, the more aluminum found in solution. They also found that at the same pH but with varying amounts of aluminum in solution, the plants were injured in proportion to the concentration of aluminum. They found that concentrations of 1 p.p.m. (parts per million) or greater were unfavorable to barley and corn in culture solutions; and one might expect to find 1 p.p.m. or more soluble aluminum in a soil below a pH of 5.

Manganese solubility increases as the pH is decreased, and it has been shown by Kelley (19) and others that manganese may be absorbed by plants in amounts sufficient to be toxic. Morris and Pierre (27) found that 5 p.p.m. of manganese in culture solutions was extremely toxic to lespedeza, while 0.1 to 1 p.p.m. of soluble manganese resulted in about the same growth, with 0.1 p.p.m. being somewhat more favorable.

Acidifying Soils. It is sometimes desirable, particularly in gardening, to acidify soils in order to grow an iron-loving (or acid-loving) plant.

There are at least three suitable materials for lowering the pH of soils, namely, sulfur, ferrous sulfate, and aluminum sulfate (alum). Sulfur is the cheapest material, but ferrous sulfate is more satisfactory in most cases. Ferrous sulfate performs the dual function of lowering the pH and providing soluble iron.

The amount of sulfur or ferrous sulfate to apply can be calculated in exactly the same manner as the lime requirement. It is necessary to estimate the exchange capacity, determine the pH, and decide on the desired pH. By using an appropriate pH–base-saturation chart one can calculate the pounds per acre of sulfur needed to obtain the desired pH.

Example:

pH 6.5, exchange capacity 30 meq./100 g.

pH 5.0 = desired

pH 6.5 = 89% base saturation

pH 5.0 = 68% base saturation

21% of 30 is 6.3, or 6.3 meq./100 g.

Equivalent weight of sulfur equals 16.

$$6.3 \times 16 \times 20 = 2016 \text{ lb. sulfur/acre}$$
$$\frac{2016}{4840} = 0.41 \text{ lb./sq. yd.}$$

This amount should be sufficient to lower the pH in this particular example to 5 for the top 6⅔ in. If the soil is to be acidified to lower depths, more sulfur will have to be added. It is advisable, however, to put on just enough in the initial application to acidify the surface soil (6⅔ in.).

Saline and Alkali Soils. Under conditions of poor drainage with a high rate of evaporation from the surface of the soil there is a tendency for soluble salts to accumulate. Such conditions are common in river valleys of arid and semiarid regions, in old lake beds in arid regions, and along coast lines where the evaporation is high and the rainfall is low. The salt accumulations may result in the development of highly alkaline soils or in the development of soils containing enough neutral salts to be inhibitory to the growth of economic plants.

Soils which have formed under conditions of excess salts are generally classed as saline or alkali.

Saline soils have a high content of neutral salts and have a pH generally above 7.3 and not over 8.5. Such soils are commonly referred to as *white alkali* because of the tendency to form white crusts on the dry soil surface. They belong to the great soil group Solonchak, from a Russian term meaning salt.

The excess (usually above 0.2 per cent) salts of saline soils are usually mixtures of chlorides, sulfates, carbonates, and bicarbonates of sodium, calcium, magnesium, and potassium. Sodium usually amounts to less than 15 per cent of the exchangeable bases in saline soils. The successful management of saline soils requires the removal of salts by the establishment of a drainage system and the leaching or washing of the salts from the soils.

Alkali soils are those containing enough excess sodium salts, particularly sodium carbonate and sodium bicarbonate, to raise the pH above 8.5. Furthermore, the per cent of exchangeable bases in an alkali soil will exceed 15 per cent sodium. Alkali soils are often referred to as *black alkali* because of the tendency of the organic matter to dissolve and disperse through the soil, thus giving it a dark color.

Alkali soils belong to the great soil group Solonetz, from another Russian term associated with salt. Alkali soils present several problems in management. Their structure is poor and drainage through them is very slow, even though tile is laid for drainage. The presence of the excess sodium causes dispersion or deflocculation, and the soil tends to run together as an impervious mass. Another problem is that of the high pH which is associated with the low solubility of iron, manganese, copper, and zinc. Furthermore, the salt concentration itself may be high enough to be inhibitory to the growth of economic plants.

Correction of Alkali Conditions. The most important step in the correction of alkali is to remove the cause of the trouble. The cause of the alkali is usually the high water table, and therefore drainage is usually the most important step.

Plants can stand from two to three times as much sodium sulfate as sodium carbonate. An effective method of converting sodium carbonate to sodium sulfate is to add sulfur. The process of changing sodium carbonate to sodium sulfate also lowers the pH of the soil.

Gypsum is frequently used for correction of black alkali where it can be obtained at low cost. Gypsum has the advantage of supplying calcium to displace sodium, sulfur to react with the sodium carbonate to form sodium sulfate (which is about neutral and is soluble), and calcium carbonate (which is less soluble than sodium carbonate), a combination which lowers the pH of the soil.

Addition of organic matter helps the soil by lowering the pH, improving the structure, and improving the capacity of the soil to provide available nitrogen to the crops. Organic matter is especially helpful where sulfur is added to correct the alkalinity. The organic matter stimulates the oxidation of the sulfur to the sulfate form. McGeorge (23) recommends a combination of sulfur, manure, and gypsum for maximum benefits in correcting alkali soils.

TABLE 29. REMOVAL OF SODIUM CARBONATE FROM AN ALKALI SOIL BY
USE OF SULFUR (18)

Time	Sulfur added, lb./acre	Sulfur oxidized, per cent	CO_3, lb./acre in solution	HCO_3, lb./acre in solution	pH
Before treatment (original soil 0.60 $CaCO_3$)....	....	..	510	1890	9.6
After 2 weeks.....	800	9	330	1678	9.2
	1600	8	284	1632	9.2
After 15 weeks....	800	74	0	868	7.5
	1600	75	0	580	7.3

High-lime Soils. High-lime soils occur in the humid region where the parent material was high in calcium and the water table near the surface and where capillary water has caused the rise of excess calcium to the surface. Many of the high-lime spots have as much as 10 per cent or more of excess calcium carbonate.

Crops are affected differently on these high-lime soils. Oats lodge (especially in wet years), corn shows potassium-starvation symptoms, soybeans are chlorotic, and yet sweet clover does well on these soils.

Nelson and Allaway (28) found that chlorosis in soybeans on high-lime soils of Iowa was due to iron deficiency. They found that the chlorotic condition could be corrected by spraying the plants with ferrous sulfate.

The high-lime spots in Iowa showed up more in 1948 than in 1947, which was a rather dry summer, particularly in July and August; 1948 was dry during the spring, but the rains were almost ideal for corn production throughout the summer. Nitrate production was high during the summer of 1948. The high nitrate production and low available potassium probably account for the lodging of oats. The potassium starvation in corn is the result of several unfavorable conditions. The high nitrates in the soil cause a greater need for potassium by corn, and at the same time the excess calcium and magnesium in solution suppress the uptake of potassium. Still another factor is that the soils are poorly drained and poorly aerated, and poor aeration decreases the plants' ability to take up potassium.

Allaway and Pierre (2) found that high-lime soils had less exchangeable potassium than adjacent normal soils. Part of their data are shown in Table 30. They found that potassium fertilization increased corn yields from 10 to 151 per cent on high-lime soils.

TABLE 30. RELATION OF HIGH LIME TO EXCHANGEABLE POTASSIUM AND RESPONSE TO POTASH FERTILIZER (2)

Field	Yield of corn untreated, bu./acre	Response to K, per cent	Exchangeable K, lb./acre
Patterson:			
High lime................	45.4	74*	205
Normal...................	....	....	381
Nolte:			
High lime................	30.7	77†	148
Normal...................	....	....	273
DeWolf:			
High lime................	42.5	10†	148
Normal...................	82.1	....	401
Conway:			
High lime................	60.0	26†	189
Normal...................	....	....	392
Vaudt:			
High lime................	25.0	151†	195
Normal...................	....	....	278

* 125 lb. 0-20-10.   † 100 lb. KCl per acre.

In managing high-lime soils, there are several important points to keep in mind:

1. Nitrogen fertilizers are usually omitted in Minnesota and Iowa but are used on calcareous soils of Southern states.

2. Manures are beneficial because of the high availability of potassium in manure and also because they produce acids and organic colloids, which have a neutralizing effect on alkalinity.

3. Potassium should be applied each time corn is planted.

4. Soybeans, oats, and legume hays do not respond to potassium to as great an extent as corn.

5. Drainage is essential to successful production on high-lime soils. A good drainage system will have the effect of lowering the salt concentration of the surface soil and improving aeration, which increases the uptake of potassium.

6. Gypsum or sulfur may be injurious to corn, since the effect will be to increase the salt content of the soil solution. There is evidence to indicate that the higher the concentration of salts in the soil solution, the less potassium there will be in relation to calcium in solution.

7. The application of ferrous sulfate is recommended for soybeans where a deficiency of iron shows up. Nelson and Allaway (28) recommended the following: 10 lb. of ferrous sulfate in 50 gal. of water as a spray (used directly on the leaves of the affected plants). Rain water or cistern water is preferable, since hard water causes precipitation of the ferrous sulfate and may clog up the spray nozzle. The cost of the ferrous sulfate is about 5 cents a pound in 100-lb. lots.

REFERENCES

1. Alexander, L. T., S. B. Hendricks, and R. A. Nelson, Minerals Present in Soil Colloids. II. Estimation in Some Representative Soils, *Soil Sci.*, **48**:273–279, 1939.
2. Allaway, Hubert, and W. H. Pierre, Availability, Fixation and Liberation of Potassium in High-lime Soils, *J. Am. Soc. Agron.*, **31**:940–953, 1939.
3. Allison, F. E., E. M. Roller, and Janet H. Doetsch, Ammonium Fixation and Availability in Vermiculite, *Soil Sci.*, **75**:173–180, 1953.
4. Barshad, Isaac, Vermiculite and Its Relation to Biotite as Revealed by Base Exchange Reactions, X-Ray Analysis, Differential Thermal Curves and Water Content, *Am. Mineralogist*, **33**:655–678, 1948.
5. Barshad, Isaac, Soil Development, Chap. 1 in Firman E. Bear (ed.), "Chemistry of the Soil," Reinhold, New York, 1955.
6. Baver, L. D., The Effect of Organic Matter upon Several Physical Properties of Soils, *J. Am. Soc. Agron.*, **22**:703–708, 1930.
7. Black, C. A., "Soil-Plant Relationships," Iowa State College, Department of Agronomy, 1954 (mimeo. textbook).
8. Bower, C. A., Availability of Ammonium Fixed in Difficultly Exchangeable Form by Soils of Semi Arid Regions, *Soil Sci. Soc. Amer. Proc.*, **15**:119–122, 1951.
9. Bower, C. A., and E. Truog, Base Exchange Capacity Determinations as Influenced by Nature of the Cation Employed and Formation of Base Exchange Salts, *Soil Sci. Soc. Amer. Proc.*, **5**:86–89, 1941.
10. Coleman, N. T., M. L. Jackson, and A. Mehlich, Mineral Composition of the Clay Fraction, *Soil Sci. Soc. Amer. Proc.*, **14**:81–86, 1949.
11. Dean, L. A., and E. J. Rubins, Anion Exchange in Soils, *Soil Sci.*, **63**:377–406, 1947.
12. Gieseking, J. E., The Clay Minerals in Soils, *Advances in Agron.*, **1**:159–294, 1949.
13. Gieseking, J. E., and Hans Jenny, Behavior of Polyvalent Cations in Base Exchange, *Soil. Sci.*, **42**:273–280, 1936.
14. Grim, R. E., Modern Concept of Clay Materials, *J. Geol.*, **50**:225–275, 1942.
15. Grim, R. E., Relation of the Composition to the Properties of Clays, *J. Am. Ceramic Soc.*, **22**:141–151, 1939.
16. Jackson, M. L., and G. Donald Sherman, Chemical Weathering of Minerals in Soils, *Advances in Agron.*, **5**:221–318, 1953.
17. Kelley, W. P., and S. M. Brown, Replaceable Bases in Soils, *Calif. Agr. Expt. Sta. Tech. Paper* 15, 1924.
18. Kelley, W. P., and E. E. Thomas, The Removal of Sodium Carbonate from Soils, *Univ. Calif. Pub. Tech. Paper* 1, 1923.
19. Kelley, W. P., The Function and Distribution of Manganese in Plants and Soils, *Hawaii Agr. Expt. Sta. Bull.* 26, 1912.
20. Larson, W. E., W. H. Allaway, and H. F. Rhoades, Characteristics of Three Soils

from the Chernozem and Chestnut Soil Regions of Nebraska, *Soil Sci. Soc. Amer. Proc.*, **12**:420–423, 1947.

21. Marshall, C. E., Ionization of Calcium from Soil Colloids and Its Bearing on Soil-Plant Relationships, *Soil Sci.*, **65**:57–68, 1948.

22. Marshall, C. E., "The Colloid Chemistry of the Silicate Minerals," Agronomy Monograph 1, Academic Press, New York, 1949.

23. McGeorge, W. T., The Productive Capacity of Semi-arid Soils and the Present Emergency, *Ariz. Agr. Expt. Sta. Bull.* 182, 1942.

24. Mehlich, A., Base Unsaturation and pH in Relation to Soil Type, *Soil Sci. Soc. Amer. Proc.*, **6**:150–156, 1941.

25. Mehlich, A., The Significance of Percentage Base Saturation and pH in Relation to Soil Differences, *Soil Sci. Soc. Amer. Proc.*, **7**:167–174, 1942.

26. Miller, E. V., and N. T. Coleman, Colloidal Properties of Soils from Western Equatorial South America, *Soil Sci. Soc. Amer. Proc.*, **16**:239–244, 1952.

27. Morris, H. D., and W. H. Pierre, The Effect of Calcium, Phosphorus, and Iron on the Tolerance of Lespedeza to Manganese Toxicity in Culture Solutions, *Soil Sci. Soc. Amer. Proc.*, **12**:382–386, 1947.

28. Nelson, L. B., and W. H. Allaway, unpublished data, Iowa State College.

29. Olson, R. V., and K. C. Berger, Boron Fixation as Influenced by pH, Organic Matter Content and Other Factors, *Soil Sci. Soc. Amer. Proc.*, **11**:216–220, 1946.

30. Pierre, W. H., G. G. Pohlman, and T. C. McIlvaine, Soluble Aluminum Studies. I. The Concentration of Aluminum in the Displaced Soil Solution of Naturally Acid Soils, *Soil Sci.*, **34**:145–160, 1932.

31. Pierre, W. H., and G. D. Scarseth, Determination of the Percentage Base Saturation of Soils and Its Value in Different Soils at Definite pH Values, *Soil Sci.*, **31**:99–114, 1931.

32. Russell, M. B., and J. L. Haddock, The Identification of the Clay Minerals in Five Iowa Soils by the Thermal Method, *Soil Sci. Soc. Amer. Proc.*, **5**:90–94, 1940.

33. Toth, S. J., Anion Adsorption by Soil Colloids in Relation to Change in Free Iron Oxides, *Soil Sci.*, **44**:299–314, 1937.

34. Truog, E., Soil Reaction Influence on Availability of Plant Nutrients, *Soil Sci. Soc. Amer. Proc.*, **11**:305–308, 1946.

35. Wilkinson, G. E., and Fenton Gray, A Clay Mineralogical Study of Certain Reddish Prairie Soils of Oklahoma, with an Estimation of the Montmorillonite and Illite Content, *Soil Sci. Soc. Amer. Proc.*, **18**:264–268, 1954.

CHAPTER 8

THE PRINCIPLES AND PRACTICE OF LIMING

The use of lime is one of the oldest practices known in soil management and is the fertility practice that farmers think they know most about. The ultimate effects of liming soils, however, are not generally understood by farmers.

Liming is a practice that will permanently improve soil fertility if used in a properly managed crop rotation; in a poorly planned cropping system, it may serve as a stimulant, producing good crops immediately, followed by gradual impoverishment of fertility.

There is an old and time-tested German expression which illustrates the effects of lime on soils: *"Kalk macht die Väter reich, aber die Söhne arm"* (lime makes the fathers rich, but the sons poor). This expression probably originated in an area where it was the custom to lime the soil in a cropping system that returned little or no organic matter to the soil. Lime stimulates the decomposition of soil organic matter, thereby hastening the exploitation of nutrients held in organic combination. Therefore a man who follows such a system may reap profits from his soil, but he leaves an impoverished soil for those who follow him.

The diagram in Fig. 70 illustrates the effect of liming on crop yields compared to the same management practices without lime. The diagram is based on a liming experiment in Pennsylvania (3).

The stimulating effect of lime is primarily the effect of liberating nitrogen from organic matter by increasing the activity of soil microorganisms. The increased availability of nitrogen and other favorable effects of lime (to be mentioned later) cause an immediate improvement in crop yields, but after a few years nitrogen may become the most important limiting factor in the growth of nonlegumes.

Another old saying is that "Lime, and lime without manure, will make both farm and farmer poor." This expression might have originated in an area where an exploitive system of liming without organic-matter return was observed beside a system of liming in conjunction with manuring or liming in conjunction with a legume rotation. Lime plus an adequate

198

supply of decomposing organic matter are basic to maintenance of soil fertility. Either one of the practices alone will not prove successful on acid soils. The use of a legume in crop rotation is one of our most important means of maintenance of organic matter, and lime is essential to success in growing legumes on acid soils.

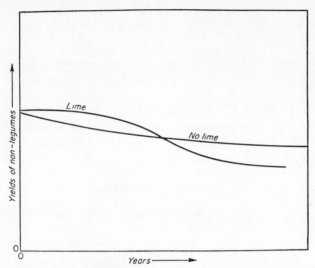

Fig. 70. A schematic diagram showing the relative yields of limed and unlimed soils where organic matter is allowed to decline.

There are two distinctly different ways in which liming of an acid soil might affect the organic-matter content. One is the short-time effect on the humus content that has accumulated over many years, because lime does stimulate decomposition of the residual organic matter of soils. The other effect is that liming of an acid soil where legumes are grown may actually cause an increase in organic-matter content. In the first case there is no addition of nitrogen, and the increased microbial activity resulting from liming causes a more rapid disappearance of nitrogen and a reduction in organic-matter content. In the second case the legume growth is encouraged by lime; a greater amount of nitrogen is fixed by symbiotic bacteria, and as nitrogen increases, the organic-matter content of the soil increases.

Economic Gains from Use of Lime. The use of lime on unfertilized plots at Wooster, Ohio, more than doubled the yields of crops in a 5-year rotation from 1917 to 1931. Lime on fertilized plots almost doubled the yields of the crops during the same period, and the profits from lime were greater on the fertilized plots than on the unfertilized plots. The returns on the dollar invested for lime were about $4 on unfertilized plots and nearly

$5 on fertilized plots. Table 31 shows the Ohio experiment, and the authors of the Ohio publication (4) refer to the balance in value due to liming as a "cost of failure to use lime."

Once a soil is limed to about pH 6.5 it will take from 50 cents to $1 worth of lime per acre per year to maintain the desired reaction. This estimate is based on an annual loss of 250 to 500 lb. of $CaCO_3$ per acre per

TABLE 31. AVERAGE YIELDS AND VALUE OF CROPS ON LIMED AND UNLIMED PLOTS (4)
Wooster, Ohio, 1917–1931

| Crop | Average yields per acre | | | |
| | Unfertilized | | Fertilized | |
	Unlimed	Limed	Unlimed	Limed
Corn, bu...............	7.7	24.9	23.6	45.8
Oats, bu...............	19.5	38.7	36.0	49.0
Wheat, bu.............	4.9	14.5	17.7	27.9
Clover, lb..............	546	2045	1288	3405
Timothy, lb............	1018	2955	1496	3806

| Economic analysis | Value of crops per acre | | | |
| | Unfertilized | | Fertilized | |
	Unlimed	Limed	Unlimed	Limed
Total value............	$20.37	$57.11	$49.87	$91.79
Gain for liming.........	....	36.74	....	41.92
Cost of lime............	....	7.50	....	7.50
Balance...............	....	$29.24	....	$34.42

year by leaching and crop removal. The cost of lime is estimated at $4 per ton. The increase in return for this investment is about as high as any increase expected from any enterprise on the farm. Table 32 shows average yield increases due to lime from many experiments conducted in Iowa on acid soils over a period of about 20 years (2). These crops were grown in rotations, and the effects of lime on corn, oats, and wheat may be partially due to greater quantities of legume residues left to decompose to supply nitrogen.

Lime Requirements of Legumes and Nonlegumes. There are probably many reasons why legumes require a soil of near neutrality, and not the least important reason is the high calcium requirement. Table 33 shows the relative amounts of calcium and magnesium in several legumes compared to several nonlegumes.

Alfalfa and sweet clover are commonly known as "lime-loving crops" because they have a high lime (calcium and magnesium) requirement and they thrive on alkaline soils.

TABLE 32. RESPONSE OF SOME IOWA SOILS TO LIME

Crops	No. of crops	Manure	Lime and manure	Increase for lime, per acre
Corn.............	255	58.5	63.5	5.0 bu.
Oats.............	131	48.9	52.6	3.7 bu.
Wheat............	22	25.5	28.9	3.4 bu.
Mixed hay........	94	1.4	1.7	0.3 ton
Alfalfa...........	11	1.2	2.7	1.5 ton

Soybeans and lespedeza both are legumes with high calcium requirement, yet both crops grow best at pH values lower than the optimum for alfalfa or sweet clover. Both lespedeza and soybeans show chlorosis (iron starvation, particularly) when grown on some alkaline soils where alfalfa

TABLE 33. AVERAGE AMOUNTS OF CALCIUM AND MAGNESIUM IN LEGUMES AND NONLEGUMES
In pounds per 1000 lb. dry plant materials

Crop	Calcium	Magnesium
Corn...................................	2.24	0.86
Oats...................................	1.65	0.98
Wheat.................................	1.45	0.87
Alfalfa.................................	13.91	3.55
Lespedeza.............................	13.87	
Red clover............................	11.42	2.70
Soybeans..............................	12.29	3.88

and sweet clover grow successfully. Red clover has about the same minimum pH value for optimum growth as soybeans, but red clover will succeed at a higher pH value than will soybeans.

Cowpeas succeed on alkaline soils and make their optimum growth at near neutrality, yet cowpeas are quite acid-tolerant.

Figure 71 shows the variations in pH values at which different crops make their optimum growth.

Each curve in Fig. 71 was prepared from several observations for each crop by McIlvaine and Pohlman of West Virginia. In the case of the non-legumes, all made 80 per cent or more of their optimum yield at pH 6 and from 95 to 100 per cent of their optimum yield at pH 6.5. Red clover, soybeans, and cowpeas made 80 per cent or more of their optimum growth at pH 6, while alfalfa and sweet clover made only about half their optimum growth at pH 6. Cowpeas did about as well at pH 6 as at pH 7, while the other legumes shown in Fig. 71 did considerably better at pH 7 than at pH 6 or 6.5.

Of the nonlegumes shown in Fig. 71, rye is the most acid-tolerant. All the nonlegumes but rye were greatly reduced in yield as the pH was reduced to values below pH 6.

Grass crops like corn, wheat, and oats take up considerably less calcium per unit of dry matter produced than legume crops like alfalfa and sweet clover. Nevertheless the grass crops respond favorably to a sys-

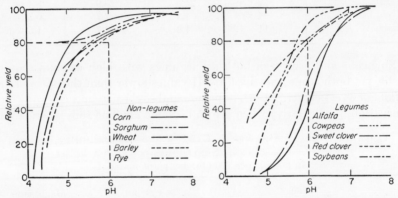

FIG. 71. Curves showing the relative yield at different pH values for several legumes and nonlegumes (6).

tem of management where lime is used on acid soils. The response is most likely due to the increased availability of nitrogen and phosphorus rather than from increased availability of calcium. The difference in the response of legumes and grasses to lime is so great that the effect on grasses is often overlooked. The difference is simply that legumes may fail without the lime while grasses might grow fairly well without lime on the same soil. The grasses respond to the lime but to a lesser extent. Figure 71 helps to see part of the reason why grasses might respond less to lime than legumes.

Grasses, in mixtures of legumes and grasses, are better equipped for competing with legumes for a limited supply of K. Conversely, legumes are better equipped than grasses in competing for Ca. The explanation is believed to be as follows. Plant roots have cation-exchange capacity, probably because of dissociation of H ions from the root surfaces. Legume roots have a higher cation-exchange capacity than grass roots. Consequently, the density of the charge, or the closeness of the negative charges, on the legume roots causes them to adsorb divalent ions more readily than monovalent ions. On the other hand, the wider spacing of the negative charges on the surface of grass roots causes them to adsorb monovalent ions more readily than divalent ions. This is the same principle that was described on page 188 for adsorption of mono- and divalent ions by clays.

The adaptation to adsorption of monovalent versus divalent ions may account in part for the composition of grasses and legumes with respect to Ca and K; but it appears also that grasses and legumes differ in their requirements for Ca and K.

Legumes have a high Ca to K requirement, while grasses have a high K to Ca requirement. Under conditions of moderate acidity, the supply of K versus Ca might be more favorable to grasses than to legumes. Lime improves the Ca to K relations for legumes but might not help the grasses from the standpoint of Ca to K nutrition; that is, potassium may have to be added also.

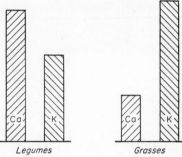

Fig. 72. The relative proportions of calcium and potassium contained in legumes and grasses.

The important consideration in growing grasses on limed soils is to ensure an adequate supply of potassium. This subject will be treated in Chap. 11, but it should be emphasized at this point that the successful growth of such grasses as corn, oats, and wheat often requires the addition of potassium on a soil which has been limed to a pH favorable for the growth of legumes.

Alfalfa, sweet clover, and sugar beets have a low tolerance for acidity and actually thrive on soils which are calcareous. In mixtures of hay and pasture crops, alfalfa and sweet clover are better competitors for nutrients under calcareous or alkaline conditions than the other crops commonly associated with them. The nutritional requirements of alfalfa and sweet clover for iron, potassium, and other nutrients are not disturbed by the high calcium saturation. However, it should not be assumed that these crops prefer a pH above 7. They may grow as well at a pH of 6.5 as at a pH of 7.5 in the presence of adequate calcium.

A very comprehensive study by the Ohio Experiment Station on the relation of pH and crop production is summarized in the table on page 204. These crops were grown in various rotations on plots which received phosphorus and potassium. The plots were limed to different pH values. The yields of the corn and small grain crops are related to the nitrogen supply furnished by the legume crops. It is expected that the nitrogen supply would be better following a high-yielding legume crop than following a low-yielding legume crop. The important feature here, however, is that, in choosing the best condition for several crops to appear in rotation, one would select a pH of 6.8 in preference to 7.5. Even if the yields were the same at pH 6.8 as at pH 7.5, the cost of maintaining the pH of 6.8 would be considerably less than the cost of maintaining a pH of 7.5.

TABLE 34. RELATIVE YIELDS OF CROPS AT DIFFERENT SOIL REACTIONS (4)

Crop	Average yields* at pH of :				
	4.7	5.0	5.7	6.8	7.5
Corn..................................	34	73	83	100	85
Wheat.................................	68	76	89	100	99
Oats..................................	77	93	99	98	100
Barley................................	0	23	80	95	100
Alfalfa...............................	2	9	42	100	100
Sweet clover..........................	0	2	49	89	100
Red clover............................	12	21	53	98	100
Alsike clover.........................	13	27	72	100	95
Mammoth clover........................	16	29	69	100	99
Soybeans..............................	65	79	80	100	93
Timothy...............................	31	47	66	100	95

* Highest yield in bushels or tons shown as 100. All other yields are shown as per cent of the highest yield.

Soybeans was injured less by acidity than any of the legumes. Among the small grains studied, oats was injured least and barley was injured most by acidity.

There is increasing interest in the production of nonlegumes in rotations where legumes are excluded. This practice was not considered feasible on a large scale before the Second World War because of the lack of nitrogen supply in the form of a cheap fertilizer; that is, it was more economical to grow legumes in rotations as a primary source of nitrogen than to buy nitrogen fertilizers for the production of such agronomic crops as corn and cotton. The supply of low-cost fertilizer nitrogen is such now that in some instances it is more economical to omit the legume from the rotation. The question arises as to the lime requirements of such crops as corn and the small grains. In the Ohio study previously described, corn, oats, and wheat were grown on soils of different pH reactions following alfalfa and on comparable plots following timothy with no legume in the rotation.

The yields of the corn and small grain were higher in the pH range from 6.8 to 7.5 whether in rotation with legumes or nonlegumes. Recent unpublished results in southern Iowa show that liming increased yields of continuous corn. Lime was as effective as an application of 30 lb. P_2O_5 per acre in increasing the yield of continuous corn. It is believed that an important effect of the lime was that of making the soil phosphorus more available. The experiments in Ohio and Iowa provide evidence for the recommendation that soils should be limed to at least a pH of 6.5 for corn and the small grains even though a legume is not grown in the rotation.

The premium is placed on the effect of lime on availability of nutrients *other than calcium* in the growth of grasses. On the other hand, the premium is on calcium nutrition for most legumes.

Desired Soil Reaction for Special Crops. It was shown in Chap. 7 that each nutrient element has a pH value or range at which it is most available. A plant that has a high requirement for iron and a low requirement for calcium would thrive best on an acid soil. There are certain plants which are actually injured by addition of lime. Such plants have frequently been called "acid-loving," but they are probably not especially favored by the high concentration of hydrogen directly, but by the increased availability of certain nutrients such as iron or manganese in the acid soil.

White potatoes do quite well on soils high in lime, but potato scab is caused by an actinomycete which thrives in soils high in calcium. To grow scab-free potatoes, therefore, an effort is made to keep soils acid by using acidifying fertilizers.

Table 35 shows a grouping of plants on the basis of probable response to addition of lime on an acid soil. Strawberries and watermelons grow

TABLE 35. GROUPING OF PLANTS ACCORDING TO RESPONSE TO LIME ON ACID SOILS

High	Medium	Low	None	May be injured
Alfalfa	Red clover	Lespedeza	Strawberry	Azalea
Sweet clover	White clover	Soybeans	Watermelon	Rhododendron
Sugar beets	Corn	Alsike clover		Cranberry
	Barley	Oats		Blueberry
	Wheat	Rye		
	Timothy	Flax		
	Orchard grass	Cotton		
	Bluegrass	Tobacco		

well on soils at near neutrality, but at the same time, no increase in yield would be expected from the addition of lime to a medium-acid soil on which these crops were growing. Azalea, rhododendron, cranberry, and blueberry are "iron-loving" plants which may be injured by liming, and to grow them successfully may require acidification with ferrous sulfate (see page 192). If the minor elements, particularly iron, could be maintained in available form at the pH of near neutrality, then these plants might respond favorably to liming.

Testing Soils for Lime Requirement. There are several methods used to estimate lime requirement. Some of the more common methods are the following:

Glass Electrode. The most reliable method for determination of pH is the use of a glass electrode pH meter. But pH alone is not sufficient information for estimating lime needs. A knowledge of the mineralogical

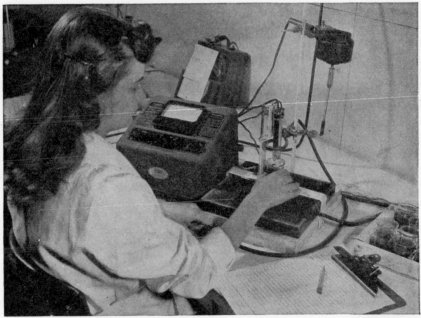

Fig. 73. Determining the pH of soil with a glass electrode pH meter. (*Soil Testing Laboratory, Iowa State College.*)

nature of the clay (whether montmorillonitic, kaolinitic, etc.), the percentage of clay, and the percentage of organic matter in the soil is necessary in order to estimate the exchange capacity of the soil and the percentage base saturation. A table must be prepared in every locality where soil testing is to be done in order that pH values for different textural classes and organic-matter percentage ranges may be converted to tons of lime requirement. A discussion of pH and base saturation is presented in Chap. 7.

Colorimetric Tests for pH. There are many different commercial quick-test kits for determining pH colorimetrically. The kits use various indicators such as *bromcresol purple* or *bromthymol blue*, which change color gradually over a wide pH range. For example, bromthymol blue is yellow at pH 6 or below, green at pH 6.5, greenish blue at pH 7.0, and deep blue at pH 7.5 or higher. One simple test is as follows: A tiny sample of soil is placed in the concave cell of a white porcelain spot plate, and a few drops of the indicator solution are then placed on the soil. The soil settles to the center of the spot plate, and the excess solution can be observed as a colored ring in the cell around the soil sample and can be compared to a color chart for estimating the pH.

Each kit contains printed directions for making the test and a table converting pH to lime requirement.

Thiocyanate Test. The thiocyanate test is one of the most popular rapid methods for estimating lime requirement and is sold commercially under various trade names. It was developed by Comber (1) and improved by Harper (5). The solution is made by dissolving 5 g. of potassium thiocyanate in 900 ml. of acetone and 100 ml. of ether.

The test is easy and rapid. About ½ in. of soil is placed in a test tube, and the solution is added so that about ½ in. of it remains on top of the soil. The contents are then shaken vigorously for a few seconds and allowed to settle. The color developed in the solution is compared to a color chart. A red color develops if there is need of lime. The red color is due to the presence of soluble iron. The more acid the soil, the more soluble the iron, and therefore the redder the color and the higher the lime requirement.

The greatest limitation to the test is that it does not provide a quantitative expression of how much lime is needed. The recommendations on the color chart are nothing more than "educated guesses." Furthermore, the test is not too reliable. Some soils will be only medium in acidity as shown by a pH meter and yet will turn blood red when the test solution is added. Other soils may be quite acid and develop only a slight red color. Other factors besides pH determine the amount of soluble iron in a soil.

Lime Meter. Woodruff (11) has recently developed a buffer solution to which soil is added. It is allowed to stand for a specified time, and the soil and buffer solution are than placed in contact with a glass electrode, which is calibrated to read lime requirement rather than pH. This procedure eliminates the necessity for estimating the clay content or percentage of organic matter in the sample of soil.

Amount of Lime to Use on Soils. Soils should be tested before deciding the amounts of lime to use. If the test is made by a commercial or state-college laboratory, the amount of lime will be recommended by the laboratory operator. If the test is accomplished by quick test, the printed directions in the test kit will indicate the amount of lime to use.

Table 36 is provided to give the reader a general idea of the amounts of ordinary limestone to use with various soil conditions.

TABLE 36. TONS OF LIME TO APPLY TO DIFFERENT SOIL CONDITIONS AT VARIOUS pH VALUES

pH	Corn Belt soils		Cotton Belt soils	
	Loam soils low in organic matter	Clay loam soils high in organic matter	Sandy loam soils low in organic matter	Clay loam soils medium in organic matter
6.0	0.75	1.5	0.25	0.5
5.5	1.5	3.0	0.5	1.0
5.0	2.25	4.5	1.0	1.5
4.5	3.0	6.0	1.5	2.0

Where Lime Is Used. Figure 74 shows a very generalized map of the United States which indicates relative lime content and acidity of various areas.

Removal of bases by leaching is the most important cause of soil acidity, and it is readily apparent in Fig. 74 that most of the soils of the humid part of the United States are in need of lime, while the subhumid, semiarid, and arid parts are rich in lime.

The forest soils of the humid part of the United States (Podzols, Brown Podzolic, Gray-Brown Podzolic, and Red-Yellow Podzolic) as a whole are generally in need of lime for legume rotations.

There are several areas of soils in the humid region of the United States which are young geologically, have developed from calcareous deposits, and are high in lime. Such areas occur in Texas, Iowa, Alabama, and Mississippi.

Judging the Efficiency of Limestone. The finer the limestone, the more quickly it reacts with the soil. Table 37 shows the relationship of fineness to the time required for the lime to dissolve.

TABLE 37. RELATIVE AVAILABILITY OF LIMESTONE PARTICLES OF DIFFERENT DEGREES OF FINENESS (8)

Fineness of particles	Percentage available within 1–3 years	Percentage available within 8–12 years
Held on 20-mesh screen..............	20	50
Through 20-mesh screen but held on 60-mesh............................	60	100
Through 60-mesh screen............	100	100

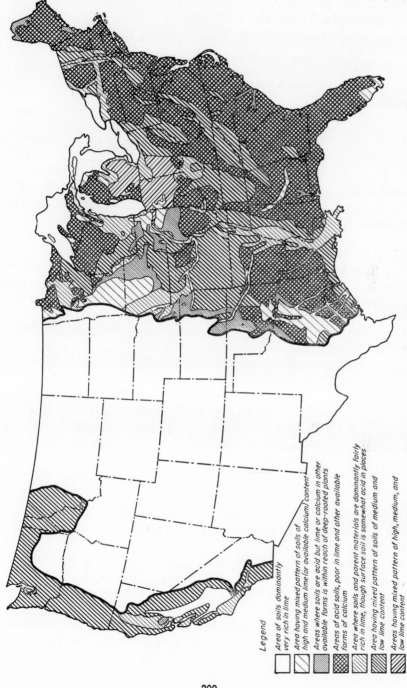

Legend

Area of soils dominantly
very rich in lime

Area having mixed pattern of soils of
high and medium lime (or available calcium) content

Areas where soils are acid but lime or calcium in other
available forms is within reach of deep-rooted plants

Areas of acid soils, poor in lime and other available
forms of calcium

Area where soils and parent materials are dominantly fairly
rich in lime, though surface soil is somewhat acid in places

Area having mixed pattern of soils of medium and
low lime content

Areas having mixed pattern of high, medium, and
low lime content

FIG. 74. The relative lime content and acidity of the soils of the United States.

The following procedure is recommended for use in calculating the efficiency of limestone from the standpoint of fineness. Effectiveness is based on the amount that becomes soluble during the first 3 years.

Material finer than 60 mesh............ 100% effective
Material from 8–60 mesh............... 40% effective
Material from 4–8 mesh................ 10% effective

Example:

10% between 4 and 8 mesh × 0.10   = 1%
40% between 8 and 60 mesh × 0.40   = 16%
50% finer than 60 mesh × 1.00   = 50%
    Total % effective during first 3 years = 67%

Another important factor is the purity of the ground limestone. The purity is based on the neutralizing effect on hydrochloric acid. The neutralizing power is expressed in terms of calcium carbonate equivalent.

In order to determine the value of the ground limestone, one should multiply the value for fineness by the value for purity. Limestone will usually have a calcium carbonate equivalency of 80 per cent or higher. As a guide, one may consider the average limestone at 90 per cent pure and 70 per cent effective (fineness). Multiplying these two figures together one gets 63 per cent efficiency for the average ground limestone.

Liming Materials. Lime is any material high in calcium (or calcium and magnesium) with a neutralizing effect on soil acidity. The cheapest and most abundant material in this country is the native limestone, which is principally calcium carbonate. Calcium carbonate is a salt of a strong base and a weak acid and is therefore alkaline in reaction. Calcium carbonate fulfills another desirable feature in liming material in that the reaction of limestone with an acid clay can go to completion, since one of the products of the reaction is removed.

$$CaCO_3 + \boxed{clay \begin{matrix} -H \\ -H \end{matrix}} \rightarrow \boxed{clay} = Ca + H_2O + CO_2\uparrow$$

Gypsum ($CaSO_4$) would not qualify under our definition, since it is a salt of a strong acid and a moderately strong base and is neutral or acid in its effect on soil reaction.

No two limestone deposits are alike. They vary in percentage of calcium and magnesium carbonate and, of course, in impurities. Furthermore, the fineness to which the limestone is ground determines how quickly it will be dissolved in the soil.

According to state laws, anyone selling limestone for agricultural use must furnish the purchaser with information relative to the percentage of calcium carbonate (or its equivalent) and the percentages of material passing through sieves of specified mesh.

Pure calcium carbonate has a molecular weight of 100. Pure magnesium carbonate has a molecular weight of 84. Therefore a sample of magnesium carbonate would be 100 ÷ 84, or 119 per cent calcium carbonate equivalent. Sometimes burned lime is used instead of limestone where the material has to be shipped long distances. One hundred pounds of calcium carbonate can be burned to drive off CO_2 and will lose 44 lb. Therefore burned lime has 100 ÷ 56, or 179 per cent calcium carbonate equivalent. Ordinary building lime is too expensive for liming a field soil but may be used for liming garden soil. Building lime is $Ca(OH)_2$ with a molecular weight of 74; its calcium carbonate equivalent is 135 per cent.

Fig. 75. Limestone is found to occur in abundance under soils in many parts of the country. The ground limestone provides a cheap and abundant source of lime. (*Courtesy of Roy W. Simonson.*)

Ordinary ground limestone contains some magnesium carbonate. When magnesium carbonate makes up an appreciable amount of the limestone, the material is called dolomitic limestone. The mineral referred to as dolomite has the formula of $CaCO_3 \cdot MgCO_3$, but the proportion of calcium carbonate to magnesium carbonate in the mineral is variable. Dolomitic limestone also varies considerably in its magnesium to calcium ratio. It is desirable to use limestone containing some magnesium. It is not generally possible, however, for a farmer to find out the ratio of calcium carbonate to magnesium carbonate in the limestone he expects to use. The desirable ratio would be about six times as much calcium carbonate as magnesium carbonate. The average humid-region soil contains about five times as many milliequivalents of exchangeable calcium as exchangeable magnesium, and it would be well to maintain this ratio. Yet dolomitic limestone may be considerably higher in magnesium than is desired, and a good plan is to alternate applications of dolomitic limestone with applications of ordinary high-calcium limestone on soils found to be deficient in magnesium.

In addition to limestone, burned lime, and hydrated lime, the following materials are available for liming soils: calcium carbide–refuse lime, sugar-factory lime, water-softening-process lime, blast-furnace slag, marl, and oyster shells.

When to Apply Lime. Lime should be applied at a time when heavy trucks will not damage the soil structure. The soil should be relatively dry or frozen at the time of application. Lime should not be spread on hilly topography when the soil is frozen, however, because thawing spring rains may cause serious losses of the lime by erosion.

In so far as the crop is concerned, limestone can be applied at any time of the year. Since it is rather insoluble at the time of application, it cannot damage the crop.

Lime should not be spread on a windy day because of losses and because uneven distribution may be the result.

It takes about 1 year for added limestone to make a significant change in the soil pH, and such a change throughout the furrow slice will occur only if the lime is thoroughly mixed with the soil. For this reason, the usual recommendation is to apply the lime in the rotation a year ahead of the legume seeding. However, one should not be misled by this recommendation. If the soil needs lime, as indicated by soil test, and a legume like alfalfa or red clover is to be seeded right away, the soil should be limed. Even if the lime is applied on the day of the seeding, there will be great benefit from the lime. The lime application has a valuable starter effect on acid soils.

Once soils have been limed to a pH of about 6.5 they should be limed again in 4 to 8 years. Well-drained soils will require liming more often than will poorly drained soils. Lime is removed from the soil by crops and by leaching at the rate of about 250 to 500 lb. of $CaCO_3$ equivalent per acre per year. Once the pH is brought into a favorable range, lime can be applied about anywhere in the rotation. The time should be determined by the physical condition of the soil surface. A systematic plan for applying the lime should be developed. A 5-year rotation on a well-drained soil will require 1 to 2 tons of lime once during the rotation. The farmer, under such a system, would apply lime to one field every year.

Too many farmers have limed their soil once and assumed that they corrected the soil acidity. Any soil which *was limed* to a pH of 6.5 more than 5 years ago should be tested for lime requirement. Chances are good that it will require lime.

Occasionally, a farmer will report favorable results from liming soils which showed a pH of about 6.5. Apparently, on some soils at pH 6.5 lime tends to have a favorable starter effect with lime-loving legumes like alfalfa. Where such experience proves the starter effect of lime, it might be desirable to apply a small application of lime each time that alfalfa is seeded in the rotation. Lime is cheap and not only supplies calcium but helps to make phosphorus more available. Care should be taken, however, to check the pH of the soil often enough to prevent overliming. The pH should not go above 7 if the soil was formerly acid.

How to Apply Lime. The spreading of lime by the dealer is to be preferred in the majority of situations. The dealer usually has a truck with a

Fig. 76. Finely ground limestone being spread on freshly plowed soil. (*Courtesy of Edwards, University of Missouri.*)

centrifugal type of spreader, and it is just about as easy for him to spread the lime as to dump it in one place on the field.

If the farmer spreads his own lime, it should be done with a regular lime spreader or an endgate seeder. Best results are obtained with even spreading, and damage can be done by getting too much in spots.

Overliming Soils. Too much lime may be worse than not enough. Figure 69 shows that too much lime reduces availability of iron, phosphorus, manganese, boron, copper, and zinc. Too much lime also suppresses the availability of potassium. Too much lime can be observed in the high-lime spots on the Clarion and Webster soil-association area of Minnesota and Iowa. Corn and soybeans become stunted and turn yellow on high-lime spots. It is not uncommon to see farmers liming calcareous soils in various parts of the country. This practice should be discouraged. The practice is costly and without returns, and yields may be depressed by adding lime where there is already more than is needed.

It is in areas where soils have very low exchange capacities that one frequently observes the effects of overliming. Very sandy soils with low exchange capacities are also more likely to be deficient in minor elements than are finer-textured soils with higher exchange capacities.

REFERENCES

1. Comber, Norman M., A Qualitative Test for Sour Soils, *J. Agr. Sci.*, **10**:420–424, 1920.
2. Firkins, B. J., Liming Iowa Soils, *Iowa Agr. Expt. Sta. Ext. Serv. Bull.* 45, 1942.
3. Frear, William, *Penn. Agr. Expt. Sta. Rep.*, 1902.
4. Handbook of Experiments in Agronomy, *Ohio Agr. Expt. Sta. Spec. Cir.* 53, 1938.
5. Harper, Horace J., and H. G. M. Jacobson, A Comparison of Several Qualitative Tests for Soil Acidity, *Soil Sci.*, **18**:75–85, 1924.
6. McIlvaine, T. C., and G. G. Pohlman, Crop Growth and Soil Reaction, *W. Va. Agr. Expt. Sta. Bull.* 337, 1949.
7. Mehlich, A., and W. E. Colwell, Influence of Nature of Soil Colloids and Degree of Base Saturation on Growth and Nutrient Uptake by Cotton and Soybeans, *Soil Sci. Soc. Amer. Proc.*, **8**:179–184, 1943.
8. Pierre, W. H., and G. G. Pohlman, Lime, Its Need and Use in West Virginia, *W. Va. Agr. Expt. Sta. Cir.* 71, 1936.
9. Spurway, C. H., Soil Reaction (pH) Preference of Plants, *Mich. Agr. Expt. Sta. Spec. Bull.* 306, 1941.
10. Truog, E., Soil Reaction Influence on Availability of Plant Nutrients, *Soil Sci. Soc. Amer. Proc.*, **11**:305–308, 1946.
11. Woodruff, C. M., Determination of Exchangeable Hydrogen and Lime Requirement of the Soil by Means of the Glass Electrode and a Buffered Solution, *Soil Sci. Soc. Amer. Proc.*, **12**:141–142, 1947.

CHAPTER 9

NITROGEN

Nitrogen is not contained in the original rocks and minerals of the earth's crust. All of the nitrogen in the soil comes from the atmosphere through processes of fixation wherein nitrogen is caused to combine with hydrogen or oxygen. The atmosphere just above the soil contains about 78 per cent nitrogen, but this nitrogen cannot be used by higher plants until it is combined with hydrogen or oxygen.

The nitrogen of the soil is combined as part of the organic matter. About 99 per cent of the nitrogen in the soil at any one time is in the organic form. An acre furrow slice of a representative humid-region soil contains about 3000 lb. of nitrogen. The average amount of inorganic nitrogen in a representative soil will probably not exceed 30 lb. per acre. The nitrogen must be in the inorganic form before it is available to higher plants. The amount of available nitrogen in any particular soil varies greatly from day to day. At one time a particular soil may have over 100 lb. of available nitrogen, and at another time the level of available nitrogen might be near zero. The amount of inorganic (and available) nitrogen in a particular soil depends largely on the rate at which organic matter is decomposing and on the rate of absorption by the crop growing on that soil.

It is assumed that much of the nitrogen of the soil is proteinaceous in character. However, the proteinaceous material of the soil is much more resistant to decomposition than the protein material (like that used in livestock feeds) which might be added to the soil. A high percentage, perhaps half, of the nitrogen from cottonseed meal, alfalfa, or soybean meal will become available during the first year when added to the soil. But the proteinaceous material of the soil will release less than 4 per cent in 1 year, and in some soils the percentage release of nitrogen is less than 1 per cent per year (20,27).

Ammonification and Nitrification. In the proteinaceous material of the soil, nitrogen is combined as an amino group ($-NH_2$). This group is split off as ammonia (NH_3) during decomposition of the organic matter under influence of enzymes produced by microorganisms, a process known as *ammonification*.[1]

$$R\text{—}NH_2 + H_2O \rightarrow NH_3 + R\text{—}OH + \text{energy}$$

It should be emphasized at this point that the process of ammonification occurs under conditions most favorable to growth of microorganisms. In particular, this means a moist, warm soil well supplied with nutrients and organic matter. *As the soil dries out the process slows down.*

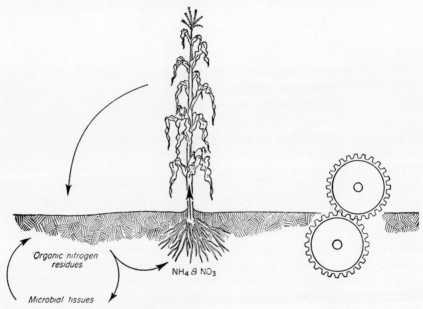

Organic nitrogen residues

$NH_4 \, \& \, NO_3$

Microbial tissues

Fig. 77. A schematic diagram showing the nitrogen cycle. The meshed gears indicate that the turnover of plant residues to the soil affects the rate of turnover of ammonia and nitrates to the growing crop.

The ammonia readily combines with water or carbonic acid to produce the ammonium ion.

$$NH_3 + H_2O \rightarrow NH_4OH \rightleftharpoons NH_4^+ + OH^-$$
$$\text{or}$$
$$NH_3 + H_2CO_3 \rightarrow (NH_4)_2CO_3 \rightleftharpoons NH_4^+ + NH_4CO_3^-$$

The ammonium ion is available to higher plants and microorganisms. Furthermore, the ammonium ion (NH_4^+) may combine with clay[2] or

---

[1] R is the symbol used to indicate the remainder of a complex organic compound.

[2] The ammonium ion may enter the crystal lattice of minerals like vermiculite (3) or illite (34). It may occupy the position between adjacent silica layers of illite in the same manner that potassium does (see page 166), and while in such position, the ammonium ion is relatively unavailable to microorganisms or higher plants. The low response of ammonia added to soils known to be high in illite or vermiculite might be explained by this mechanism.

humus where it is held as an exchangeable ion.   While held by the clay
or humus it is relatively resistant to removal by the leaching action of
percolating water.   On the other hand, while the exchangeable ammonium ion is readily available to microorganisms and higher plants, it may
be readily transformed to the nitrate form.   There are certain species of
bacteria which are aerobic and autotrophic and derive their energy by
the oxidation of ammonia to nitrite, and the nitrite to the nitrate, a process
known as *nitrification*.

$$2NH_4^+ + 3O_2 \rightarrow 2NO_2^- + 2H_2O + 4H^+ + \text{energy}$$
$$2NO_2 + O_2 \rightarrow 2NO_3 + \text{energy}$$

The two processes above are caused by different bacteria, but the conditions favorable to one are also favorable to the other.   Consequently,
very little nitrite occurs in soils, and for all practical purposes we might
consider nitrification as the oxidation of ammonia to nitrate, as follows:

$$NH_4 + 2O_2 \rightarrow NO_3^- + H_2O + 2H^+ + \text{energy}$$

The process of nitrification proceeds at the most rapid rate under
conditions of near neutrality, with good aeration and moisture near field
capacity, a temperature of about 95°F., and a favorable nutrient supply.

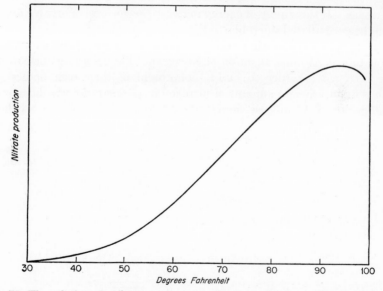

FIG. 78. The relation of soil temperature to nitrate production. [*Based on data of
several sources* (5,13,29,30).]   The data of Thompson (36) indicates that the curves
for ammonification are similar up to 95°F. but above this temperature nitrification
decreases and ammonification continues at a rapid rate.

While the temperature is below 50°F. the process is very slow, but the rate increases rapidly above 50°F.

Blackman (5) found that the addition of nitrogen to pastures in the early spring allowed earlier grazing. His work showed that at temperatures below 5 to 8°C. (42 to 47°F.), plant growth was limited because of available nitrogen. When the temperature was above 5 to 8°C., the mineralization of nitrogen was high enough so that nitrogen was not a limiting factor. He found that pastures could be grazed from 10 to 14 days earlier by the application of nitrogen early in the spring.

Mineralization and Immobilization of Nitrogen. The decomposition of organic matter and the release of inorganic compounds is called *mineralization*. The conversion of inorganic compounds to organic form is called *immobilization*.

The production of ammonia is mineralization. However, in determining the extent of mineralization of organic nitrogen it is necessary to analyze the soil for both NH_4^+ and NO_3^-. This is necessary since some of the NH_4^+ may have been converted to NO_3^-. Where conditions are favorable to nitrification, the conversion of NH_4^+ to NO_3^- may occur so rapidly that for all practical purposes one may measure nitrates and refer to nitrification as an indication of mineralization.

Immobilization may be the result of utilization of NH_4^+ or NO_3^- by higher plants or by microorganisms. Immobilization by microorganisms means that available nitrogen occurring in the soil is converted to microbial tissue. If the supply of energy material, in the form of organic matter which has stimulated microbial activity, contains less than about 1.2 per cent nitrogen (a wide carbon to nitrogen ratio) one may expect immobilization to exceed mineralization of nitrogen. The microorganisms must have nitrogen in order to build the protein of their own bodies. If there is an insufficient amount of nitrogen in the material which they are decomposing, they will use the NH_4^+ and NO_3^- of the soil around them.

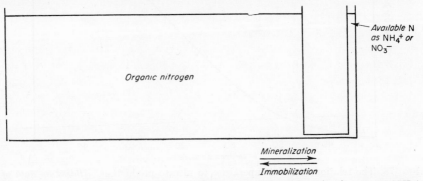

Fig. 79. A schematic diagram illustrating the relation of organic nitrogen to NH_4^+ and NO_3^-. The occurrence of NH_4^+ and NO_3^- depends on the rate of mineralization minus the rate of immobilization, assuming no losses by leaching or volatilization.

Effect of Carbon to Nitrogen Ratio on Nitrogen Mineralization. When materials like cornstalks are plowed into the soil, the activity of microorganisms is greatly increased if temperature and moisture conditions are favorable. Cornstalks have a high proportion of cellulose and hemicellulose, which are good sources of energy for microorganisms. But the low nitrogen content of cornstalks may actually limit the number of microorganisms that can develop. Those which do develop use part of the carbon as a source of material for building of their own bodies. A major part of the carbon is used in respiration as a source of energy and is released as CO_2. A large population of microorganisms and a high rate of decomposition are indicated by a high rate of CO_2 evolution. If there is plenty of available nitrogen as NH_4^+ and NO_3^- in the soil, the cornstalks will actually decompose faster than in a soil low in available nitrogen. To speed up decomposition of cornstalks requires that some nitrogen be available in addition to that contained in the cornstalks. The disappearance of available NH_4^+ and NO_3^- from the soil during the decomposition of the cornstalks would be the result of immobilization exceeding mineralization.

The wider the carbon to nitrogen ratio, the longer the period of net immobilization. The more narrow the carbon to nitrogen ratio of freshly added materials, the greater the amount of nitrogen that is mineralized in the first several weeks of decomposition (17,25). Several workers (7,41) have presented data that indicate that net immobilization can be expected if the C to N ratio is greater than 33 to 1 and that if the ratio is as narrow as 17 to 1, net mineralization can be expected. Between C to N ratios of 33 to 1 and 17 to 1, mineralization is about equal to immobilization. This can be interpreted to mean that, in the range from 33 to 1 and 17 to 1, the NH_3 that is produced during enzyme hydrolysis is immediately used by microorganisms for their own protein building.

The curve in Fig. 80 is presented to show the relation of C to N ratio to rate of decomposition. The time required for the decomposition is estimated. It is indicated that materials with a carbon to nitrogen ratio of about 40 to 1 should be allowed from 2 to 4 weeks of favorable weather for decomposition before the next crop is planted. The curve indicates that from 1 to 2 weeks should be allowed for the decomposition of materials with a carbon to nitrogen ratio of about 25 to 1. Table 38 indicates that mixed-hay (grass and legume) residues will have a ratio of about 25 to 1. This value of 25 is based on the hay being cut in the bloom stage. If the material is allowed to reach maturity before being turned under, the ratio of carbon to nitrogen will be closer to 40 to 1.

If a large amount of oat straw is turned under, it may take from 4 to 8 weeks or an even longer period of decomposition before the carbon to nitrogen ratio is narrow enough to prevent immobilization of available nitrogen of the soil.

Any addition of nitrogen reduces the carbon to nitrogen ratio and the length of time necessary for mineralization. In other words, one may add nitrogen to oat straw or cornstalks and reduce the time required before planting the next crop.

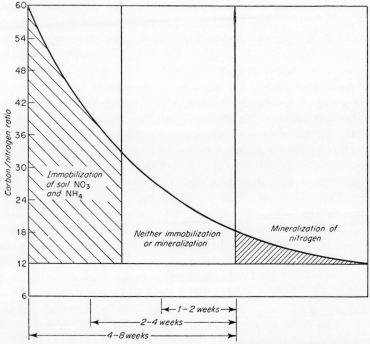

FIG. 80. A schematic diagram showing the time that crop residues should be allowed to decompose before planting the next crop, if nitrogen fertilizers are not used.

Workers in Kansas (9,31) have reported that July plowing for wheat has produced approximately 10 bu. per acre more than September plowing. They found that more nitrates were available at the time of seeding where a longer period had been allowed for decomposition. Albrecht (1) reported a similar observation shown in Fig. 81.

As the carbon to nitrogen ratio decreases during decomposition, the energy supply diminishes and the number of microorganisms decreases. The need for nitrogen in relation to carbon decreases until finally a condition is reached where NH_3 is split off during decomposition without being used by the microorganisms for their own protein building.

Cornstalks have a carbon to nitrogen ratio of about 50 to 1. If a field contained 1600 lb. of carbon per acre in residues from a 70 bu. crop of corn, there would be about 32 lb. of nitrogen in the residues. By the addition of 32 lb. of nitrogen, the ratio would be reduced to about 25 to 1, and the next crop could be planted immediately without fear of competition for nitrogen between the crop and microorganisms.[1]

One may turn under cornstalk residues and plant corn the next day, provided that about 5 to 10 lb. of nitrogen is applied in a starter fertilizer in the hill or drilled in the row. The carbon to nitrogen ratio will be favor-

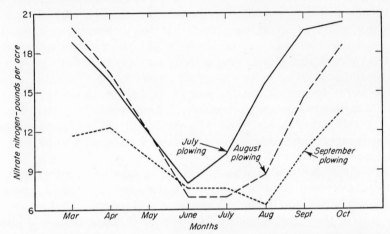

Fig. 81. Nitrate nitrogen levels in the soil under wheat are affected by the time of plowing (1).

able in the immediate vicinity of the seed, and generally there will be no harmful effects of the cornstalk residues. This same principle applies in the case of seeding of oats in the spring on cornstalk ground. Drilling of the seed with fertilizer containing 10 to 20 lb. of nitrogen provides a favorable carbon to nitrogen ratio immediately around the seed. It is therefore

TABLE 38. AVERAGE CARBON TO NITROGEN RATIO OF PLANT MATERIALS

Plant material	C, %	N, %	C to N ratio
Oat straw..........................	40	0.5	80
Cornstalks.........................	40	0.8	50
Mixed hay residues.................	40	1.6	25
Sweet clover green manure...........	40	3.0	13

not necessary to delay planting to allow for decomposition of carbonaceous residues if a small amount of nitrogen is placed near the planted seed or

[1] The addition of nitrogen is usually not necessary to decompose crop residues as long as several weeks is allowed for decomposition. The soil will usually contain enough nitrogen to effect decomposition. The extra nitrogen should be applied as a benefit of the crop to be grown, rather than be considered as necessary to decompose organic residues.

if enough nitrogen is broadcast to lower the carbon to nitrogen ratio to a favorable level.

Mineralization of nitrogen from sweet clover green manure should begin almost immediately after the material is turned under. If a very large amount of green manure is turned under (a ton or more per acre), one might allow at least a week before planting a crop, because the rapid rate of decomposition is unfavorable for seed germination and starting of growth of seedlings. One reason for this is that there may be competition for nutrients other than nitrogen (such as phosphorus), and still another is that the high rate of microbial activity may cause parasitic growth on the seedlings.

The curve for immobilization and mineralization shows that, as the ratio of carbon to nitrogen approaches 12, decomposition is about leveled off. This is rather typical of all decomposition studies. Decomposition proceeds rapidly at first and then slows down as the carbon to nitrogen ratio approaches 11 to 1.

If the decomposition were to continue for a very long time without an appreciable annual addition of organic matter, the ratio would approach that found in bacterial tissue. Waksman and Hutchings (39) have shown that soils of the desert regions have a carbon to nitrogen ratio of about 6 to 1. They explain this on the basis of desert soils receiving very little organic-matter residues annually, so that decomposition has progressed to where the humus is largely microbial residues.

Testing Soils for Available Nitrogen. There are tests for estimating the nitrate content of soils in the field. These tests, however, are generally discouraged for use by farmers. The nitrate content of the soil varies tremendously from day to day. A good soaking rain might wash the surface soil free of nitrates. Two or three days later, the soil may be high in nitrates again. If a crop is growing rapidly, it may keep a fertile soil very low in nitrates. There are too many chances for error in picking up a sample of soil in the field and estimating its nitrogen status by running a quick test for nitrates.

A very satisfactory test for nitrogen status has been developed by Stanford and Hanway (33). It is a test now used as a part of the standard procedure for determining the fertilizer needs of soils in several state college–operated soil-testing laboratories. A sample of soil is placed in a carbon filter tube (Fig. 82) between layers of expanded vermiculite.[1]

The sample is leached with water to remove any nitrates present. The tube containing the moist soil and vermiculite is then placed in a controlled-temperature room where the soil organic matter is allowed to undergo decomposition for several days under favorable conditions of

---

[1] The expanded vermiculite in this case refers to the heat-treated material which is used for insulation in houses.

moisture, temperature, and aeration. The expanded vermiculite with its high water-holding capacity and permeability to air helps in maintaining the favorable conditions of moisture and aeration. After a standard period of time the tube of soil is again leached with water. This leachate is then analyzed for nitrates. The amount of nitrates produced under these conditions of incubation serves as a basis for recommending the amount of nitrogen needed for improving crop yields.

Utilization of Ammonia and Nitrates by Plants. Plants may use either NH_4^+ or NO_3^-. The NO_3^- absorbed must be reduced to NH_4^+ by the plant before it is further changed to the amino ($-NH_2$) form for assimilation as protein or similar material.

Certain plants, like rice, wheat, and oats, seem to make good use of NH_4^+ in their early growth, while certain warm-season plants, like cotton, are adapted to using NO_3^- in their early growth. It is very difficult to determine a preference for NH_4^+ or NO_3^- in soils. Any NH_4^+ added may be nitrified before absorption by the crop. Furthermore, the associated ion added with either NH_4^+ or NO_3^- may have an influence on the results obtained. For example, in comparing $NaNO_3$ with $(NH_4)_2SO_4$ in field experiments, one would have to assume that the Na^+ or SO_4^{--} might have just as much effect on the crop as the difference between NH_4^+ and NO_3^-.

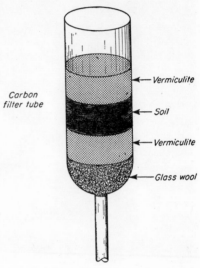

Fig. 82. Diagram of apparatus used in the Stanford-Hanway test for nitrifiable nitrogen.

As plants progress toward maturity they seem to absorb a higher proportion of NO_3^- than NH_4^+. This may be a simple adaptation to conditions that usually exist in the soil. In the case of oats, for example, the early growth occurs when the soil is cooler and less favorable to nitrification. As the season for maturity advances, the soil is more favorable to the production of nitrates.

When plants absorb more nitrogen than they need, some of the extra nitrogen exists in the cell sap as NO_3^-. This makes it possible to examine plants and estimate the nitrogen status of the soil. Alphanapthylamine is a grayish-white powder that can be used to test the cell sap for nitrates. The material turns red in the presence of nitrates. The corn plant is especially well suited to such a test. The stalk can be split to expose the white tissue on which the powder can be placed. The color developed is easily detected.　　Another test is described in Fig. 83, using diphenylamine indicator.　　This indicator is made by dissolving diphenylamine in concentrated sulfuric acid and must be used with great caution.

When tissue tests were first publicized they were used quite widely, but they are being used less now that a satisfactory soil test has been developed for estimating nitrification.　　The tissue test is rather spectacular and probably has its greatest value as a teaching aid.

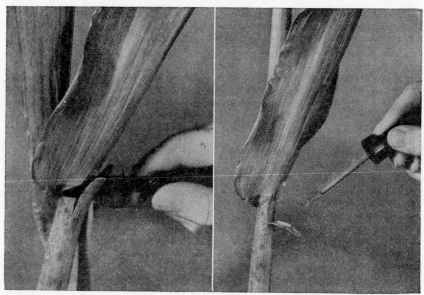

FIG. 83. Nitrate tests can be made at the base of the leaf midrib with diphenylamine without destroying the entire plant.　　This is an important consideration in making numerous tests on small experimental plots.　　The height of the plant at which nitrates are present as well as the intensity of the blue color gives an indication of the nitrate status of the plant.　　(*Courtesy of W. L. Nelson, B. A. Krantz, and L. F. Buckhart.*)

One who uses the tissue test should be aware of one problem, that is, that the nitrates accumulated in a plant are related to the moisture status of the soil.　　Two or three days after a rain the rate of nitrification is high and the rate of absorption of nitrates by the plant is high.　　Beyond 10 days after a rain the rate of nitrification slows down to a low ebb, and by that time, the nitrates absorbed by the plant may have been reduced to ammonia or assimilated for growth.

Relation of Nitrogen Mineralization to Soil Moisture.　　When a soil dries out, microbial activity slows down to an almost zero level.　　When the soil receives moisture from rainfall, following a few days of dry weather, microbial activity proceeds almost immediately.　　The rate of mineralization (assuming no excess of carbohydrates) is rapid at first and then slows down, as illustrated in Fig. 84.

Most of the decomposable organic matter which releases available nitrogen is concentrated in the top 6 in. of the soil. This part of the soil dries out first. In a prolonged droughty period, crops often show nitrogen-starvation symptoms, especially where the decomposable organic matter is of low nitrogen content. This situation can be observed in corn,

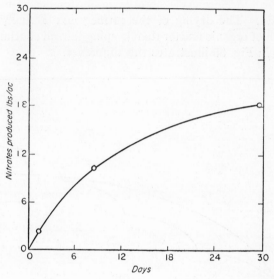

FIG. 84. The rate of nitrate production in a soil incubated at 75°F. at moisture equivalent (29).

in particular. Corn following corn will "fire" (lower leaves turn yellow down the midrib and eventually die), more than corn following a legume. Farmers refer to firing of corn as a sign of need for rain. In a certain sense, this is true. On the other hand, the firing is directly due to nitrogen starvation.

It is frequently observed that corn, which is side-dressed with an abundance of nitrogen, never fires during dry weather, while adjacent plots with no extra nitrogen frequently fire. The difference in response might be explained as follows. In the early stages of growth the corn receiving extra nitrogen may take up a large excess of nitrogen. When the dry weather prevails, the plant has sufficient nitrogen to continue to build protein for new roots which continue to grow deeper into moist soil below. The corn which receives no extra nitrogen depends on decomposition of the organic matter in the topsoil. If the rate of nitrogen mineralization is low, the plant may absorb nitrogen in the early stages only as fast as it is assimilated. When the dry weather prevails, the plant does not have a reserve of nitrates held (as excess nitrogen) in the cell sap.   In order to continue to grow, the nitrogen is translocated from the lower leaves to new growth.   This causes the lower leaves to die, the cells along the midrib dying first.   A good soaking rain may come soon enough for the firing corn to recover, and the recovery is often attributed entirely to moisture, with little thought of nitrogen starvation.

In order to have maximum yields it would be desirable to have a rain every 10 days.   A new cycle of organic-matter decomposition occurs with each rain.   The drying of the surface may actually cause more decomposition of organic matter than keeping the soil continuously moist. The diagram in Fig. 85 illustrates this difference.

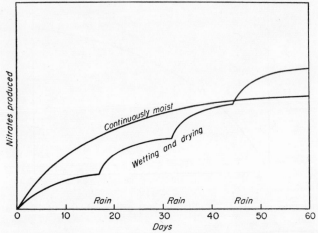

FIG. 85. A schematic diagram indicating that wetting and drying of a soil cause more nitrate production over a period of several months than would be produced if the soil were kept moist.

This should not be interpreted to mean that greater yields will always be obtained by successive wetting and drying in about 10-day cycles.   If the organic matter of the soil is depended on entirely for a source of nitrogen, this is probably true.   However, if extra nitrogen is applied in abundance and maintained at a high level, the highest yields are obtained by maintaining the soil at or near field capacity.   In using large amounts of nitrogen without irrigation in the Middle West, the yields of corn level off because of moisture limitations.   Under irrigation, however, the yields go much higher before leveling off, as illustrated on page 227.

Rate of Mineralization of Organic Matter.   Organic matter does not decompose at a constant rate.   When a sample of organic matter is allowed to decompose under favorable conditions of constant level of moisture and temperature, one finds that decomposition is very rapid at first and then slows down as illustrated by Fig. 85. The rapid decomposition continues until the easily decomposed materials disappear, and then the resistance of the remaining material causes the slowing down of the rate of decomposition.

Soils first brought into cultivation may decompose so rapidly that as much as 4 per cent of the total nitrogen may be mineralized during the first year. After many years of cultivation the rate slows down so

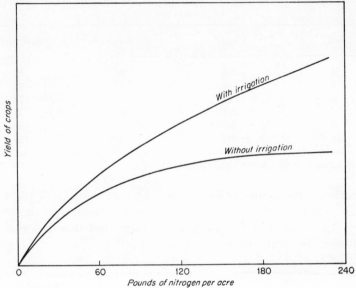

FIG. 86. A schematic diagram indicating that yields are limited by water at higher rates of fertilization.

that the percentage of total nitrogen mineralized becomes less and less. Finally, an equilibrium is reached where the organic-matter and total nitrogen content of the soil remain about constant under the prevailing conditions of management. *When the equilibrium is reached, one should expect to return as much nitrogen during a rotation as one expects to remove from the soil.* Perhaps in some cases more nitrogen than harvested will be needed in order to compensate for losses through erosion, leaching, and volatilization.

During the first few years of cultivation of a new soil the rate of nitrogen mineralization may be so high that no profitable response is obtained from the use of fertilizer nitrogen. In 1948, Carroll Brown of Rose Hill, Iowa, produced 224.2 bu. of corn per acre on 10 acres. The soil had been in bluegrass for about 50 years up to 1948. The only fertilizer treatment was the addition of 200 lb. of 0-45-0 (90 lb. of P_2O_5). The crop probably used over 400 lb. of nitrogen per acre. This means that decomposition of organic matter proceeded rapidly during the first year of cultivation in order for that much nitrogen to be mineralized. The moisture conditions were quite favorable throughout the growing season. The rains came at frequent intervals.

Data in Table 39 illustrate the difference in rate of mineralization of nitrogen in new and old soils.

TABLE 39. NITROGEN MINERALIZED IN 30 DAYS AT 35°C. (36)
In pounds per acre

Soil	Virgin*	Soil	Cultivated*
1	263	2	81
3	315	4	77
5	249	6	71
7	213	8	39
9	355	10	129
11	400	12	139

* Soils 1 and 2, 3 and 4, etc., were adjacent soils.

Attention is frequently called to the fact that the soils of the United States have lost a third or more of their organic matter in the last 100 years. This estimate is probably about right, but this does not mean that during the next 100 years another third will be lost. Figure 87

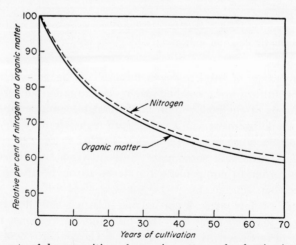

FIG. 87. The rate of decomposition of organic matter and reduction in total nitrogen under cultivated soils. The organic-matter curve is taken from Jenny (16). The nitrogen curve is shown to indicate that organic matter is reduced slightly faster than nitrogen, thereby causing a slightly narrower nitrogen to carbon ratio as soils become older under cultivation.

illustrates the way in which organic matter declines over a long period of time.

The soils of the United States are generally approaching equilibrium, some have already reached that stage, and the need for fertilizer nitrogen is becoming greater to compensate for the nitrogen formerly obtained from the residual organic matter of the soil. Of course there will always be some nitrogen available each year from the decomposition of freshly added organic matter, but without additional nitrogen these residues become less and less as yields decline.

Amounts of Nitrogen Removed from the Soil. Nitrogen disappears from the soil in the following ways: (a) volatilization, (b) erosion, (c) leaching, and (d) crop removal.

Losses of NH_3 as a gas through decomposition of organic matter on or in the immediate surface of the soil may occur. This loss is very difficult to determine, and to estimate the amount would be highly speculative. Francis Clark[1] found that NH_3 was lost to the atmosphere in decomposition of soil organic matter under conditions of incubation, where air was circulated over the surface of soils held in flasks. It would be expected that losses of NH_3 would be greater under alkaline conditions. NH_3 is readily trapped by acids to form ammonium salts which are stable, but NH_4OH is unstable and breaks down to form H_2O and gaseous NH_3.

Under conditions of poor aeration, such as obtained when all of the pore space of soil is filled with water for several days, anaerobic bacteria will reduce nitrates. The nitrogen is probably lost as nitrous oxide (N_2O) but might be lost also as free nitrogen (N_2). If the nitrogen is reduced to N_2O or N_2 it is lost from the soil. The biological production of N_2O or N_2 is referred to as denitrification.

Losses by denitrification are not considered to be of economic importance in well-drained soils, but the losses may be quite high in wet spots in fields. The addition of 40 to 60 lb. of nitrogen per acre on these spots as a top-dressing following submergence can mean the difference between a fair crop and a crop failure. Judging from experience of top-dressing these spots, it is estimated that denitrification may account for losses up to 100 lb. per acre of nitrogen in the wet spots in a single season.

The loss of nitrogen by erosion throughout the United States was estimated in 1936 by Lipman and Conybeare (22) to exceed that removed by crops. There is no doubt that the losses of nitrogen by erosion are quite high. The following data illustrate the point. The corn-oats-clover rotation plots at Clarinda, Iowa, lost 32 lb. of nitrogen per acre per year from 1932 to 1948. The figure was calculated by assuming a 1 to 20 ratio of nitrogen to organic matter. The organic-matter content

[1] Personal communication.

was 3.3 per cent. The soil loss was 9.6 tons per acre per year on the corn-oats-clover rotation plots. The slope of the plots at Clarinda is 9 per cent. The continuous-corn plot lost an average of 38.2 tons of soil per acre (8). This would amount to an annual loss of about 126 lb. of nitrogen per acre per year.

The losses of nitrogen by leaching represent serious economic losses, particularly in the regions where the soil is not frozen during the winter months. Nitrates are readily leached from the topsoil to lower depths and into the water table. Professor A. J. Sterges,[1] formerly of Texas A & M College, once found that nitrates moved from the surface to a depth of 2 ft. in a soaking rain that occurred in College Station, during one 24-hr. period. There are several factors which affect leaching losses, among them are (a) the rate of nitrification, (b) amount of rain, (c) permeability of the soil and its water-holding capacity, and (d) the crop growing on the soil.

A sandy soil without a cover crop would be extremely susceptible to leaching losses because of rapid permeability and low water-holding capacity. A soil with low permeability and high water-holding capacity would permit less leaching if other conditions are equal.

The following data indicate that a growing crop greatly reduces leaching losses.

TABLE 40. LOSSES OF NITROGEN UNDER DIFFERENT SYSTEMS OF MANAGEMENT (4)
Lysimeter studies on Dunkirk silty clay loam

Management practice	Annual nitrogen losses, lb./acre
Bare	69.0
Rotation	7.8
Grass	2.5

The losses by leaching in the Corn Belt on Prairie soils are probably not very significant under ordinary systems of management. The soils are protected by frost during most of the season when *no* crop is growing. The amounts of nitrogen lost by leaching while the crop is growing are negligibly small. There may be some loss of nitrogen in spring before corn is planted, but the losses in the spring with oats and meadow crops are negligibly small.

Farmers who apply nitrogen in advance of planting corn run less risk of losing nitrates by leaching if they use ammonia rather than nitrate nitrogen. Some farmers apply nitrogen in the fall for the following crop of corn. They are advised to use ammonia nitrogen applied after the topsoil has reached an average temperature of less than 50°F. if they do choose to apply nitrogen in the fall.

Furthermore, fall applications of nitrogen for the following season

[1] Personal communication.

should be restricted to soils with high water-holding capacity and slow permeability and in regions where soil is protected by frost.

On soils subject to rapid leaching losses, one should apply a small amount of nitrogen as part of the starter fertilizer and apply the remainder after the crop has started growing.

For most soils, the most important loss of nitrogen is through crop removal. A bushel of corn removes about 1 lb. of nitrogen if only the grain is harvested. A bushel of oats removes about 0.6 lb. of nitrogen. The continuous production of corn and small grain rapidly depletes soils of their nitrogen. A legume crop may, if inoculated, add more nitrogen than is harvested in forage or seed. A consideration of this subject follows.

Table 41 is shown to indicate the approximate amounts of nitrogen removed by different crops. These represent average values. The nitrogen content of a crop varies with the fertility status of the soil and other factors to be described in Chap. 15.

Nitrogen Fixation by Azotobacter. The Azotobacter organism is a bacterium that is aerobic and heterotropic. It derives its source of energy from organic residues of the soil. In the absence of sufficient available nitrogen in the medium in which it is growing, Azotobacter will use the free nitrogen (N_2) of the air. For this reason it is referred to as a *nonsymbiotic*, or *free-living*, nitrogen-fixing organism in contrast to the *symbiotic* bacteria which fix nitrogen in the nodules on the roots of legume plants.

Nitrogen fixation by Azotobacter can be readily demonstrated in the laboratory. Much speculation has been made as to the amounts of nitrogen that might be added to the soil by Azotobacter under field conditions. In several instances the increase in nitrogen content of grass plots in fertility experiments has been attributed to Azotobacter. The recent trend (2,11,27) is to minimize the contribution of nitrogen to crops by Azotobacters.

Lipman (21) and Waksman and Starkey (40) have shown that about 100 parts of carbon are used in respiration for every 1 part of nitrogen fixed. In our own laboratory (37) it was found that about 500 p.p.m. of nitrogen was fixed in a 10-week period by Azotobacter in soil material to which sugar and a nutrient solution (except nitrogen) were added weekly. The efficiency of fixation was no greater, however, than that reported by Waksman, Starkey, and Lipman; that is, about 100 parts of carbon was used in respiration for each 1 part of nitrogen fixed. Furthermore, the fixation occurred in soil material that contained no measurable amount of nitrogen in the beginning of the experiment.

Martin et al. (26) studied the occurrence of Azotobacter in Iowa soils and concluded that they generally occurred in soils with a pH above 6.

Martin also showed a positive correlation between Azotobacter numbers and available phosphorus.

It appears that the following conditions are required for any significant amount of nitrogen fixation by Azotobacter.

1. A wide carbon to nitrogen ratio in added residues (in excess of 33 to 1) or, expressed in another way, plant residues containing less than 1.5 per cent nitrogen

2. Lack of available nitrogen in the soil to meet the needs of the multiplying organisms decomposing the residues

3. A pH above 6

4. An adequate, preferably high, supply of available phosphorus

TABLE 41. AVERAGE AMOUNTS OF NUTRIENTS REMOVED BY CROPS
Calculated from various sources by J. D. Romaine

Crop	Yield	Part of crop	N, lb.	P_2O_5, lb.	K_2O, lb.
Cotton...............	500 lb.	Lint	38	18	14
	1000 lb.	Seed			
	1500 lb.	Stalks, leaves	27	7	36
Tobacco..............	1500 lb.	Leaves	55	10	80
		Stalks	25	10	35
Corn................	60 bu.	Grain	57	23	15
	2 tons	Stover	38	12	55
Wheat...............	30 bu.	Grain	35	16	9
	1.25 tons	Straw	15	4	21
Oats........	50 bu.	Grain	35	15	10
	1.25 tons	Straw	15	5	35
Barley...............	40 bu.	Grain	35	15	10
	1 ton	Straw	15	5	30
Potatoes.............	300 bu.	Tubers	65	25	115
		Tops	60	10	55
Sweet potatoes........	300 bu.	Roots	45	15	75
		Tops	30	5	40
Sugar beets...........	15 tons	Roots	55	22	53
		Tops	60	23	92
Tomatoes............	10 tons	Fruit	60	20	80
		Vines	40	15	95
Soybeans.............	25 bu.	Grain	110	35	40
	1.25 tons	Straw	15	5	20
Peanuts..............	1 ton	Nuts	60	10	10
	3 tons	Vines	25	5	40
Alfalfa..............	3 tons	Hay	140	35	135
Sweet clover..........	5 tons	All	185	45	165
Red clover...........	2 tons	Hay	80	20	70
Lespedeza............	3 tons	Hay	130	30	70
Cowpeas.............	2 tons	All	125	25	90
Timothy.............	1.5 tons	Hay	40	15	45

One would most likely find the conditions described above in a system of continuous culture of grass crops in the absence of legumes, the most favorable system being that of uncultivated grass plots where all the residues are left on the surface. There are two well-known experiments where these conditions prevailed; one was at the Rothamsted Experiment Station in England and the other was at the Cornell University Agricultural Experiment Station (24). The data from these experiments have been widely cited as a basis for predicting nitrogen fixation by Azotobacter.

Where crops are grown in rotation with legumes and where manure and fertilizer nitrogen are used in the rotation, there is little opportunity for Azotobacter to fix nitrogen in residues of wide carbon to nitrogen ratio in soils deficient in available nitrogen at the time of plowing down of the residues.

Under conditions of cultivation the contribution of Azotobacter probably amounts to less than 10 lb. per acre per year. The amount is so small that it can be neglected in planning a fertility program where legumes and fertilizer nitrogen will be included.

Fixation of Nitrogen by Legume Bacteria. Studies in the amounts of nitrogen added to soils by legumes have met with difficulties in analytical work. A reasonable error in the total-nitrogen determination in soils is about 50 lb. per acre. The error of sampling in the field is even greater. Therefore it is not possible to analyze a soil, grow a legume, analyze the soil again, and determine the nitrogen fixed by the legume at the end of a year in the field with accuracy comparable to greenhouse studies. The most reliable data are based on greenhouse studies, and again, the plants do not grow in the same way in the greenhouse as they do in the field.

The amount of nitrogen fixed by the bacteria (in nodules on the roots of legumes) varies with the carbohydrate supply in the plant and with the available nitrogen in the soil (42,43). When the carbohydrate supply in the plant is high and the nitrogen supply of the soil is low, the symbiotic bacteria will fix larger quantities of nitrogen than when the carbohydrate supply is low or when the available nitrogen supply in the soil is high. Carbohydrate supply is higher in plants on long clear days with optimum temperature for photosynthesis.

It is possible to predict only in a general way the amount of nitrogen a plant will cause to be fixed. Legumes can be rated, however, for purposes of estimating nitrogen fixation. Hopkins (15) estimated that a legume will contain about two-thirds of the total nitrogen in the tops and about one-third in the roots. He also suggested that, on the average, inoculated legumes will obtain about one-third of the nitrogen needs from the soil and about two-thirds from the air. In other words, according to Hopkins, the nitrogen contained in the tops is about equal to the nitrogen obtained from the air.

Fig. 88. Nitrogen is taken from the air by bacteria which live in the nodules on the roots of alfalfa, clover, and other legume plants. (*Soil Conservation Service.*)

Table 42 illustrates the point that if all the tops of a leafy crop like alfalfa or clover are removed, the balance of the soil nitrogen is left about the same. The data further illustrate the point that removing all the aboveground parts of soybeans and field peas may cause a reduction in

TABLE 42. EFFECT ON SOIL NITROGEN OF CUTTING LEGUMES FOR HAY
Calculated by C. A. Black from data of Pieters (28)

Legume	Roots, per cent of entire crop	Nitrogen in roots, lb./ton of hay removed	N, lb./ton removed	Nitrogen lost from the soil, lb./ton of hay removed
Red clover*....	33.5	23.6	54.0	2.3
Alfalfa*.......	33.5	20.5	51.2	3.4
Sweet clover*..	26.5	14.7	48.2	6.3
Soybeans*.....	12.2	5.3	51.6	13.7
Field peas.....	4.3	2.3	56.0	17.1

* One cutting of hay only.

the soil-nitrogen level. In this table it is assumed that two-thirds of the nitrogen contained in each of the crops was derived from the air and the remainder from the soil.

A farmer does not remove all the tops of a legume in cutting for hay. He may leave ½ ton or more of residues after the last cutting of hay; therefore a legume-hay crop in the rotation does contribute nitrogen to the soil. Furthermore, legumes seeded with oats on cornstalk ground probably take as much as 90 per cent of their nitrogen from the air.

An average crop of alfalfa will produce nearly 3 tons of aboveground parts containing about 50 lb. of nitrogen per ton. Assuming that the nitrogen in tops equals the nitrogen fixed, we find that about 150 lb. of nitrogen is fixed by an average crop of alfalfa. The nitrogen contained in 18 bu. of soybeans amounts to about 70 lb. Assuming that the nitrogen in the seed equals the nitrogen fixed, one may estimate that an average crop of soybeans will fix about 70 lb. of nitrogen per acre. The information in Table 43 is based on such calculations and agrees well with the data of Erdman (12), who based his estimates on greenhouse studies. The only disagreement is in the case of alfalfa (see Tables 43 and 44).

TABLE 43. RELATIVE NITROGEN-FIXATION VALUES FOR LEGUMES GROWN UNDER IOWA CONDITIONS
Estimated

Crop	Nitrogen fixed, lb.
3 tons of alfalfa	150
2½ tons of sweet clover	125
2 tons of red clover	100
18 bu. of soybeans	70

The nitrogen content of the same species, and even the same variety within a species, varies greatly, and it should be remembered that the figures in Table 43 are only for rough calculations. Furthermore, the amount of nitrogen fixed by any legume is determined by many factors such as photosynthetic rate, growth rate, and available nitrogen. If an inoculated legume is grown in sand where all nutrients are added except nitrogen, then all nitrogen contained in the plant (roots and tops) represents nitrogen fixed. Figure 89 illustrates the idea that the percentage of nitrogen fixed is a function of available nitrogen in the soil, assuming that other factors are held constant. It shows a parabolic curve to indicate that there might be some nitrogen fixed regardless of the level of available nitrogen in the soil.

TABLE 44. AVERAGE AMOUNTS OF NITROGEN FIXED BY LEGUMES (12)
Based on greenhouse studies

Crop	Nitrogen fixed, lb.
Alfalfa	100
Sweet clover	117
Red clover	89
Soybeans	63

Recent studies with lysimeters in Kentucky (19) have shown that 2452 lb. of nitrogen (per acre basis) was fixed during an 11-year period by alfalfa when grown alone. The studies show that Korean lespedeza fixed 2265 lb. of nitrogen per acre during the same period. The Kentucky studies show that when considered in relation to the amount of legumes produced, fixation of nitrogen was considerably larger in the

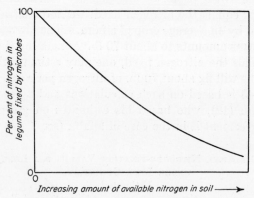

FIG. 89. A schematic diagram showing the effect of available nitrogen on nitrogen fixed by legume bacteria.

case of mixed growth than where legumes were grown alone. This information is of great significance in helping us explain the benefits of growing legumes in rotations where hay is removed. There is the popular concept that where legume hay is removed, the nitrogen balance of the soil is left the same. While direct proof is lacking, there is good reason to suspect that legumes grown with a grass companion crop will fix nearly all the nitrogen contained in the legume tops and roots.

In the Corn Belt, legumes are usually seeded with oats or wheat on cornstalk ground. Available nitrogen is in short supply under such conditions. The wheat or oats absorb most of the available nitrogen and "force" the legume to fix its own nitrogen. This competition continues until the grain is harvested. The oat or wheat straw is normally left on the ground by the combine harvester. The residue of the wheat or oats cause immobilization of available nitrogen by microorganisms of the soil. Again the legume is forced to fix its own nitrogen. To repeat, there are at least four contributing factors in causing high fixation of nitrogen by legumes in the rotations described. The legume seeding follows corn, which leaves available nitrogen in short supply. The cornstalks have a wide carbon to nitrogen ratio and cause some immobilization of available nitrogen while the legume is getting started. The grain crop competes with the legume for available nitrogen. Finally, the straw and roots of the harvested grain crop cause immobilization of available nitrogen in the late summer.

Direct proof is lacking for these statements, but it is quite likely that red clover contributes an average of 75 lb. of nitrogen and alfalfa (2 years of meadow), an average of 125 lb. of nitrogen in Corn Belt rotations, even though hay is removed. Anyone questioning these figures should look

Fig. 90. A good stand of red clover provides an excellent cover in protecting soils from the impact of falling raindrops and offers almost complete protection from erosion. (*Iowa State College.*)

into yield data for rotations like corn-oats-red clover or corn-oats-alfalfa-alfalfa. There are many farmers who are producing over 100 bu. of corn and 60 bu. of oats in a corn-oats-alfalfa-alfalfa rotation and harvesting hay from the alfalfa meadows. A crop of 100 bu. of corn removes about 100 lb. of nitrogen, and a 60-bu. crop of oats removes about 36 lb. of nitrogen. In order for a farmer to maintain organic matter under such yields and a rotation of corn-oats-alfalfa-alfalfa, he must count on the alfalfa contributing about 125 lb. of nitrogen per acre per rotation. Experimental "evidence" along this line may be found in Chap. 16.

Lyon and Bizzell (23) carried out an interesting study which is of particular value in rating the different legumes. Their data, shown in Table

45, indicate that alfalfa is considerably more efficient than red clover or soybeans in fixing nitrogen. Their value for vetch is probably low compared to its efficiency farther south.

TABLE 45. AMOUNT OF NITROGEN FIXED BY VARIOUS LEGUMES UNDER FAVORABLE CONDITIONS (23)
In pounds per acre

Crop	Nitrogen in all crops	Nitrogen in soil loss or gain	Apparent nitrogen fixation		
			Total	Annual	Relative
Alfalfa..............	1804	607	2411	241	100
Red clover...........	868	532	1463	146	60
Alsike clover........	830	595	1362	136	56
Soybeans............	1058	−42	1016	102	42
Hairy vetch..........	549	97	646	65	27
Field beans..........	672	−100	572	57	23
Field peas............	493	−32	461	46	19
No legume—barley, rye, or oats each year....	223	−52	171	17	
Alfalfa continuously...	2179	505	2684	268	

The legumes were grown in alternate years (except where indicated) over a 10-year period, with barley or rye occupying the soil the other years. Thus there were five crops of the legumes. The annual fixation was calculated on the basis of 10 years. Crops were grown out of doors in frames containing a mixture of 60 per cent Dunkirk silty clay loam and 40 per cent sand. The soil was limed, and phosphorus and potassium were added.

There has been considerable work done on the benefits of having a legume in the mixture with grasses. The data in Table 46 illustrate these studies. There is definite effect of the legume in raising the protein content of the associated grass if the grasses and legumes are grown together over a period of several years. The net effect is that more nitrogen is available to the grass if there is a legume growing nearby. The question immediately follows, whether there is excretion from the nodule or whether the grass gets its nitrogen after there has been a sloughing of cellular tissue by the legume. The belief is that nitrogen is not excreted from the nodule except under very unusual conditions. Virtanen (38) showed that excretion did occur, but he was working in Finland where the day is very long during the summer and the photosynthetic period is long enough to permit high carbohydrate supply in the plant, and this factor increases nitrogen fixation. It is most likely that nitrogen is made available to the grass through sloughing of cellular tissue of the legume roots, which releases nitrogen upon decomposition.

TABLE 46. EFFECT OF GROWING KENTUCKY BLUEGRASS AND WILD WHITE CLOVER ALONE AND IN ASSOCIATION (18)

Analyses	Grown alone		Grown in association		
	Bluegrass	Clover	Bluegrass	Clover	Total
Dry weight, lb./acre......	881	3072	2243	2742	4985
Protein:					
Total, lb./acre.........	159	1075	561	960	1521
Percentage............	18	35	25	35	

Nitrogen Added in Rainfall. The amounts of nitrogen added to the soil by rainfall appear to be only a few pounds annually. The amount is small and may be no more than leaching losses in humid regions. It may be a significant factor in subhumid regions where no leaching losses occur, in so far as soil formation is concerned. Over periods of hundreds of years, rainfall nitrogen may constitute an appreciable part of the total nitrogen in subhumid soils.

Collison and Mensching (10) reported that about 9 lb. of nitrogen was added annually by rainwater at Geneva, New York, over a 10-year period. Karraker and associates (19) found that about 10 lb. of nitrogen was added per year in Kentucky.

From a review of the literature, Lyon and Buckman (24) suggest that an average of about 6 lb. of nitrogen (as ammonia and nitrate) is added annually in soils in humid regions.

From a soil-management point of view, the amount of nitrogen received annually by rainfall may be considered to be equal to nitrogen losses by leaching in Corn Belt states where a legume rotation is followed. Leaching losses may be reduced to rainfall income of nitrogen by growing a winter cover crop in Southern rotations.

REFERENCES

1. Albrecht, W. A., Why Do Farmers Plow? *Better Crops with Plant Food*, **27**(6): 23, 1943.
2. Allison, F. E., V. L. Gaddy, L. A. Pinck, and W. H. Armiger, Azotobacter Inoculation of Crops. II. Effect on Crops under Greenhouse Conditions, *Soil Sci.*, **64**:489–497, 1947.
3. Allison, F. E., E. M. Roller, and Janet H. Doetsch, Ammonium Fixation and Availability in Vermiculite, *Soil Sci.*, **75**:173–180, 1953.
4. Bizzell, J. A., and T. L. Lyon, Composition of Drainage Waters from Lysimeters at Cornell University, *Proc. Intern. Congr. Soil Sci.*, **2**:342–349, 1927.

5. Blackman, G. E., The Influence of Temperature and Available Nitrogen Supply on the Growth of Pasture in the Spring, *J. Agr. Sci.*, **26**:620–647, 1936.

6. Bower, C. A., Availability of Ammonium Fixed in Difficultly Exchangeable Form by Soils of Semi-arid Regions., *Soil Sci. Soc. Amer. Proc.*, **15**:119–122, 1951.

7. Broadbent, F., "Factors Influencing Nitrogen Transformations in Soils as Determined by Means of Isotopic Nitrogen," Master's Thesis, Iowa State College, 1946.

8. Browning, G. M., Save That Soil, *Iowa Farm Sci.*, February, 1948.

9. Call, L. E., The Effect of Different Methods of Preparing a Seed Bed for Winter Wheat upon Yield, Soil Moisture and Nitrates, *J. Am. Soc. Agron.*, **6**:249–259, 1914.

10. Collison, R. C., and J. E. Mensching, Lysimeter Investigations. II. Composition of Rainwater at Geneva, N.Y., for a 10-year Period, *N.Y. Agr. Expt. Sta. Tech. Bull.* 193, 1932.

11. Ensminger, L. E., and R. W. Pearson, Soil Nitrogen, *Advances in Agron.*, **2**:81–111, 1950.

12. Erdman, Lewis W., Legume Inoculation: What It Is; What It Does, *U.S. Dept. Agr. Farmers' Bull.* 2003, 1948.

13. Frederick, Lloyd R., The Formation of Nitrates from Ammonia in Soils. I. Effect of Temperature, *Soil Sci. Soc. Amer. Proc.* (in press).

14. Gainey, P. L., Effect of Inoculating a Soil with Azotobacter upon Plant Growth and Nitrogen Balance, *J. Agr. Research*, **78**:405–411, 1949.

15. Hopkins, C. G., "Soil Fertility and Permanent Agriculture," Ginn, Boston, 1910.

16. Jenny, Hans, Soil Fertility Losses under Missouri Conditions, *Mo. Agr. Expt. Sta. Bull.* 324, 1933.

17. Jensen, H. L., On the Influence of the Carbon: Nitrogen Ratios of Organic Material on the Mineralization of Nitrogen, *J. Agr. Sci.*, **19**:71–82, 1929.

18. Johnstone-Wallace, D. B., The Influence of Grazing Management and Plant Associations on the Chemical Composition of Pasture Plants, *J. Am. Soc. Agron.*, **29**:441–455, 1937.

19. Karraker, P. E., Charles E. Bortner, and E. N. Fergus, Nitrogen Balance in Lysimeters as Affected by Growing Kentucky Bluegrass and Certain Legumes Separately and Together, *Ky. Agr. Expt. Sta. Bull.* 557, 1950.

20. Klemme, A. W., and O. T. Coleman, Evaluating Annual Changes in Soil Productivity, *Mo. Agr. Expt. Sta. Bull.* 405, 1939.

21. Lipman, J. G., quoted by S. A. Waksman and R. L. Starkey in "The Soil and the Microbe," Wiley, New York, 1931.

22. Lipman, J. G., and A. B. Conybeare, Preliminary Note on the Inventory and Balance Sheet of Plant Nutrients of the United States, *N.J. Agr. Expt. Sta. Bull.* 607, 1936.

23. Lyon, T. L., and J. A. Bizzell, A Comparison of Several Legumes with Respect to Nitrogen Accretion, *J. Am. Soc. Agron.*, **26**:651–656, 1934.

24. Lyon, T. L., and H. O. Buckman, "The Nature and Properties of Soils," Macmillan, New York, 1943.

25. Martin, T. L., Decomposition of Green Manures at Different Stages of Growth, *Cornell Univ. Agr. Expt. Sta. Bull.* 406, 1921.

26. Martin, William P., R. H. Walker, and P. E. Brown, The Occurrence of Azotobacter in Iowa Soils and Factors Affecting Their Distribution, *Iowa Agr. Expt. Sta. Res. Bull.* 217, 1937.

27. Norman, A. G., Recent Advances in Soil Microbiology, *Soil Sci. Soc. Amer. Proc.*, **11**:9–15, 1946.

28. Pieters, A. L., "Green Manuring," Wiley, New York, 1927.

29. Russel, J. C., E. G. Jones, and G. M. Bahrt, The Temperature and Moisture Factors in Nitrate Production, *Soil Sci.*, **19**:381–398, 1925.

30. Sabe, B. R., W. V. Bartholomew, and John Pesek, Influence of Temperature on Nitrification in Soils, *Soil Sci. Soc. Amer. Proc.* (in press).

31. Sewell, M. C., and P. L. Gainey, Effect of Tillage Treatments on Soil Nitrogen and Carbon, *J. Am. Soc. Agron.*, **24**:221–227, 1932.

32. Sievers, F. J., and H. F. Holtz, The Significance of Nitrogen in Soil Organic Matter Relationships, *Wash. Agr. Expt. Sta. Bull.* 206, 1926.

33. Stanford, George, and John Hanway, Predicting Nitrogen Fertilizer Needs of Iowa Soils. II. A Simplified Technique for Determining Relative Nitrate Production in Soils, *Soil Sci. Soc. Amer. Proc.*, **19**:74–77, 1955.

34. Stanford, George, and W. H. Pierre, The Relation of Potassium Fixation to Ammonium Fixation, *Soil Sci. Soc. Amer. Proc.*, **11**:155–160, 1946.

35. Thompson, L. M., "The Mineralization of Organic Phosphorus Nitrogen and Carbon in Virgin and Cultivated Soils," Ph.D. Thesis, Iowa State College, 1950.

36. Thompson, L. M., "Mineralization of Organic Phosphorus in Clarion and Webster Soils," Master's Thesis, Iowa State College, 1947.

37. Thompson, L. M., C. A. Black, and F. E. Clark, The Accumulation and Mineralization of Microbial Organic Phosphorus, *Soil Sci. Soc. Amer. Proc.*, **13**:242–245, 1948.

38. Virtanen, A. I., "Cattle Fodder and Human Nutrition," Cambridge, London, 1938.

39. Waksman, Selman A., and I. J. Hutchings, Chemical Nature of Organic Matter in Different Soil Types, *Soil Sci.*, **40**:347–363, 1935.

40. Waksman, Selman A., and R. L. Starkey, "The Soil and the Microbe," Wiley, New York, 1931.

41. Waksman, Selman A., and Florence G. Tenney, The Composition of Natural Organic Materials and Their Decomposition, *Soil Sci.*, **24**:317–333, 1927.

42. Wilson, Perry W., "The Biochemistry of Symbiotic Nitrogen Fixation," University of Wisconsin Press, Madison, Wis., 1940.

43. Wilson, Perry W., The Carbohydrate-Nitrogen Relation in Symbiotic Nitrogen Fixation, *Wis. Agr. Expt. Sta. Res. Bull.* 129, 1935.

CHAPTER 10

PHOSPHORUS

Phosphorus is absorbed by plants chiefly as the monovalent ortho-phosphate ion, $H_2PO_4^-$, ordinarily referred to as phosphate. It is one of the three macroanions used by plants, the other two being nitrate and sulfate. All three of these macronutrients are stored to a great extent in soil organic matter. Nitrogen, phosphorus, and sulfur combine readily with other elements to form organic compounds, and while organically combined they are not available to plants.

Relation of Phosphate to Nitrate and Sulfate. Phosphate ions differ greatly from nitrate and sulfate ions in terms of solubility (or activity). Both nitrate and sulfate ions leach from soils in significant quantities, but phosphate ions do not leach from the soil to any appreciable extent because of low solubility. Only traces of phosphate ions are found in drainage water from lysimeters. Storage of nitrogen and sulfur in well-drained soils is dependent on organic-matter accumulation, and as soil organic matter decomposes, nitrates and sulfates tend to leach downward if they are not removed by a growing crop. Sulfate ions are fairly soluble and active in the soil, although some sulfate may be precipitated by calcium under certain conditions. Sulfate ions are held as exchangeable anions by clays only to a limited extent. Nitrates are active enough that they do not form insoluble inorganic compounds, and they are not adsorbed and held by clays as exchangeable anions to any appreciable extent. On the other hand, phosphate does form insoluble inorganic compounds and is adsorbed as an exchangeable anion by clays (6). Phosphorus is stored in organic matter to a large extent in some soils, but the retention of phosphorus by soils is not dependent on organic-matter accumulation.

A high concentration or an excessive amount of nitrate in the soil solution depresses the uptake of phosphate by plants (1,15). A high concentration of sulfate has a similar but not nearly so great effect as the more active nitrate. This is due primarily to competition between the anions for entry into the plant root.

Forms of Phosphorus in Soils. Although it is recognized that phosphate is held as an exchangeable anion by clays, it is believed that contact exchange is not important in phosphorus nutrition of plants (7,26). In other words, plant roots exchange an anion for $H_2PO_4^-$ directly from the soil solution rather than by exchanging an anion for the $H_2PO_4^-$ which is adsorbed by the clay.

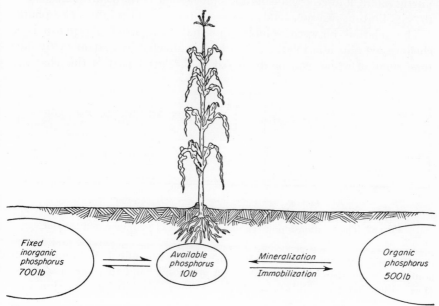

Fixed inorganic phosphorus 700 lb

Available phosphorus 10 lb

Mineralization

Immobilization

Organic phosphorus 500 lb

FIG. 91. A schematic diagram showing the relationship between the different forms of phosphorus. The amounts of phosphorus are suggested as being representative for the acre furrow slice of Prairie soils.

The amount of phosphate in solution in the soil at any one time is extremely small; in most soils this will be less than a pound per acre and even less than 0.1 lb. in some soils (27). The amount of phosphate in the soil solution at any one time is not nearly as important as the rate at which the phosphate will be dissolved. Plants can make satisfactory growth with a very small concentration of soluble phosphate, as long as the concentration is maintained. This means that conditions must be favorable for rapid release of phosphate from the organic and/or the fixed inorganic forms in order to maintain an adequate supply of the available form.

The relation of soluble phosphate to organic phosphorus and fixed phosphate is shown graphically in Fig. 92. In Fig. 92 soluble phosphate is in chemical equilibrium with fixed phosphates. As additional soluble phosphate is added to a soil as fertilizer, the equilibrium tendency is toward the left. As organic phosphorus decomposes, the amount of soluble phosphate is increased temporarily, but the equilibrium tendency would drive the reaction to the left, so that after a period of time the original level of soluble phosphate would be restored.

If soluble phosphate is removed by plant absorption, the equilibrium reaction moves to the right to restore the level of soluble phosphorus. Furthermore, if microorganisms immobilize some of the soluble phosphate, the equilibrium reaction tends to restore the level of solution phosphate.

The relation between soluble phosphate and fixed phosphate is a chemical-equilibrium relationship which is affected by a great many factors, some of which will be discussed in the latter part of this chapter.

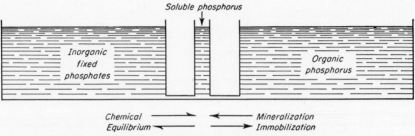

FIG. 92. The relationship of the different forms of phosphorus in the soil.

There are some management practices that will affect the amount of soluble phosphate that will occur in a given soil, and there are practices that will affect the rate at which the chemical-equilibrium reaction will move to the right or to the left.

The factors affecting immobilization and mineralization are associated with microbial activity. When the population is expanding rapidly, the organisms may deplete the soil of soluble phosphate temporarily. As the population declines again, some of the phosphorus of microbial tissue is mineralized. Mineralization and immobilization are reversible, but the reaction is not one of equilibrium.

Total Phosphorus Content of Soils. The total phosphorus content of soils is extremely variable but generally low. The soils developed from limestones, calcareous shales, marls, and chalks generally have more total phosphorus than those derived from acidic or noncalcareous deposits. One reason for this is that much of the calcium carbonate of these calcareous deposits owes its origin to the remains of aquatic animals, the skeletons and shells of which are high in both calcium and phosphorus. The limestone soils of Kentucky and Tennessee are notably high in total phosphorus. The content of total phosphorus in the blacklands of Alabama, Mississippi, and Texas is higher than found in the associated Red-Yellow Podzolic soils of those states. Likewise, the calcareous Reddish

Prairie soils of Kansas and Oklahoma have more total phosphorus than the soils developed from noncalcareous materials.

The amount of total phosphorus in soils expressed as P_2O_5 rarely runs over 0.5 per cent, and a more typical figure would be about 0.15 per cent, which would be 1500 p.p.m., or about 3000 lb. per acre furrow slice.

The following table shows the total phosphorus content of 12 soils selected from various parts of the country. It is significant that the topsoil often contains more total phosphorus than either the subsoil or parent material.

TABLE 47. TOTAL PHOSPHORUS CONTENT OF SOILS FROM DIFFERENT SECTIONS OF THE UNITED STATES (21)

Soil type	Great soil group	Per cent P_2O_5		
		Horizon A	Horizon B	Horizon C
Becket fine sandy loam.........	Podzol	0.13	0.08	0.08
Sassafras sandy loam..........	Gray-Brown Podzolic	0.11	0.08	0.07
Miami silt loam..............	Gray-Brown Podzolic	0.08	0.07	0.08
Maury silt loam..............	Gray-Brown Podzolic	0.31	0.36	0.55
Davidson clay loam...........	Red-Yellow Podzolic	0.10	0.20	0.24
Carrington silt loam..........	Prairie	0.10	0.03	0.12
Marshall silt loam............	Prairie	0.12	0.10	0.16
Barnes silt loam..............	Chernozem	0.23	0.15	0.15
Holdrege silt loam............	Chernozem	0.20	0.21	0.22
Richfield clay loam	Reddish Chestnut	0.10	0.04	0.09
Houston Black Clay..........	Rendzina	0.15	0.17	0.09

Figure 93 illustrates the tendency in phosphorus accumulation in soils where no erosion occurs and where remains of plants (and remains of animals consuming the plants) are returned to the soil. Owing to the low solubility of phosphorus there is little removal by leaching in soils that are young or mature. In very old soils, however, where organic-matter content declines, one would expect some loss of phosphorus from the A horizon, as indicated by studies of Godfrey and Riecken (13).

The diagram in Fig. 93 assumes a mature soil profile. It is assumed that the content of phosphorus was the same in all three horizons when the soil started forming from the exposed parent material. The depletion of phosphorus from the subsoil is due to root absorption, and the enrichment of the topsoil is due to the accumulation of the remains of generation after generation of plants.

Organic phosphorus accumulates in the soil profile in accordance with the distribution of soil organic matter (28). This subject will be dealt with in detail in subsequent sections.

There is fairly high correlation between total phosphorus content of soils and organic-matter content. The author found this to be the case with a large number of soils. Table 48 shows this general relationship.

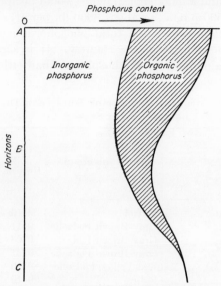

Fig. 93. A schematic diagram showing the distribution of inorganic phosphorus and organic phosphorus in a typical grassland soil profile.

Jackman (17) recently reported a similar relation for several soils of New Zealand.

The relationship that might exist between total nitrogen and total phosphorus was first brought to the author's attention by a publication

TABLE 48. RELATIONSHIP BETWEEN TOTAL NITROGEN AND TOTAL PHOSPHORUS (33)

Number of soils in each group	Total phosphorus, p.p.m.	Organic matter,* average per cent
2	800–999	7.50
25	600–799	6.50
17	400–599	4.52
4	200–399	3.02
2	0–199	2.22

* Calculated by multiplying total nitrogen by 20.

of Bear and Salter (3) who investigated the effects of different treatments applied to soils for 15 years at the West Virginia Experiment Station. They found a high correlation between total nitrogen and total phosphorus. The ratio between nitrogen and phosphorus remained almost constant with the different treatments.

A large supply of phosphorus contributes to a large amount of plant growth, thereby maintaining a larger supply of organic matter than is found on soils of the same region, which are low in total phosphorus.

Organic Phosphorus in Soils. Almost half of the phosphorus in the topsoils of Prairie soils is contained in organic combination. There is high correlation between total nitrogen and organic phosphorus (28,34). The ratio between total nitrogen and organic phosphorus is about 10 to 1 in soils of Iowa, but widens in soils to the south in the United States. Garman (11) found the ratio to be about 15 to 1 in Oklahoma soils. The author found the ratio to be even wider in three virgin Prairie soils of Texas. While nearly half the total phosphorus in Iowa soils is in organic combination, the percentage is smaller for Southern soils. Fuller and McGeorge (10) reported that 31 per cent of the total phosphorus was in organic form in 19 Arizona soils.

Table 49 shows the relationship between total nitrogen and organic phosphorus in certain soils of Iowa, Colorado, and Texas. These data show that the ratio of nitrogen to organic phosphorus is much wider in

TABLE 49. NITROGEN AND PHOSPHORUS CONTENT OF SURFACE SOILS (28,34)

Soil series and state	Total N, per cent	N/organic P ratio	Organic phosphorus	
			p.p.m.	Per cent of total P
Carrington, Iowa................	0.20	8.3	246	45.3
Marshall, Iowa..................	0.20	7.6	264	37.8
Edina, Iowa....................	0.22	7.0	316	64.2
Grundy, Iowa...................	0.21	10.4	205	40.2
Fayette, Iowa...................	0.34	9.6	352	72.6
Weller, Iowa....................	0.26	8.2	319	50.7
Garwin, Iowa...................	0.41	10.5	393	35.4
(Unknown) Colorado............	0.18	15.3	119	21.5
(Unknown) Colorado............	0.17	18.1	94	18.3
Wilson, Tex....................	0.19	28.8	66	32.5
Houston, Tex...................	0.35	29.4	121	17.5

the Colorado soils than in the Iowa soils. It has already been pointed out that Southern soils of the United States contain less organic phosphorus in relation to the total nitrogen content than is found in Iowa, presumably because of the higher soil temperatures of the South, which might hasten the mineralization of organic phosphorus. The difference in temperature between Iowa and Colorado would not explain the wider ratio of total nitrogen to organic phosphorus in the Colorado soils. Data of Thompson, Black, and Zoellner (34) are presented graphically in Fig. 94. These data indicate that as the pH increases, the ratio of total nitrogen to organic phosphorus becomes wider.   This is a possible explanation for the wider ratio of total nitrogen to organic phosphorus of the Colorado soils.   The Colorado soils were almost neutral in reaction, both having a pH of 6.4.   Other evidence on the nature of organic phosphorus in Colorado soils has been provided recently by Greb (14) who found that several calcareous soils of Colorado contained an average 23 per cent of the total phosphorus in organic form.   The two Texas soils shown in Table 49 have quite different percentages of phosphorus in organic form, yet these soils were both collected in the same county. The Houston series with the very low percentage of organic phosphorus was calcareous, with a pH of 7.4, while the Wilson series was very slightly acid with a pH of 6.3.

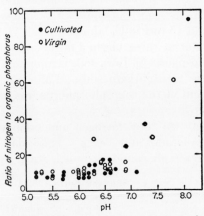

Fig. 94. Ratio of total nitrogen to organic phosphorus as a function of soil pH.

It is believed that pH is a major factor in determining the proportion of the total phosphorus that might exist in organic form.   This knowledge is of particular importance because it leads to the suggestion that raising the pH of acid soils might "unlock the storehouse" of phosphorus tied up in organic matter.   The more acid soils tend to accumulate more organic phosphorus, for reasons yet unknown.

The author studied 20 pairs of virgin and cultivated soils from Iowa. Each member of the pair was collected a few yards from the other.   They were collected from sites unaffected by erosion.   The data for total nitrogen and organic phosphorus for these 40 soils are shown graphically in Fig. 95.

The ratio between total nitrogen and organic phosphorus was 11.09 to 1 for the 20 virgin soils and 9.86 to 1 for the cultivated soils, which indicates that nitrogenous compounds have decomposed to a slightly greater extent in the latter soils than have the organic phosphorus compounds.   Nevertheless, it was apparent that both nitrogen and organic phosphorus were being mineralized.   The graph shows two slanting lines.   The top one represents the average of the virgin soils, and the bottom line represents the average of the cultivated soils.   They are remarkably similar in slope, the virgin soils having more nitrogen and more organic phosphorus than the cultivated soils, which accounts for one line being above the other.

Utilization of Organic Phosphorus by Plants.   The soils described above were moistened to field capacity and incubated for 25 days at 40°C. (104°F.). The amounts of organic nitrogen, phosphorus, and carbon mineralized during the 25 days were determined. The data are shown in Figs. 96 and 97. There was high correlation between mineralized phosphorus and mineralized nitrogen. There was also high correlation between mineralized phosphorus and mineralized carbon.

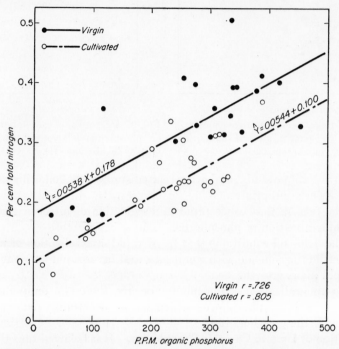

FIG. 95. The relation of total nitrogen to organic phosphorus in 20 pairs of virgin and cultivated soils of Iowa (33).

The study indicated that the ratio of nitrogen mineralized to phosphorus mineralized was 11.5 for cultivated soils and 7.6 for virgin soils. This relationship leads one to believe that there is a fraction of easily mineralized organic phosphorus in virgin soils that soon disappears under cultivation. This bears out an observation frequently made of Corn Belt soils as one reviews their history. During the first few years of cultivation they frequently did not respond to either nitrogen or phosphorus fertilization. After a few years of cultivation phosphorus became the first limiting factor. As long as a fraction of the organic phosphorus was decomposing rapidly, the crops were well supplied with available phosphorus. As this fraction decomposed, the remaining organic phosphorus decomposed relatively slowly.

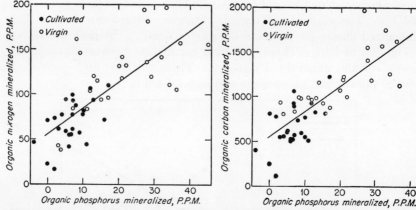

Fig. 96. Regression of nitrogen mineralized on phosphorus mineralized during laboratory incubation (34).

Fig. 97. Regression of carbon mineralized on phosphorus mineralized during laboratory incubation (34).

From the above study, and other related studies, the following generalizations seem appropriate:

1. The factors that cause rapid mineralization of nitrogen also cause rapid mineralization of phosphorus.

2. The field-soil conditions that favor rapid mineralization of nitrogen and phosphorus coincide with conditions that favor rapid nutrient uptake and rapid plant growth.

3. As mineralization of phosphorus occurs, there is a temporary high content of soluble phosphorus which might be rapidly removed from solution by the growing crop.

Relation of Lime to Organic Phosphorus. It is believed that the addition of lime would hasten the mineralization of phosphorus in the short-time incubation period. This belief is based on two bits of evidence. Kaila (18) reported a study of Finland soils in which liming greatly decreased the organic phosphorus content of soils. The other bit of evidence is shown graphically in Fig. 98. The data indicate that the percentage of total phosphorus combined in organic form decreases as the pH increases.

It has long been recognized that the addition of lime to an acid soil increases the availability of phosphorus. It is entirely logical to assume that a substantial share of the benefit of lime on availability of phosphorus might be due to the unlocking of a storehouse of resistant form of organic phosphorus.

Availability of Inorganic Phosphorus. The inorganic forms of phosphorus in soils include the primary mineral combination, such as apatite, and the secondary forms in which the phosphate ion is held immobile by clays, iron and aluminum hydroxides, and calcium and magnesium. Secondary forms are referred to as "fixed" phosphate.

The exchangeability of fixed phosphate is very slow, so slow in fact that the term exchangeable phosphate hardly applies. One thinks of the exchangeable cations as being readily available; however, only a small share of the fixed phosphate is readily available.

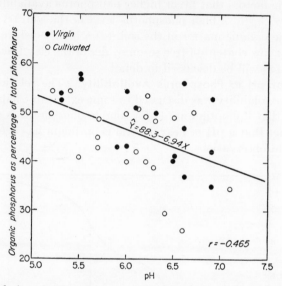

FIG. 98. The relation of pH to the percentage of total phosphorus existing as organic phosphorus (33).

Soluble phosphate in the soil may be less than 0.1 lb. per acre. As the soluble phosphate is absorbed by the plant, more phosphorus is dissolved to restore the equilibrium.

The amount of "available phosphate" is usually determined by the use of a weak acid, like carbonic acid, or 0.002 normal sulfuric acid, or by the use of ammonium fluoride in 0.025 normal hydrochloric acid solution. The amounts of available phosphate expressed as elemental phosphorus range from less than 5 to more than 20 lb. per acre, with 10 lb. per acre a representative figure where ammonium fluoride hydrochloric acid is used as the extracting solution. The extracting solution removes much more phosphate than exists in the soil solution. The reasoning behind the use of a relatively strong extracting solution is that one may estimate the fraction of phosphate which readily dissolves to maintain the equilibrium condition of the soil solution.

Such a test is empirical and must be closely correlated with experimental results from the use of fertilizers. For example, if by a certain method of extracting available phosphate one finds about 5 lb. per acre in several soils and that fertilizer phosphorus gives good response in such cases, one might then predict that the next soil testing below 5 lb. per acre of phosphorus would respond favorably to fertilizer.

The soil test is a rapid and economical way of determining the phosphorus status of a soil. There are a number of factors, however, that affect phosphorus availability, some of which a farmer can modify or control. The factors that favor higher phosphorus availability are (a) a pH of 6.5 to 7.5, (b) a high phosphorus level in the soil, (c) a supply of decomposable organic matter in the soil, (d) a high moisture level in the soil, and (e) a low content of free sesquioxides in the clay fraction. Each of these factors will be discussed in detail.

Relation of pH to Phosphorus Availability. The relation of pH to phosphorus availability was discussed to some extent in Chap. 7. It was emphasized that the optimum pH for soluble phosphorus is about 6.5 to 7.5. The fact that a pH of near neutral is optimum has been confirmed by many field observations.

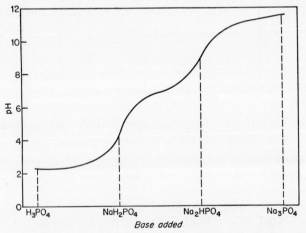

Fɪɢ. 99. Titration of orthophosphoric acid with sodium hydroxide.

In the pH range in which we find soils (about 4 to 10) there are three forms of orthophosphate, the monovalent $H_2PO_4^-$, the divalent HPO_4^{--}, and the trivalent PO_4^{---}. The existence of any one or more of these ions is a function of pH. Figure 99 is a curve showing the stepwise titration of orthophosphoric acid with sodium hydroxide. The first end point is reached at about pH of 4. The second end point is reached at about pH of 9. In the range of about 9 to 10 the PO_4^{---} ion appears in solution to a slight extent.[1] In the pH range of 4 to 9 there are two orthophosphate ions, $H_2PO_4^-$ and HPO_4^{--}, that might exist in solution. The pro-

[1] The trivalent form exists in a wider pH range in soils, but in mineral form.

portion of these two anions is a function of pH. The concentration of $H_2PO_4^-$ is greatest at a pH of about 4 and declines to zero at about the pH of 9. The opposite relation applies to HPO_4^{--}. The HPO_4^{--} ion first appears in solution at a pH of 4 and increases to a maximum at a pH of 9. The HPO_4^{--} and $H_2PO_4^-$ ions are about equal at a pH of 7.2.[1]

The concentration of $H_2PO_4^-$ would be especially low in a calcium-saturated soil, which would most likely prevail in the range from pH 7.5 to 8.5. Furthermore, the HPO_4^{--} ion is precipitated by calcium to form dicalcium phosphate, which is relatively insoluble in water.

In the pH range above 8.5, the soil is most likely to be high in exchangeable sodium. Sodium combined with HPO_4^{--} is relatively more soluble than calcium combined with HPO_4^{--}, and it is recognized that phosphate is more soluble in soils in the range of 8.5 to 9 than in the range from 7.5 to 8.5 (Fig. 69, page 191). Although the solubility of phosphorus is higher above pH 8.5 than between 7.5 and 8.5, the availability to plants is low above pH 8.5.

In the pH range below 6.5, the solubility of free iron and aluminum hydroxides increases with decreasing pH (Fig. 42, page 113). Either iron or aluminum hydroxides will precipitate $H_2PO_4^-$ ions from solution. The lower the pH, the greater the likelihood of having $H_2PO_4^-$ ions precipitated from solution by iron and aluminum. There is evidence to indicate that iron and aluminum phosphate are more insoluble than phosphates held as anions by silicate clays or as precipitates of calcium. For example, Toth (35) found that phosphorus solubility was increased by the removal of iron oxide from soils. While it has long been recognized that iron and aluminum reduce phosphorus solubility in acid soils, it should be recognized that they are not the only factors responsible for low phosphorus solubility in acid soils. Kaolinite will attract phosphate ions,[2] and recent work with radioactive phosphorus indicates that phosphate will even migrate from within a plant root to kaolinite when roots are transferred from a medium without kaolinite to a kaolinite clay suspension (7).

Raising the pH of a soil by liming to 6.5 reduces the solubility of iron and aluminum and increases calcium saturation, which should increase the opportunity for the formation of the more soluble calcium phosphate. Furthermore, the more abundant OH^- ions resulting from liming of an acid soil will compete with $H_2PO_4^-$ ions for anion-exchange positions.

Yet, with this apparently favorable combination of conditions, the

[1] This value was calculated from data of Abbott and Bray by Sterling Olsen. See Chap. IV of "Soil and Fertilizer Phosphorus," Vol. IV of "Agronomy," a monograph edited by W. H. Pierre and A. G. Norman.

[2] Low and Black (20) have found that phosphate combines with kaolinite and, in the process, seems to decompose the kaolinite crystal to form an aluminum phosphate with a loss of silica.

amount of phosphate in solution remains very low. But, in conclusion, it appears that phosphate availability should be at a maximum somewhere in the range of 6.5 to 7.5. In this range, the most available of the $H_2PO_4^-$ ions not in solution are probably those which are held on surfaces, or perhaps held by calcium linkage to clay and organic anions as follows:

$$\boxed{\begin{array}{c} \text{Clay} \\ \text{or} \\ \text{organic} \\ \text{anion} \end{array}} \text{—Ca—H}_2\text{PO}_4$$

Effect of Added Phosphorus on the Level of Available Phosphorus. The addition of phosphorus fertilizer to a soil has the effect of increasing the level of available phosphate. The fixation of added soluble phosphate occurs quite readily, particularly if the phosphate is mixed with the soil, and after several days any additional phosphate in solution might be insignificant because of the equilibrium relationship that exists between soluble phosphate and fixed phosphate (19). The availability of phosphorus to plants is increased, however, probably because the addition of phosphorus fertilizer provides a greater surface area of phosphorus compounds in contact with the soil solution (19). In other words, as the phosphorus is removed from the soil solution by plant absorption, the rate of replacement is faster with the additional phosphorus fertilizer. Stated in still another way, the equilibrium reaction to the right is faster.

That the content of acid-soluble or available phosphorus is increased by fertilization as well as by liming is illustrated in the data of Table 50.

TABLE 50. PHOSPHORUS IN LIMED AND UNLIMED OHIO FERTILITY PLOTS (25)
Expressed in pounds per acre

Phosphorus added during 30 years	Unlimed soil		Limed soil	
	Total	Acid-soluble	Total	Acid-soluble
0	952	44	829	64
200	1152	93	934	114

Effect of Organic Matter on the Availability of Phosphorus. Organic matter of the soil is (predominately) negatively charged. It is often referred to as a "humate" because the humus compounds combine with cations to form an "organic salt." There are many different kinds of organic compounds in the soil which are negatively charged. Some are true organic acids, and some are merely negatively charged compounds, but all are referred to as "humic acids" or "organic acids" in the same way that we think of clay crystals acting as weak acid radicals.   Organic acids at this time should be thought of as *organic anions*.

Organic anions combine with such cations as $Fe(OH)_2^+$ and $Al(OH)_2^+$ to form immobile complexes.[1]   As long as the iron and aluminum are immobilized in such a manner, they cannot precipitate $H_2PO_4^-$ ions out of solution.   Swenson *et al.* (32) found that soil organic matter, which they referred to as humus, and lignin increased the solubility of phosphate in a laboratory experiment.   Figure 100 was taken from their publication. It shows that increasing amounts of organic compounds caused further increase in solubility of phosphate.

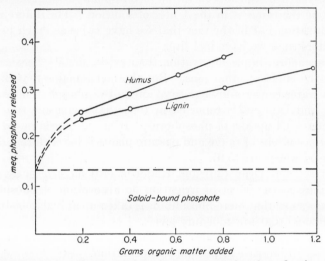

FIG. 100. Ability of humus and lignin to prevent phosphate fixation (32).

The phosphate anion $H_2PO_4^-$ is most soluble in the presence of anions which form precipitates and is least soluble in the presence of soluble and mobile anions.   The silicate clay minerals function as precipitating anions and do combine with $Fe(OH)_2^+$ and $Al(OH)_2^+$.   Additional precipitating anions like the organic anions help to keep the phosphate ions from combining with $Fe(OH)_2^+$ and $Al(OH)_2^+$ and other anion-exchange materials.

The addition of manure with superphosphate helps to keep the phosphate more available.   Midgley and Dunklee (22) have demonstrated this relationship with higher crop yields by applying manure and phosphate together than by applying them separately.

Organic anions "run interference" for phosphate ions.   To a certain extent, OH^- ions produced by liming perform the same function.

[1] There are other cations of iron and aluminum, but these two will be used in this chapter for purposes of illustration.

Relation of Moisture Level in the Soil to the Amount of Available Phosphorus. In order to describe the relation of moisture level to phosphate availability a simple laboratory illustration will be used. The insoluble (or relatively insoluble) compounds have a certain *solubility-product constant.* This means that only a certain amount of the compound will dissolve in the solution around it. Suppose one places a gram of tricalcium phosphate in a liter of water. A very small amount will dissolve. Adding another gram of the compound will not increase the amount of the material in solution. Now suppose one places a gram of tricalcium phosphate in a flask holding 2 liters of water. When equilibrium is reached, the concentration of phosphate in the 2 liters of solution will be the same as in the 1 liter of solution. The difference is not in concentration but in the fact that we have twice as much in solution with 2 liters than we have in 1 liter.

This is a more simple illustration than exists in soils, because in soils we have the effect of other ions. But the fact remains that dilution of soil with water causes a greater total amount of phosphate in solution.

Miller and Duley (24) reported in 1925 that increasing soil moisture caused increased uptake of phosphorus. It has also been noted that the phosphorus content of range and pasture plants is lower during dry years than during wet years (5,9).

Overstreet and Dean (26) and Haddock (15) have recently reported that studies on the effect of irrigation on absorption of phosphorus by sugar beets show that more phosphorus is taken up at high moisture levels than is taken up at low moisture levels.

Table 51 illustrates the idea that increasing the content of water in soils causes an increase in phosphate in solution.

TABLE 51. CONCENTRATION OF PHOSPHATE UNDER DIFFERENT RATIOS OF SOIL TO WATER (4)

Soil	Phosphate in p.p.m. under soil to water ratio of:		
	1:1	1:2.5	1:5
Fresno fine sandy loam............	69	92	115
Kimball fine sandy loam..........	9.6	22	40

Relation of the Silica to Sesquioxide Ratio to Available Phosphorus. The amount of free iron and aluminum (that which is not combined in the clay crystal) greatly affects the solubility of phosphorus. As silicate minerals undergo weathering, there is a loss of silica with an increase in iron and aluminum. As the ratio of iron plus aluminum to silica increases, there is also an increase in active iron and aluminum combined with phosphates to form rather insoluble compounds. The addition of phosphorus to soils high in iron and aluminum compared to silica requires careful treatment with lime and organic matter before phosphate is applied. Lime decreases the solubility of iron and aluminum and increases the amount of soluble calcium in the soil. If phosphorus combines with calcium it is more soluble than if combined with iron or aluminum.

Soils with a low silica to sesquioxide ratio are usually more strongly weathered and contain more free iron and aluminum. The data in Table 52 show the silica to sesquioxide ratio of the total colloid, which includes the clay crystal as well as free iron and aluminum. The lower the ratio the more free iron and aluminum one might expect.

TABLE 52. CORRESPONDENCE BETWEEN SILICA TO SESQUIOXIDE RATIO OF SOIL COLLOID AND EFFICIENCY OF SUPERPHOSPHATE (12)*

Soil series (surface soils)	$\dfrac{SiO_2}{Al_2O_3 \cdot Fe_2O_3}$ ratio of colloid	Average efficiency of superphosphate in soil-sand mixtures
Sharkey.................	3.23	148
Wabash.................	3.16	198
Stockton................	2.87	146
Marshall................	2.82	142
Carrington..............	2.75	54
Miami..................	2.50	62
Clarksville..............	2.18	71
Hagerstown.............	1.91	11
Huntington.............	1.86	72
Sassafras...............	1.85	75
Orangeburg.............	1.83	66
Chester.................	1.77	38
Manor..................	1.74	50
Norfolk.................	1.67	6
Cecil...................	1.34	28
Nipe...................	0.41	1

* Soils applied at rate of 50 g. of colloid per pot, superphosphate at rate of 0.05 g. or P_2O_5. A nutrient solution was added to supply elements other than phosphorus. Millet was grown as the test plant. The figures for the efficiency of superphosphate give the amount of growth relative to the growth in sand alone taken as 100.

The highest efficiency from the use of phosphate is associated with soils of high silica to sesquioxide ratio, as indicated in Table 52. Another way of expressing this relationship is that high efficiency from the use of soluble phosphate is associated with soils low in free iron and aluminum, other conditions being equal.

Soils high in free iron and aluminum have a high fixing capacity for phosphate. The addition of organic matter helps to satisfy a part of that fixing capacity. The increase in OH^- ions, through raising the pH of an acid soil by liming, also immobilizes $Al(OH)_2^+$ and $Fe(OH)_2^+$ and occupies anion-exchange positions on silicate clay crystals.

Sell and Olson (30) found that in an acid Georgia soil, which had a high fixing capacity for phosphorus, liming increased the availability of phosphorus. They also found that the higher the amount of phosphorus applied, the greater the amount of phosphorus available and the farther downward the phosphorus penetrated.

TABLE 53. EFFECT OF TOP-DRESSED LIME AND RATE OF PHOSPHATE APPLICATION ON AVAILABLE P_2O_5 AT VARIOUS SOIL DEPTHS (30)
Two years after surface application of phosphate

| Depth, in. | Available P_2O_5, lb./acre, after application at: | | | | | | | |
| | 40-lb. rate | | 80-lb. rate | | 160-lb. rate | | 320-lb. rate | |
	Unlimed	Limed	Unlimed	Limed	Unlimed	Limed	Unlimed	Limed
0–1	6.9	14.1	21.0	30.0	59.0	52.3	112.5	172.8
1–2	0.4	1.5	0.8	7.7	17.7	12.6	49.7	41.4
2–4	0.0	0.0	0.4	0.4	12.9	11.1	40.2	45.3
4–6	0.0	0.0	0.0	1.2	2.7	5.7	13.8	29.4
6–8	0.0	0.0	0.0	0.0	2.1	0.6	9.6	13.2

The results of Sell and Olson's work (Table 53) indicate that a soil has a certain capacity to fix phosphorus, and after that capacity has been filled, phosphorus may move downward in the soil.

Time and Method for Applying Soluble Phosphate Fertilizer for Clean-tilled Crops. The low solubility of phosphate and its resistance to leaching has been emphasized again and again. This feature of low immobility is illustrated by the data of Table 54. The soil studied in this case has a relatively high fixing capacity for phosphate, but it does illustrate the point to be emphasized.

The interesting feature of these data, however, is that much of the applied phosphate remained in available form (as measured by the use of 0.002 normal sulfuric acid extractant), but did not move downward to any appreciable depth. Very little phosphate moved below the 1-in. depth.

Although many soils (low in free iron and aluminum and high in organic matter) would allow phosphate to penetrate to a greater extent than was observed in this soil, the fact remains that phosphate is quite immobile. It should be placed where the roots can reach it.

Where a clean-tilled crop is to be grown, the phosphate should either be plowed under or placed in the soil to a depth of 2 in. or more. If the phosphate is applied to the surface and disked in the surface 2 in., it remains in the surface 2 in. The roots will not be feeding in the top 2 in. to any great extent because of tillage and because of rapid drying of the top 2 in. in most seasons.

TABLE 54. PENETRATION OF SUPERPHOSPHATE (23)
In plots receiving 300 and 600-lb. 20% superphosphate

Depth of plots, in.	Available phosphorus in soil, p.p.m.*		
	Check	300-lb. rate	600-lb. rate
Sampled June 25			
0–½	12.2	80.0	155.0
½–1	4.8	6.0	18.0
1–2	3.2	3.8	6.0
2–3	3.0	3.4	3.4
Sampled Oct. 13			
0–½	10.0	54.0	100.0
½–1	4.0	14.0	38.0
1–2	3.6	5.0	8.0
2–3	4.0	4.0	3.6

* Truog-Meyer method.

It is also known that soluble phosphate is more available when first applied. The question is often raised as to when phosphate should be plowed under. The answer is that there are other factors that are more important than phosphate application in determining when the soil should be plowed. Therefore if phosphate, other than starter fertilizer, is to be applied to a clean-tilled crop, it should be plowed under whenever the plowing best fits into the farm-management program. This may mean fall application of phosphate for a spring seeded crop in some instances.

Time and Method for Applying Soluble Phosphate to Broadcast or Drilled Crops. It would be desirable to have some phosphate plowed under for broadcast crops, but the problem is that many broadcast crops are seeded on a disked surface rather than a plowed surface. If phosphate is needed, part or all should ordinarily be applied at seeding time either broadcast or drilled.

The drilled or broadcast crop soon protects the surface 2 in. from rapid drying. Tillage does not follow seeding as in the case of clean-tilled crops. Therefore the roots develop to a great extent in the surface 2 in. where they can feed on the surface-applied phosphate.

Top-dressing of Phosphate. Phosphate top-dressing (or side-dressing of phosphate) for the growing crop is not recommended on clean-tilled crops but is quite satisfactory on meadow and pasture crops. Although the phosphorus does not penetrate very deep in the soil, there is an abundance of roots feeding in the immediate surface of pasture and meadow crops.

FIG. 101. Rock-phosphate mining operation at Bartow, Florida. Hydraulic pump in foreground, dragline in background. The rock phosphate is ground and sold as rock phosphate, or is treated with sulfuric acid or phosphoric acid to produce super-phosphate. (*The Davison Chemical Corporation.*)

Hanway *et al.* (16) have reported a very efficient recovery by plants of phosphate applied as a top-dressing on a meadow. Again it should be emphasized that the degree of efficiency of surface-applied phosphate will depend on the phosphate-fixing capacity of the soil and the moisture status of the surface soil.

Availability of Phosphate of Subsoils. Generally speaking, phosphate of subsoils is less available than phosphate of the A horizon of acid soils of humid regions. The clay content as well as the iron and aluminum content of the B horizon is greater than that of the A horizon. The organic-matter content of the A horizon is greater than in the B horizon. Moreover, the A horizon may even contain a greater quantity of phosphorus than is found in the B horizon.

Removal of the A horizon by erosion usually creates a greater problem of phosphate management than experienced with noneroded soils. An experiment was conducted by Stelly (31) to determine the availability of phosphorus from different layers of two soil profiles. He grew different plants in pots of soil collected from various depths in the two soils. Selected data from his study are shown in Table 55. His data indicate

TABLE 55. AVAILABLE PHOSPHORUS OF DIFFERENT SOIL HORIZONS (31)
Measured by plant response to phosphorus fertilization

Horizon	Depth of samples, in.	Dilute acid-soluble P, p.p.m.	Alfalfa, g. per pot grown on soils	
			With no phosphorus added	With added phosphorus
Grundy silt loam:				
A_1	0–6	16	6.0	10.9
B_1	14–22	13	0.9	7.7
B_2	26–30	39	5.6	7.3
C_1	36–48	176	7.0	9.2
Tama silt loam:				
A_1	0–6	8	7.9	10.9
B_1	13–18	7	1.3	8.1
B_3	24–32	32	5.6	8.3
C_1	36–45	106	7.1	8.4
C	48–54	184	7.2	7.7

that the phosphate was less available from the B horizon than from the A horizon in terms of plant responses. On the other hand, he found that the phosphate in the C horizon of these soils was as available to alfalfa as the phosphate of the A horizon. These soils contained free calcium carbonate in the C horizon. The phosphate was probably combined as dicalcium phosphate and tricalcium phosphate. It is generally recognized that alfalfa can make better use of these forms of phosphate than grass crops. Other studies of Stelly confirmed this observation. Neither corn nor Sudan grass grew as well on the phosphate of the C horizon as on the phosphate of the A horizon.

Use of Rock Phosphate. When Cyril G. Hopkins wrote his famous textbook "Soil Fertility and Permanent Agriculture" in 1910, there was a serious controversy on the relative merits of rock phosphate and superphosphate. The subject will still start an argument among farmers who reside in some communities where soils are acid. If the argument has not been settled in 50 years there must be something to be said in favor of both sides.

There is one argument that can easily be settled. Rock phosphate is not a satisfactory fertilizer for soils with a pH above 7.5. A soil with a pH above 7.5 is base-saturated, and free calcium carbonate usually exists in the surface as well as in lower depths. A soil with free calcium carbonate will effervesce with hydrochloric acid and is referred to as a calcareous soil. The naturally occurring phosphates of the soil are precipitated largely as tricalcium phosphate, $Ca_3(PO_4)_2$, with some dicalcium phosphate, $Ca_2H_2(PO_4)_2$. Either of these compounds is more soluble in a dilute acid than ground raw rock phosphate which has the formula $[Ca_3(PO_4)_2]_3CaF_2$.

FIG. 102. This corn was grown on a calcareous soil which was deficient in available phosphorus. The plot on the left received superphosphate; the plot on the right received rock phosphate. (*Iowa State College.*)

The problem is that the phosphate of the naturally occurring tricalcium phosphate is so slowly available that crop production is limited. Applying a less available material would not be a wise investment.

There is something to be said for ground raw-rock phosphate. The material is cheaper than superphosphate, and satisfactory results can be obtained on moderately acid soils (below pH 6.5) well supplied with crop residues or manure. There have been times when there was not enough superphosphate to supply the farmer demand while rock phosphate was available. It is well to know its limitations. The reason for a better response to rock phosphate on an acid soil is shown as follows:

$$\boxed{\begin{matrix}\text{Clay or}\\\text{humus}\end{matrix}} \begin{matrix}-\text{H}\\-\text{H}\\-\text{H}\\-\text{H}\end{matrix} + Ca_3(PO_4)_2 \rightarrow \boxed{\begin{matrix}\text{Clay or}\\\text{humus}\end{matrix}} \begin{matrix}=\text{Ca}\\ \\=\text{Ca}\end{matrix} + CaH_4(PO_4)_2$$

One would expect better results from rock phosphate on unlimed soils than on limed soils, and such was found to be the case in studies in Illinois (2). However, the better response of rock phosphate on unlimed soils is not a good reason for not liming an acid soil. And the neutralizing effect of rock phosphate is so small that its effect on pH is hardly measurable.

Table 56 shows results of long-time experiments on several soils in Iowa. They show a difference in favor of superphosphate for corn and a decided difference in favor of superphosphate for oats. The average annual rate of application was 250 lb. of 32 per cent rock phosphate and 90 lb. of 20 per cent superphosphate.

TABLE 56. RESPONSE OF CORN AND OATS TO DIFFERENT PHOSPHATE FERTILIZERS ON SEVERAL IOWA SOILS RECEIVING MANURE (29)

Soil type	No. of crops	Rock phosphate	Superphosphate
Increased yield of corn, bu./acre			
Carrington loam................	15	3.2	5.6
Carrington silt loam.............	9	6.0	5.4
Clarion loam...................	19	3.9	4.5
Grundy silt loam...............	6	5.2	3.6
Grundy silt loam...............	9	7.3	11.3
Marshall silt loam..............	6	2.7	3.6
Increased yield of oats, bu./acre			
Carrington loam................	9	2.6	5.2
Carrington silt loam.............	6	3.0	3.2
Clarion loam...................	8	2.5	4.7
Clarion loam...................	22	2.6	5.7
Grundy silt loam...............	4	7.0	9.9
Grundy silt loam...............	9	12.0	18.9
Grundy silt loam...............	77	3.1	11.6
Marshall silt loam..............	3	4.6	7.5

Legumes, which have a high calcium requirement, appear to respond more to rock phosphate than do nonlegumes. The removal of calcium from the dicalcium or tricalcium phosphate molecule and the replacement of calcium with hydrogen would increase the solubility of the phosphate. Table 57 is a partial list of crops showing their relative efficiency in the utilization of phosphorus from raw-rock phosphate.

Young seedlings are not as capable as older plants in removal of phosphorus from rock phosphate. For this reason it is wise to start small grain and legumes with superphosphate even though rock phosphate is the principal phosphate used.

Where an application of 750 to 1000 lb. of rock phosphate is made as a basic application, it is recommended that superphosphate be used in regular applications of starter fertilizer for small grain and legume seedings.

TABLE 57. A CLASSIFICATION OF PLANTS IN ACCORDANCE WITH THEIR EFFICIENCY IN THE UTILIZATION OF RAW-ROCK PHOSPHATE (7)

Most efficient	Moderately efficient	Least efficient
Lupines	Alfalfa	Cotton
Buckwheat	Peas	Cowpeas
Sweet clover	Rape	Bur clover
Mustard	Cabbage	Rice
Swiss chard		Oats
Vetch		Barley
		Millet
		Rye
		Wheat

This recommendation is based on the fact that available phosphorus in superphosphate helps to give the crops a good start. The older plants, probably because of their more extensive root systems, are better able to utilize the phosphorus from rock phosphate.

Colloidal phosphate is a claylike material containing phosphorus in the same form as in rock phosphate. Recommendations regarding the use of rock phosphate are also applicable to colloidal phosphate.

REFERENCES

1. Arnon, Daniel I., The Physiology and Biochemistry of Phosphorus in Green Plants, Chap. 1 in W. H. Pierre and A. G. Norman (eds.), "Soil and Fertilizer Phosphorus in Crop Nutrition," Academic Press, New York, 1953.
2. Bauer, F. C., and Associates, Effect of Soil Treatment on Soil Productivity, *Ill. Agr. Expt. Sta. Bull.* 516, 1945.
3. Bear, Firman E., and Robert M. Salter, The Residual Effects of Fertilizers, *W.Va. Expt. Sta. Bull.* 160, 1916.
4. Burd, John S., and J. C. Martin, Water Displacement of Soils and the Soil Solution, *J. Agr. Sci.,* **13**:265–295, 1923.
5. Daniel, H. A., and H. J. Harper, The Relation Between Effective Rainfall and Total Calcium and Phosphorus in Alfalfa and Prairie Hay, *J. Am. Soc. Agron.,* **27**:644–652, 1935.
6. Dean, L. A., Fixation of Soil Phosphorus, *Advances in Agron.,* **5**:391–411, 1949.
7. Dean, L. A., and Maurice Fried, Soil Plant Relationships in the Phosphorus Nutrition of Plants, Chap. 2 in W. H. Pierre and A. G. Norman (eds.), "Soil and Fertilizer Phosphorus in Crop Nutrition," Academic Press, New York, 1953.

8. Dean, L. A., and E. J. Rubins, Anion Exchange in Soils, *Soil Sci.*, **63**:377–406, 1947.

9. Eckles, C. H., T. W. Gullickson, and L. S. Palmer, Phosphorus Deficiency in the Rations of Cattle, *Minn. Agr. Expt. Sta. Tech. Bull.* 91, 1932.

10. Fuller, W. H., and W. T. McGeorge, Phosphate in Calcareous Arizona Soils. II. Organic Phosphorus Content, *Soil Sci.*, **71**:45–50, 1951.

11. Garman, William L., Organic Phosphorus in Oklahoma Soils, *Okla. Acad. Sci. Proc.*, **28**:89–100, 1948.

12. Gile, Philip L., The Effect of Different Colloidal Soil Materials on the Efficiency of Superphosphate, *U.S. Dept. Agr. Tech. Bull.* 371, 1933.

13. Godfrey, Curtis L., and F. F. Riecken, Distribution of Phosphorus in Some Genetically Related Loess-derived Soils, *Soil Sci. Soc. Amer. Proc.*, **18**:80–84, 1954.

14. Greb, B. W., "Organic Phosphorus in Calcareous Colorado Soils," Master's Thesis, Colorado A & M College, 1952.

15. Haddock, Jay L., The Influence of Soil Moisture Condition on the Uptake of Phosphorus from Calcareous Soils by Sugar Beets, *Soil Sci. Soc. Amer. Proc.*, **16**:235–238, 1952.

16. Hanway, John, George Stanford, and H. R. Meldrum, Effectiveness and Recovery of Phosphorus and Potassium Fertilizers Topdressed on Meadows, *Soil Sci. Soc. Amer. Proc.*, **17**:378–382, 1953.

17. Jackman, R. H., Organic Phosphorus in New Zealand Soils under Pasture, *Soil Sci.*, **79**:293–299, 1955.

18. Kaila, Armi, Viljelysmaan Orgaaniseta Fosforista, *Vation Maatalouskoetoiminnan Julkaisuja* 129, 1948.

19. Kittrick, J. A., and M. L. Jackson, Common Ion Effect on Phosphate Solubility, *Soil Sci.*, **79**:415–421, 1955.

20. Low, P. F., and C. A. Black, Phosphate-induced Decomposition of Kaolinite, *Soil Sci. Soc. Amer. Proc.*, **12**:180–184, 1947.

21. Marbut, C. F., "Atlas of American Agriculture," Part III, Soils of the United States, 1935.

22. Midgley, A. R., and D. A. Dunklee, The Availability to Plants of Phosphates Applied with Cattle Manure, *Vt. Agr. Expt. Sta. Bull.* 525, 1945.

23. Midgley, A. R., The Movement and Fixation of Phosphates in Relation to Permanent Pasture Fertilization, *J. Am. Soc. Agron.*, **23**:788–799, 1931.

24. Miller, M. F., and F. L. Duley, The Effect of a Varying Moisture Supply upon the Development and Composition of the Maize Plant at Different Periods of Growth, *Mo. Agr. Expt. Sta. Res. Bull.* 76, 1925.

25. *Ohio Agr. Expt. Sta. Ann. Rept.* 48, 1930 (for 1928–1929).

26. Overstreet, Roy, and L. A. Dean, The Availability of Soil Anions, pp. 79–105, in E. Truog (ed.), "Mineral Nutrition of Plants," University of Wisconsin Press, Madison, Wis., 1951.

27. Parker, F. W., and W. H. Pierre, The Relation between the Concentration of Mineral Elements in a Culture Medium and the Absorption and Utilization of Those Elements by Plants, *Soil Sci.*, **25**:337–343, 1928.

28. Pearson, R. W., and Roy W. Simonson, Organic Phosphorus in Seven Iowa Soil Profiles, Distributions and Amounts Compared to Organic Carbon and Nitrogen, *Soil Sci. Soc. Amer. Proc.*, **4**:162–167, 1939.

29. Report Prepared by the Agronomy Department, Iowa State College, *Proc. Corn Belt Sec. Am. Soc. Agron.*, 1940.

30. Sell, O. E., and L. C. Olson, The Effect of Surface-applied Phosphate and Limestone on Soil Nutrients and pH of Permanent Pasture, *Soil Sci. Soc. Amer. Proc.*, **11**:238–245, 1946.

31. Stelly, Mathias, "Forms of Inorganic Phosphorus in Lower Horizons of Some Iowa Soils as Indicated by Availability and Chemical Methods," Ph.D. Thesis, Iowa State College, 1942.

32. Swenson, Richard M., C. Vernon Cole, and Dale H. Sieling, Fixation of Phosphate by Iron and Aluminum and Replacement by Organic and Inorganic Ions, *Soil Sci.*, **67**:3–22, 1949.

33. Thompson, Louis M., "The Mineralization of Organic Phosphorus, Nitrogen and Carbon in Virgin and Cultivated Soils," Ph.D. Thesis, Iowa State College, 1950.

34. Thompson, L. M., C. A. Black, and J. A. Zoellner, Occurrence and Mineralization of Organic Phosphorus in Soils, with Particular Reference to Associations with Nitrogen, Carbon, and pH, *Soil Sci.*, **77**:185–196, 1954.

35. Toth, S. J., Anion Adsorption by Soil Colloids in Relation to Changes in Free Iron Oxides, *Soil Sci.*, **44**:299–314, 1937.

CHAPTER 11

POTASSIUM

Potassium is absorbed by plants as the K^+ ion, but it has long been the custom to express the potassium content of soils and fertilizers in terms of K_2O. In order to distinguish between K_2O and K^+, the term *potash* will be used to describe K_2O in this book and the term *potassium* will refer to K^+.

Potassium is one of the three macrocations used by plants. It is one of the bases held in exchangeable form by clay and organic anions. It is quite mobile as a cation in the soil and in the plant, but while combined as a part of a crystal structure, it is highly immobile and relatively resistant to removal by processes of weathering.

Potassium–organic-matter Relationships. Considerable emphasis has been placed on organic matter in studying nitrogen and phosphorus. While nearly half the phosphorus in the topsoil may be in organic combination and nearly all the nitrogen is in organic combination, only a small fraction of potassium is held by organic compounds.

Potassium does not enter into organic combinations in the plant as do nitrogen, phosphorus, and sulfur. Potassium remains active in the plant and is readily released to the soil when the plant tissue is turned under.

Distribution of Potassium in Soils. Because of the resistance of potassium-bearing minerals to weathering, potassium is one of the more abundant bases in the soil profile. During long periods of weathering some minerals decompose and their constituents leach away. The more resistant minerals remain behind to make up the soil. Potassium-bearing minerals are generally resistant, and the A and B horizons of well-developed profiles frequently contain a higher per cent of potassium than their parent materials. Table 58 shows the percentage of K_2O in the profiles of 16 soils from different sections of North America. Eight of the soils contained a lower per cent of K_2O in the C horizon than was contained in the A and B horizons. A representative soil of the United States will contain about 2.0 per cent K_2O throughout the profile. The variation is great enough, however, that one should be cautious in using an average figure.

Highly differentiated soil profiles developed from sandy-marine deposits in the Red-Yellow Podzolic great soil group are generally low in total K_2O. The Norfolk sandy loam was selected as representative of the sandy profiles. Although the Red-Yellow Podzolic soils are generally recognized as a strongly weathered group, there are some soils with a large amount of K_2O. The Cecil clay loam was developed from a parent material quite high in potassium-bearing minerals. The Grenada silt loam was developed from a loess deposit along the Mississippi River and represents a less-weathered material than is found in the marine deposits of that region.

TABLE 58. DISTRIBUTION OF K_2O IN THE PROFILES OF SEVERAL GREAT SOIL GROUPS (25)

| | | Horizon | | |
| | | A | B | C |
Soil type	Great soil group	Per cent K_2O		
Becket fine sandy loam.........	Podzol	2.06	3.45	3.79
Sassafras sandy loam..........	Gray-Brown Podzolic	1.62	1.97	2.07
Miami silt loam...............	Gray-Brown Podzolic	2.03	2.03	1.81
Norfolk sandy loam............	Red-Yellow Podzolic	0.11	0.16	0.19
Greenville fine sandy loam......	Red-Yellow Podzolic	0.35	0.32	0.23
Grenada silt loam.............	Red-Yellow Podzolic	2.10	2.24	2.33
Cecil fine sandy loam..........	Red-Yellow Podzolic	1.04	1.16	1.00
Cecil clay loam...............	Red-Yellow Podzolic	2.24	1.88	5.84
Marshall silt loam.............	Prairie	2.23	2.08	1.94
Putnam silt loam..............	Planosol	1.63	1.96	2.20
Canadian soil, unknown type...	Chernozem	2.03	1.85	1.85
Barnes silt loam...............	Chernozem	1.95	2.01	1.61
Vernon clay loam..............	Reddish Chestnut	2.57	2.18	2.85
Mohave loam.................	Red Desert	2.72	1.80	2.18
Gray soil from...............	Nevada	3.10	2.61	1.46
Gray soil from...............	Utah	2.49	2.09	1.50

As a broad generalization, soils of the western half of the United States contain more K_2O than soils of the eastern half of the country.

A typical soil profile with 2.0 per cent K_2O will contain about 40,000 lb. of potash per acre furrow slice. Yet potash is one of the three constituents of an ordinary *complete* fertilizer. Although a typical starter fertilizer for corn includes about 20 lb. of K_2O per acre, the acre of soil on which it is applied may contain 20 tons of K_2O in the top $6\frac{2}{3}$ in. The main reason is that the potassium-bearing minerals weather very slowly.

Sources of Potassium in Soils. Potassium is an important constituent of many of the silicate minerals. Some of the important minerals which supply potassium on weathering are muscovite, biotite, and orthoclase.

While the potassium is a part of the crystal structure, it is considered to be *nonexchangeable*. As the minerals weather, the potassium is released as the K⁺ ion, which may exist in solution to small extent or occupy an exchange position on a clay crystal or an organic anion. The K⁺ ion is exchangeable and quite mobile. The nonexchangeable potassium is quite immobile.

The resistance to weathering of potassium silicate is due largely to the size of the potassium atom. Its diameter is just slightly smaller than that of an oxygen atom. The silica tetrahedral layers of micas and clay

Fig. 103. Mechanical loading of raw potash salts into conveyor cars in a potash mine near Carlsbad, New Mexico. (*American Potash Institute.*)

minerals have oxygen atoms arranged in such a manner that they appear as hexagonal rings when viewed from the surface. The center of the ring is a space about the size of an oxygen atom or a potassium atom. Once the potassium enters this space between two adjacent silica layers during the formation of a mineral, it is very difficult to remove. The displacement of the potassium must accompany a certain amount of expansion of the adjacent silica layers during weathering.

In clay minerals of the 2 to 1 crystal lattice type, potassium ions may move into spaces between adjacent silica layers (32). If the clay mineral is caused to contract, the potassium ions become entrapped. They are no longer exchangeable, because of their lack of mobility. The potassium thus entrapped would be called nonexchangeable. The entrapment of potassium and its change in mobility are called "fixation."

There are three forms of nonexchangeable potassium, (a) that which occurs in primary minerals as a part of the crystal structure, (b) that which occurs as a part of the structure of a secondary mineral like illite, and (c) "fixed" potassium. It is generally believed that fixed potassium is relatively more available than the other forms of nonexchangeable potassium (15,16,41).

Roughly 99 per cent of the potassium in most soils is combined in non-exchangeable form. This is fortunate in one way and creates a problem in another. It is fortunate that potassium minerals weather so slowly and that fixation does occur, because, as an exchangeable ion, K^+ is quite mobile and leaches from soils much more readily (in proportion to the total exchangeable base content) than calcium or magnesium. The slowness to weather and tendency toward fixation create a problem in that additional available potassium as fertilizer may be necessary for satisfactory crop production.

The resistance of potassium minerals to weathering and the tendency toward fixation probably account to a large extent for the fact that the land surface of the earth is high in potassium while the oceans are high in sodium. Both sodium and potassium are quite mobile as cations. The big differences are that (a) sodium minerals weather somewhat faster than potassium minerals, (b) the sodium ion does not become fixed because it is surrounded by water molecules, making it act as a relatively large ion, and (c) exchangeable Na^+ is more easily displaced from the surface of clays and organic anions than K^+ ions.

Nonexchangeable potassium is well distributed throughout the soil profile, as indicated by data in Table 58. The data represent total K_2O, but about 99 per cent of total K_2O would be nonexchangeable.

Nonexchangeable potassium is fairly well distributed in the sand, silt, and clay fractions of most soils. The exception would be in soils where quartz makes up most of the sand or possibly the silt fractions. The weathering of potassium-bearing minerals may be important in any one of the fractions, sand, silt, or clay. The relative importance of any one of the three fractions would depend on the degree of weathering and on the nature of the clay. Strongly weathered clays are a poor source of potassium, and fixation of potassium does not occur in kaolinitic clays. On the other hand, slightly weathered clays containing a high proportion of illite are a good source of potassium. In soils with low fixing capacity for potassium, one might expect the silt and sand fractions to supply an important part of the potassium on weathering.

As a general rule, one finds that K^+ release increases with decrease in particle size (31). The greater surface exposed by finer particles probably accounts for this relationship.

Forms of Potassium Available to Plants. It is generally accepted that plant roots exchange H⁺ ions for cations. In the case of potassium, plant roots may exchange H⁺ ions for K⁺ ions in solution or for K⁺ ions held on the surfaces of clay crystals or organic anions. The latter exchange is referred to as contact exchange.

The relative importance of contact exchange feeding versus feeding from solution probably depends more on the water supply of the soil than any other one factor. As the water content of the soil increases, the amount of K⁺ ions in solution increases. On the other hand, as the water supply of the soil is exhausted by evaporation and root absorption, the amount of K⁺ in solution decreases. Plant roots may absorb an appreciable amount of K⁺ ions from an area of soil drier than the wilting point provided that turgidity of the plant is maintained by absorption of water from another area of the root zone (40).

Rather than debate the relative importance of feeding from solution versus contact-exchange feeding, it is best to consider both of them important and essentially one process. Both the K⁺ in solution and the exchangeable K⁺ are available to plants.

The K⁺ in solution amounts to a few pounds per acre furrow slice. But there is an equilibrium tendency between K⁺ in solution and exchangeable K⁺ (33). As K⁺ ions are removed from solution they tend to be replaced by K⁺ ions from the exchangeable form.

In the determination of exchangeable K⁺, one includes K⁺ in solution; therefore, for all practical purposes, one might consider available K⁺ and exchangeable K⁺ as synonymous. The amount of exchangeable K⁺ ranges from less than 100 to over 400 lb. per acre in different soils.

In soils of high exchange capacity the exchangeable K⁺ amounts to less than 1 per cent of the total exchangeable cations, but in soils of very low exchange capacity one may find exchangeable K⁺ amounting to about 5 per cent of the exchangeable cation content. A typical Prairie soil with a cation exchange capacity of 25 meq. contains about 0.2 to 0.3 meq. of K⁺ per 100 g. of soil. This would amount to about 156* to 234 lb. per acre of exchangeable K⁺ per acre. Of this amount perhaps 5 lb. might be in solution when the soil is at field capacity.

A good crop of alfalfa on 1 acre will take up about 150 lb. of K⁺ in 1 year. Yet the topsoil of that acre may contain only 150 lb. of exchangeable K⁺. Of course, some of the potassium taken up comes from the subsoil, but a high proportion of potassium taken up by the crop is absorbed from the topsoil. In order to grow such a crop year after year, the potassium-bearing minerals must weather rapidly enough to release as much K⁺ as is removed by crops and by leaching in order to maintain a level of, say,

* Meq. $\times$ 20 $\times$ equivalent weight, or 0.2 $\times$ 20 $\times$ 39 = 156 lb.

150 lb. of exchangeable K⁺.   Some soils contain minerals which weather
fast enough to maintain a good supply of exchangeable K⁺.   Others do
not, and fertilization becomes necessary for high crop production.

In a general way, there is an equilibrium tendency between nonexchangeable potassium, exchangeable potassium, and potassium in solution.

$$\text{Nonexchangeable K} \rightleftharpoons \text{exchangeable K} \rightleftharpoons \text{solution K}$$

The change from nonexchangeable to exchangeable potassium is illustrated by Fig. 104.   If one were to construct a liquid system as in Fig. 104
so as to siphon water out of section D, the capillary C leading into section D would have to be equal to diameter B in order to maintain a
constant level during the siphoning.

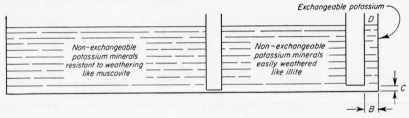

FIG. 104. A schematic diagram showing the equilibrium between nonexchangeable
and exchangeable potassium.   This may be thought of as an equilibrium system
tending to maintain a constant level.

Soils are somewhat like the diagram in the way in which they liberate
potassium from nonexchangeable sources.   As the plant takes up potassium, the exchangeable potassium level is lowered during the growing
season; but a few months after the crop has been removed, the original
level of exchangeable potassium may be restored.   This is why we often
find more exchangeable potassium in the spring than in the fall in the same
soil (14).   In other words, crops take out the potassium faster during the
growing season than the nonexchangeable potassium can become exchangeable potassium.

Over a long period of cultivation, the easily weathered minerals are
gradually reduced in quantity and the virgin level of exchangeable potassium is likewise reduced.   The highly resistant minerals do not weather
rapidly enough to maintain the exchangeable potassium at the virgin
level.   As a consequence of leaching and crop removal, the level of
exchangeable potassium is finally reduced low enough to cause response
to potash fertilization.

The equilibrium tendency is either to the right or to the left.   If one
applies large amounts of potassium fertilizer to a soil, the amount of K⁺
in solution is high temporarily, but the equilibrium reaction would be
toward the left (see the equation given above), which would cause a

temporary increase in exchangeable K^+. But again, the equilibrium tendency would cause some of the exchangeable K^+ to become fixed as nonexchangeable K^+.

Such a relationship suggests two principles of management. One is that potassium should be applied annually, or to each crop that is planted, rather than be applied once in a rotation, assuming, of course, that potassium is needed (6). The other is that concentration of the potassium (as in the hill or in the plow sole) would reduce contact with the soil, which, in turn, would reduce fixation. Fixed potassium, which was added as a fertilizer, is generally more available, however, than native nonexchangeable potassium.

Factors Affecting the Release of Potassium. The term *release* applies to the change from nonexchangeable potassium to exchangeable potassium.

Potassium which is fixed from applied fertilizer is not as readily available as exchangeable potassium but appears to be somewhat more available than the potassium contained in primary minerals. The fixation occurs in a random or irregular manner such that expansion of adjacent silica layers occurs with ease and displacement is accomplished relatively easily. In contrast, primary minerals formed in a particular geologic formation tend to build up crystals with a high degree of regularity and uniformity. Primary minerals are more likely to have close and regular packing of atoms.

Secondary minerals like illite and the mixed-layer silicate minerals associated with vermiculite release potassium more readily than primary minerals like muscovite or biotite. It should be pointed out, however, that these are the minerals that also fix potassium. The point to be emphasized here is that the native potassium occurring in illite is released more readily than native potassium from a primary mineral like muscovite, but probably not as readily as "fixed" potassium from added fertilizer.

To illustrate the variation in release of K from soils, the data of Hoagland and Martin (18) are shown in Table 59. Two of the soils examined actually supplied as much potassium from nonexchangeable sources as was removed in crops. These were greenhouse studies, and release of potassium may be greater in the greenhouse than in the field.

Fraps (17) showed that nonexchangeable potassium supplied almost half the potassium needs of corn, kafir, and sorghums in 72 soils. His data are shown in Table 60. This was also a greenhouse study, in which two crops were grown in 5-kg. samples of soil in pots. The first crop was usually corn, and the second was kafir or sorghums. The data are interesting from a number of points of view. One is that the more exchangeable potassium there was in the soil, the more potassium was removed by the crop. The second point is that, even with high amounts of exchange-

TABLE 59. POTASSIUM ABSORBED BY ONE TOMATO CROP FROM SOILS OF
DIFFERENT CHARACTERISTICS
Values as parts per million of oven-dry soil

Potassium absorbed	Soil 29	Soil 78	Soil 80	Soil 90	Soil 95	Soil 100	Soil 101
N-P treatment:							
Total K absorbed by crop..............	87	14	47	69	48	52	90
Loss of exchangeable K from soil........	25	0	16	43	0	24	26
K absorbed from nonexchangeable form..	62	14	31	26	48	28	64
K absorbed from nonexchangeable form, %	71	100	66	38	100	54	71
N-P-K treatment:							
Total K absorbed by crop..............	137	149	77	242	83	106	149
Loss of exchangeable K from soil........	110	146	33	239	15	80	137
K absorbed from nonexchangeable form..	27	3	44	3	68	26	12
K absorbed from nonexchangeable form, %	20	2	57	1	82	25	8
Added K fixed in nonexchangeable form, %	6	7	62	22	77	56	20

$Ca(NO_3)_2$ and treble phosphate were added to all soils. K_2SO_4 was added to the K-fertilized set at the rate of 1500 lb. per acre (acre basis).

TABLE 60. RELATIONSHIP BETWEEN EXCHANGEABLE POTASH IN SOIL AND
UPTAKE OF POTASH BY CROPS (17)
As parts per million K_2O in soil

Number of soils	Group according to potash removed by crops, lb.	Potash in crops	Exchangeable potash		
			Before cropping	After cropping	Lost by cropping
11	0–50	42	120	100	20
20	51–100	79	132	102	30
31	101–200	145	201	140	61
1	201–300	238	184	130	54
1	401–500	460	521	244	277
3	501–600	527	661	350	311
4	601–700	639	564	343	221
1	701–800	735	771	380	391

able potassium, the soil was still providing nearly half the crop needs from nonexchangeable sources.

It is generally recognized that young soils are a better source of potassium than strongly weathered or old soils. In younger soils, one usually finds a relatively high content of exchangeable K^+ as well as a rapid rate of release of K^+. The soils of the western half of the United States are generally well supplied with potassium (35). The Chernozems, Reddish Chestnuts, Rendzinas, and drier soils generally west of these great soil groups require little or no potassium fertilization. The Prairies, the Podzolic, and associated soils generally require potassium fertilization. This is a high correlation between degree of weathering (and leaching) and the potash needs of soils. As a general rule, one would expect soils which are weathered and leached enough to require lime to also require potash fertilization. There are exceptions, of course, and a soil test is desirable before purchasing potash fertilizer. Not only will the test indicate whether or not there is a need for potash, but it will also indicate how much might be needed.

Relation of pH to Release of Potassium. The effect of adding lime on the release of potassium has been studied by several investigators. The results are highly conflicting.

Lawton (21) studied the rate of release of potassium in Iowa soils by removing all exchangeable bases and then saturating the soils with H^+, Ca^{++}, or H^+ plus Ca^{++}. He then incubated the soils for varying periods of time. He found that more potassium was released from nonexchangeable form in the hydrogen-saturated soils than in the calcium-hydrogen-saturated soils, and least in the calcium-saturated soils. He observed that an amount of potassium equal to 55.5 to 89.0 per cent of the original exchangeable potassium was released in 360 days in 12 Iowa soils which were brought to the original pH with addition of calcium and hydrogen. The data for one of Lawton's soils are shown in Table 61.

TABLE 61. RATE OF POTASSIUM RELEASE IN CLYDE SILT LOAM (21)
Expressed in pounds per acre

| Soil treatment | Initial pH | Initial exchangeable K | Exchangeable K for incubation periods of | | | | K released as per cent of original |
			30 days	60 days	120 days	360 days	
Original soil.........	6.25	243	240	243	245	288	18.4
H^+-saturated........	4.00	...	119	162	220	233	95.9
Ca^{++} H^+-saturated..	6.25	...	70	95	112	145	60.0
Ca^{++}-saturated.....	7.42	...	33	63	75	93	38.3

H. C. Dean (13) found that the addition of lime to two Iowa soils in sufficient quantity to cause excess base saturation actually reduced the content of exchangeable potassium.

Lawton's and Dean's experiments indicate that calcium depresses the rate at which nonexchangeable potassium is released to exchangeable form. Allaway and Pierre (2) and Stanford, Kelly, and Pierre (37) found that high-lime soils of Iowa contained less exchangeable potassium than adjacent soils low in lime, and that high-lime soils had a greater capacity to fix potassium in nonexchangeable form than neutral or acid soils. The data of Stanford and his associates are shown in Table 62, page 281.

McClelland (23) incubated primary mica and feldspars with Ca and H bentonite (montmorillonite). He found that the release of K increased as hydrogen saturation increased, which is the same relationship found by Lawton.

In some soils, apparently, the addition of limestone would have the effect of decreasing the rate of release of potassium from nonexchangeable forms. We may state further that excess calcium carbonate (over 100 per cent base saturation) actually drives the equilibrium reactions to the left; that is, the addition of an excess of calcium carbonate will reduce the amount of potassium in solution and decrease the amount of exchangeable potassium. This last statement is supported by the work of Kelly (20), who has shown that high-lime soils contain less potassium in solution than adjacent low-lime soils.

A recent review by Reitemeier (34) points to the opposite effect of calcium on the release of potassium. He cites the recent work of Ayres (4), Merwin (29), and York and Rogers (43) as evidence that the addition of calcium to a hydrogen-saturated clay increases the rate of release. Ayres was working in Hawaii, Merwin in New York, and York and Rogers in Alabama.

It is quite possible that the chemical nature of the clay or the organic anions of the soil would account for the differences observed on the relation of calcium to the release of potassium. The following is a possible explanation.

The soils of Iowa are high in montmorillonite. Apparently Ca^{++} is adsorbed more strongly than H^+ by montmorillonite (24), whereas H^+ is adsorbed more strongly than Ca^{++} by kaolinite (28). The high activity of the H^+ ions of montmorillonite may help to displace the nonexchangeable potassium of the minerals with which it comes in contact. By a similar mechanism the high activity of Ca^{++} ions on kaolinite may help in displacing nonexchangeable potassium.

The above sounds like a simple cation-exchange mechanism. It is not so simple, but there is an exchange of one cation for another as nonexchangeable K becomes exchangeable K^+. The difference is one of mobility of the K. One point of significance here is that artificial fixation of K^+ with illite-montmorillonitic clay (laboratory-induced fixation) causes a reduction in exchange capacity corresponding in milliequivalents to the amount of K^+ fixed (39). It would be expected, therefore, that a release of K^+ from nonexchangeable form might be accompanied by a slight increase in exchange capacity of the soil because the ion which displaced the K^+ might remain mobile and exchangeable. This slight change would be difficult to measure, however, and might go without being observed in many studies.

Effect of Calcium on the Amount of Potassium in the Soil Solution. The amount of potassium in solution in a soil depends on several factors. One factor already mentioned is the moisture content of the soil; that is, an increase in moisture causes an increase in the amount of potassium in solution. Other factors include the ratio of exchangeable calcium to exchangeable hydrogen and the ratio of exchangeable calcium to exchangeable potassium.

The effect of Ca to H ratio and the Ca to K ratio on potassium in solution is related to the nature of the colloid, that is, the kind of clay and the nature of the organic anions (26,27). These relationships will be discussed under two headings, since there appear to be two distinctly different colloidal conditions affecting the amount of potassium in solution. One is the colloid that holds calcium with greater energy than hydrogen. This includes montmorillonites. The other is the colloid that holds hydrogen with greater energy than calcium. This includes organic anions like those found in organic soils and kaolinite and to a certain extent illite (11) and biedellite (a 2 to 1 mineral where aluminum has replaced silicon to a very large extent).

Montmorillonite holds exchangeable calcium quite strongly, whereas exchangeable hydrogen is relatively easily displaced. In terms of weak and strong acids, montmorillonite is a stronger acid when hydrogen-saturated than kaolinite when hydrogen-saturated. This is shown by the pH–base-saturation curves on page 186. The pH is lower for the hydrogen-saturated montmorillonite. The degree of dissociation of H^+ ions is greater for montmorillonite. On the other hand, calcium is held rather strongly by montmorillonite, and a high percentage of saturation with calcium is necessary to reach a pH of 7. The curve on page 186 shows 95 per cent base saturation at a pH of 7.

The principle known as the "complementary ion effect" applies in this case. Where percentage of exchangeable K^+ is held constant, the addition of the *more strongly adsorbed* Ca^{++} resulting in displacement of the *more weakly adsorbed* H^+ causes a greater activity of potassium. In other words, the addition of calcium to montmorillonite increases the amount of K^+ in solution (19). It should not be overlooked, however, that the increase in percentage of Ca^{++} saturation of montmorillonite also increases the amount of Ca^{++} in solution.

It is well known that in montmorillonitic soils, the ratio of exchangeable Ca to exchangeable K^+ can be as wide as 100 to 1 with normal potassium nutrition. This is not the case with kaolinitic soils, as will be described later.

In order to maintain sufficient active calcium in a montmorillonitic soil a high percentage of base saturation is necessary; a saturation of about 90 per cent is desirable. Although the higher calcium saturation appears to increase the amount of K^+ in solution, assuming exchangeable K^+ is held constant in montmorillonitic soils, the ultimate effect is that an increase in base saturation increases a need for potash fertilizer. The exchangeable potassium level will decline following liming for at least two reasons: (a) the higher calcium saturation reduces the rate of release of potassium from minerals associated with montmorillonite, (b) the increase in calcium saturation may encourage greater crop production and a greater demand for available potassium.

Kaolinitic clays appear to hold hydrogen with greater energy than with which they hold calcium. Hydrogen-saturated kaolinite acts as a weaker acid than hydrogen-saturated montmorillonite. Exchangeable H^+ is not as readily dissociated from kaolinite as it is from montmorillonite. On the other hand, exchangeable Ca^{++} is easily dissociated from kaolinite. As a consequence of the high activity of Ca^{++} with kaolinite, at a pH of 7 we may find only about 60 per cent base saturation; see pH–base-saturation curves on page 186.

If the content of exchangeable K^+ is held constant in a kaolinitic clay and the exchangeable H^+ is replaced by exchangeable calcium, there is a tendency to decrease the amount of K^+ in solution. In other words, the equilibrium tendency will be to the left in the case of K^+.

$$\text{Exchangeable } K^+ \rightleftharpoons K^+ \text{ in solution}$$
$$\text{Exchangeable } Ca^{++} \rightleftharpoons Ca^{++} \text{ in solution}$$

The higher exchangeable Ca^{++} causes a larger amount of Ca^{++} to appear in solution, which will cause less K^+ ions to appear in solution.

The compensating factor favoring the maintenance of available K^+ is that a higher calcium saturation of a kaolinitic soil causes a more rapid release of nonexchangeable K, which, of course, is available to plants through contact exchange.

Bear *et al.* (5) have suggested that for New Jersey soils it is desirable to maintain a ratio of about 13 to 1 for exchangeable Ca^{++} to exchangeable K^+. For soils high in kaolinite this appears to be quite logical. A kaolinitic soil with about 80 per cent base saturation containing about 65 per cent Ca^{++}, 10 per cent Mg^{++}, and 5 per cent K^+ would provide a satisfactory balance of these macrocations. Such a combination in a montmorillonitic soil with high exchange capacity would not be satisfactory because there would be "luxury" consumption of K^+ and not enough Ca^{++} for most crops.

Although the effect of lime on a kaolinitic soil appears to increase the rate of release of nonexchangeable K, the ultimate effect of lime is to increase the need for potash fertilizer. The fertility tests in North Carolina (42) have shown that very little response is obtained from addition of potash to unlimed soils. On the other hand, potash-starvation symptoms on cotton and corn on limed plots which received no potash were observed. In general, good responses to potash on limed soils were obtained. These results were explained on the basis that liming increased the growth of the legume crops, which took up more potassium and left less for the following crops of cotton or corn.

Fig. 105. View of Searles Lake and potash refining near Trona, California. (*American Potash Institute.*)

Relation of Liming a Soil to the Losses of Potassium by Leaching.

Many studies have shown over a period of many years that less potassium is lost by leaching from lysimeters after the soils were limed. Reitemeier (34) cited the evidence published by many investigators which indicates this relationship.

The discussion in the previous section supports the view that an increase in calcium saturation should reduce the amount of potassium in solutions draining from a soil. In kaolinitic soils, lime apparently increases the rate of release of K from nonexchangeable to exchangeable form but reduces the amount in solution. In montmorillonitic soils, lime increases the activity of K^+ but reduces the release of K^+ from nonexchangeable form with an ultimate effect of reducing the amount of K^+ that might appear in solution.

Table 13 on page 81 shows the relative losses of CaO, MgO, and K_2O

from a soil by leaching. The amounts expressed in pounds per acre lost from a bare soil were 557.2 for CaO, 104.4 for MgO, and 86.8 for K_2O. The usual order of leaching loss is Ca > Mg > K. When one considers the wide ratio of exchangeable Ca to exchangeable K in soils (as wide or wider than 100 to 1), it is significant to note the more narrow ratio of Ca to K found in drainage waters. The ratio runs from about 5 to 1 to 10 to 1 in drainage water and in soil solutions. Table 19 on page 114 shows that river water contains a ratio of Ca to K of nearly 10 to 1. The activity of the K^+ ion is much greater than the Ca^{++} ion. It is not uncommon for Prairie soils to have a ratio of 100 to 1 for exchangeable Ca to K and a ratio of 10 to 1 for Ca to K in solution and a ratio of 1 to 1 for Ca to K contained in the legumes grown on that soil.

The amount of K^+ lost by leaching in humid regions exceeds the amount of K^+ removed in crops and exceeds the amount added in fertilizer. This raises a question of the possible losses resulting from added potash fertilizer. Potassium added as a fertilizer becomes exchangeable K^+ in the zone to which applied. The enriched area contains a high proportion of exchangeable K^+ to other cations for a period of several months. Through the aid of water movement, through the migratory action of the K^+ ions, and through fixation, an equilibrium is eventually approached so that the ratio of K^+ ions to other cations becomes more or less the same throughout the soil body. The point is that as much K^+ might be lost by leaching as added in fertilizer in 1 year, but the K^+ in the drainage water may not be identified as the same K^+ that was added as fertilizer.

Use of Potash on Naturally Neutral and Calcareous Soils. Soils which are naturally neutral are well supplied with bases. They usually have a high content of Ca^{++} and Mg^{++}. It should be remembered that calcium and magnesium minerals generally weather faster than sodium- and potassium-bearing minerals. The existence of a naturally high base-saturation with Ca^{++} and Mg^{++} is an indication of youth and a high rate of release of Ca^{++} and Mg^{++}. Under such youthful conditions one would expect a rapid release of K^+ from primary and secondary minerals. The fact that no lime is needed is a good indication that potash may not be needed.

Calcareous soils of the subhumid, semiarid, and arid regions rarely respond to potash fertilization. The calcareous Rendzina soils of the blackland prairies of Texas are also high in available potassium.

The high-lime soils of Illinois and Iowa are quite different from the usual calcareous soil. The high-lime soils do not appear to contain easily weathered potassium-bearing minerals. Furthermore, they contain large amounts of illite and montmorillonite (and probably vermiculite) minerals which have a high capacity for fixing potassium. It is well known that alkalinity favors potassium fixation (3). The high-lime soils of Iowa have lower amounts of exchangeable K^+ than found on nearby similar but low-lime soils. This may be due to a depletion of easily weathered potassium minerals as well as to a tendency toward fixation. Table 62 illustrates this relationship. High-lime soils usually respond

TABLE 62. RELATIONSHIP BETWEEN EXCHANGEABLE POTASSIUM AND YIELD OF CORN ON NORMAL AND HIGH-LIME AREAS OF WEBSTER SOILS (37)

Field number	Area sampled	Exchangeable potassium, lb./acre	Corn yield (1940) bu./acre
1	Normal	383	56.0
	High-lime	147	33.1
2	Normal	309	73.8
	High-lime	172	39.7
3	Normal	270	62.8
	High-lime	116	22.4
4	Normal	405	71.3
	High-lime	116	16.9

quite favorably to a top-dressing of about 100 lb. of K_2O for each crop of corn in Iowa if other factors are favorable.

Relation of Ammonium Fixation to Potassium Fixation. The NH_4^+ ion is about the same size as the potassium ion. It is fixed in apparently the same manner as the K^+ ion (38). Soils which are known to have high fixing capacities for K^+ may also fix NH_4^+ in significant quantities. Whether or not this relationship is of great economic importance has not been thoroughly investigated. It is known, for example, that the Webster soils of north central Iowa do not respond as much to treatment with NH_4NO_3 as the other soil areas of the state. These soils have high organic-matter contents, and the low response to nitrogen may be due to a rapid release of nitrogen from the organic matter. Yet it is known that these soils have a high fixing capacity for K^+. One should consider the possibility of NH_4^+ fixation in soils known to respond poorly to NH_4^+ and known to fix K^+ quite readily.

Relation of Available Potassium to Crop Yields. There appears to be a high correlation between the level of exchangeable K^+ in some soils and the crop yield. This has been shown by Attoe of Wisconsin (36) and many others.

The usual method for determining potash needs in soil-testing laboratories involves an estimate of the exchangeable K^+.

The graph in Fig. 106 was taken from the work of Bray (10) in Illinois. Bray found good correlation between the amount of exchangeable potassium in the soil and the response to potash fertilization.

It may be concluded from a study of Bray's curve that soils containing 100 lb. of exchangeable potassium gave yields of corn about 70 per cent as high as soils fertilized with potassium.   It is also of interest that the curve begins to level off rapidly above the 70 per cent level of sufficiency. Furthermore, the scattering of dots above 70 per cent sufficiency indicates that correlation between exchangeable potassium and yield is not very high.   On the other hand, Bray's data show good correlation between exchangeable potassium and corn yield on soils containing less than 100 lb. of exchangeable potassium.

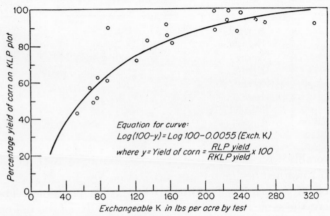

FIG. 106. Relationships between exchangeable potassium and corn yields on plots receiving no K_2O (10).

The problem in many areas is that practically all soils contain more than 100 lb. of exchangeable potassium, and it is in soils containing more than 100 lb. of exchangeable potassium that we find poor correlation between response to potash fertilization and amounts of exchangeable potassium in the soil.   Table 63 was taken from a summary prepared by members of the agronomy department of Iowa State College.   None of the soils contained less than 100 lb. of exchangeable potassium.

It is apparent from examination of Table 63 that we cannot always depend on getting a significant increase in yield of corn from the use of fertilizer potassium on soils containing between 100 and 175 lb. of exchangeable potassium.   Only half the soils containing 100 to 175 lb. of exchangeable potassium showed a significant increase in yield from use of potassium fertilizer.   Only one out of seven soils responded to potassium fertilizer where the soils contained over 175 lb. of exchangeable potassium per acre.   It is believed, however, that good response to potash fertilizer can be expected in nearly all cases, if the soils contain less than 100 lb. of exchangeable potassium.

Since we cannot depend only on the level of exchangeable potassium

TABLE 63. RESPONSE OF CORN TO APPLICATION OF POTASSIUM ON SOILS
OF IOWA

Year	Soil Series	County	Yield check	K_2O applied, lb.	pH	Increase, bu./acre		
						With corresponding exchangeable K of		
						100–175 lb.	175–275 lb.	275 lb.

Significant increase

1946	Weller	Harrison	83.5	20	6.1	9.3*		
	Haig	Lucas	77.1	20	5.3	5.5*		
	Clarion	Kossuth	83.2	48	6.0	.....	7.8*	
1947	Weller	Henry	56.9	20	7.0	5.5*		
	Weller	Henry	56.9	40	7.0	10.5*		
	Weller	Henry	56.9	80	7.0	10.5*		
	Webster	Buena Vista	54.9	20	7.5	8.0*		
	Webster	Buena Vista	54.9	40	7.5	5.0*		

No significant increase

1946	Tama	Tama	114.1	20	5.1	.....	....	1.8
	Carrington	Buchanan	49.5	20	4.8	3.1		
	Bremer	Louisa	73.6	20	6.2	.....	0.5	
	Edina	Appanoose	66.4	20	5.9	1.9		
	Taintor	Wapello	60.0	20	4.8	3.0		
	Webster	Jasper	101.3	48	5.9	3.7		
	Clarion	Boone	54.3	48	5.7	.....	5.8	
1947	Carrington	Benton	33.5	60	...	.....	0.6	
	Carrington	Iowa	51.3	60	...	.....	1.6	
	Taintor	Henry	37.5	60	...	.....	2.9	
	Clarion	Polk	27.2	60	...	0.6		
	Webster	Webster	41.6	20	...	2.0		
	Webster	Buena Vista	54.9	80	7.5	1.5		

* Highly significant.

as a criterion for making fertilizer recommendations, it is desirable that
we look into some of the factors that affect the availability of potassium
to plants.

Influence of Aeration on Uptake of Potassium by Plants. Lawton (22)
found that forced aeration of soils increased potassium uptake by plants.
He also found that decrease of aeration, by compaction of soils, caused a
decrease in the uptake of potassium. In another experiment, Lawton
varied the percentage of water and air in two soils and found that an

increase in moisture (with a consequent decrease in aeration) caused a reduction in potassium uptake by corn. Chang and Loomis (12) found that bubbling CO_2 through nutrient solutions caused depression in potassium absorption by wheat and actually caused excretion of potassium by corn.

Sandy soils are better aerated than heavier soils, and soils with granular structure are better aerated than soils in a puddled condition or with a cloddy or blocky structure. Poorly drained soils are poorly aerated soils, and poorly drained soils have a greater need for potash fertilization than do well-drained soils.

While sandy soils are well aerated, they have low exchange capacities and therefore have small amounts of exchangeable potassium. Sandy soils often contain less than 100 lb. of exchangeable potassium per acre.

Several years ago, Bower, Browning, and Norton (9) started some studies on different tillage practices. They noticed that soils which were subsurface-tilled showed potash starvation in corn, while adjacent similar soils which had been plowed showed no potash starvation. The plowing increased aeration compared to the subsurface tillage, and the increased aeration favored the uptake of potassium by corn.

The greatest response to potassium is expected during cool and wet seasons. A wet season means poor aeration, particularly on soils which are normally poorly drained.

Response of Crops to Potash Fertilizers. The response of crops to potassium is related to at least two important plant characteristics. One is that some plants require a higher ratio of potassium to calcium than others, and the other is that some plants need a larger amount of potassium over a short period of time.

Corn responds more to potassium than most other field crops grown in the Corn Belt. Table 64 shows the average amounts of potassium and calcium taken up by several crops. The data represent averages of large numbers of samples of each crop. It is realized that the potassium and calcium percentages vary greatly in plants in accordance with availability of potassium and calcium in soils. It is believed, however, that averages of large numbers of samples will be helpful in the interpretation of observations of crop response to potassium fertilization.

Corn is a warm-weather crop, which means that it is storing carbohydrates during the hottest part of the summer, when the rate of respiration is greatest. Furthermore, corn makes most of its growth during a relatively short period of the summer. Nightingale (30) points out that during the time that the photosynthetic rate and uptake of nitrates are high, plants need an abundant supply of potassium. Potassium is involved in the reduction of nitrates in protein synthesis and is also involved in carbohydrate production. The absence of sufficient potassium may cause nitrates to accumulate. In such case, the deficiency of potassium is reflected in low carbohydrate production and in failure of nitrate reduction. The point to be emphasized is that potassium is required in large amounts during the time of most rapid growth.

Albrecht (1) has suggested that plants which are notably high in carbohydrate production and low in protein production have a higher potassium to calcium requirement than leguminous plants which are notably high in protein.

TABLE 64. AVERAGE POTASSIUM AND CALCIUM CONTENTS OF SEVERAL CROPS (7)

Crop	K, per cent	Ca, per cent
Alfalfa (half bloom)............................	2.22	2.01
Red clover (various stages of maturity)............	1.62	1.53
Sweet clover (various stages of maturity)...........	1.30	1.33
Soybean hay (various stages of maturity)...........	1.24	1.12
Oats (above-ground parts in milk stage)............	0.96	0.22
Corn:		
60 cm. high.................................	9.89	0.68
Before bloom...............................	6.24	0.55
Beginning to bloom..........................	7.12	0.66
Milk stage..................................	2.62	0.50
Corn stover (mature)...........................	0.74	0.32
Corn grain....................................	0.40	0.015

Corn has a high potassium to calcium requirement and needs an abundant supply of potassium during a very short period of time. The liming of a soil, to provide more calcium for legumes in rotation with corn, reduces the availability and solubility of potassium, and at the same time, the increased growth of the legume due to liming causes a greater removal of potassium. In short, liming to increase legume growth usually calls for potassium fertilization for corn. The same is apparently true for cotton in rotation with legumes.

It was pointed out in Chap. 7 that potash is needed for corn on high-lime soils of Iowa and Illinois. The discussion in this chapter reemphasizes the need for potassium on high-lime soils.

Poor drainage and poor aeration cause an increased need for potassium. Soils with impervious subsoils require more potassium than do well-drained soils, even though both types may contain the same amount of exchangeable potassium.

Oats and legume seedings do not show as much response to potash as does corn. Crops that grow over a long period (and gradually take up potassium) may respond very little to potash fertilizer, since nonexchangeable potash may be released rapidly enough to meet the crop needs. Soybeans respond to potash on soils where the exchangeable potassium drops to 100 lb. per acre or below. Soybeans have not generally responded to potash fertilization in Iowa, where the exchangeable potassium is almost invariably above 100 lb. per acre. On the other hand, soybeans are frequently fertilized with potash in Illinois and in other states to the east and southeast of Iowa.

Partial substitution of sodium for potassium by oats may account for smaller response to potash on oats than is observed for corn. Bower and Pierre (8) have shown that, while corn takes up less than 1 meq. of sodium per 100 g. of plant material, oats will take up as much as 11.8 meq. of sodium per 100 g. of plant material.

Another factor affecting the differential response of crops to potassium is their place in the rotation. Oats and legume seedings usually follow cotton, soybeans, or corn. The residues of the latter crops contain most of the potassium which was taken up by the growing crops. The potassium contained in the residues of cotton, soybeans, and corn is, for the most part, readily available to the oats and legumes.

Most of the potassium in a crop is distributed in the leaves and stems. If the crop is harvested for hay or silage there is a larger amount of potassium removed than if only the seed or grain is harvested. In a corn, oats, legume-hay rotation the removal of a large amount of potassium in the hay crop increases the need for potassium fertilizer (in many instances) for the benefit of the corn that follows.

REFERENCES

1. Albrecht, William A., Calcium-Potassium-Phosphorus Relation as a Possible Factor in Ecological Array of Plants, *J. Am. Soc. Agron.*, **32**:411–418, 1940.
2. Allaway, Hubert, and W. H. Pierre, Availability, Fixation and Liberation of Potassium in High-lime Soils, *J. Am. Soc. Agron.*, **31**:940–953, 1939.
3. Attoe, O. J., Potassium Fixation and Release in Soils Occurring under Moist and Drying Conditions, *Soil Sci. Soc. Amer. Proc.*, **11**:145–149, 1946.
4. Ayres, A. S., Release of Non-exchangeable Potassium in Hawaiian Sugar Cane Soils, *Univ. Hawaii Agr. Expt. Sta. Tech. Bull* 9, 1949.
5. Bear, Firman E., Arthur L. Prince, and John L. Malcolm, Potassium Needs of New Jersey Soils, *N.J. Agr. Expt. Sta. Bull.* 721, 1945.
6. Bear, Firman E., and Stephen J. Toth, Influence of Calcium on Availability of Other Soil Cations, *Soil Sci.*, **65**:69–74, 1948.
7. Beeson, K. C., The Mineral Composition of Crops with Particular Reference to the Soils in Which They Were Grown, *U.S. Dept. Agr. Misc. Pub.* 369, 1941.
8. Bower, C. A., and W. H. Pierre, Potassium Response of Various Crops on a High-lime Soil in Relation to Their Contents of Potassium, Calcium, Magnesium, and Sodium, *J. Am. Soc. Agron.*, **36**:608–614, 1944.
9. Bower, C. A., G. M. Browning, and R. A. Norton, Comparative Effects of Plowing and Other Methods of Seedbed Preparation on Nutrient Element Deficiencies in Corn, *Soil Sci. Soc. Amer. Proc.*, **9**:142–146, 1944.

10. Bray, Roger H., Soil Plant Relations. I. The Quantitative Relation of Exchangeable Potassium to Crop Yields and to Crop Response to Potash Additions, *Soil Sci.*, **58**:305–324, 1944.

11. Bray, Roger H., Ionic Competition in Base Exchange Reactions, *J. Am. Chem. Soc.*, **64**:954–963, 1942.

12. Chang, H. T., and W. E. Loomis, Effect of Carbon Dioxide on Absorption of Water and Nutrients by Roots, *Plant Physiol.*, **20**:221–232, 1945.

13. Dean, H. C., The Effects of Liming on the Liberation of Potassium in Some Iowa Soils, *Iowa Agr. Expt. Sta. Res. Bull.* 197, 1936.

14. DeTurk, E. E., L. K. Wood, and R. H. Bray, Potassium Fixation in Corn Belt Soils, *Soil Sci.*, **55**:1–12, 1943.

15. Evans, C. E., and O. J. Attoe, Potassium-supplying Power of Virgin and Cropped Soils, *Soil Sci.*, **66**:323–334, 1948.

16. Fine, L. O., "Potassium Fixation and Availability," Ph.D. Thesis, University of Wisconsin, 1941.

17. Fraps, G. S., Relation of the Water-soluble Potash, the Replaceable, and Acid-soluble Potash to the Potash Removed by Crops in Pot Experiments, *Tex. Agr. Expt. Sta. Bull.* 391, 1929.

18. Hoagland, D. R., and J. C. Martin, Absorption of Potassium by Plants in Relation to Replaceable, Nonreplaceable and Soil Solution Potassium, *Soil Sci.*, **36**:1–34, 1933.

19. Jenny, H., and A. D. Ayers, The Influence of the Degree of Saturation of Soil Colloids on the Nutrient Intake by Roots, *Soil Sci.*, **48**:443–459, 1939.

20. Kelly, J. B., "Composition of the Displaced Soil Solution and Exchangeable Potassium Content of High-lime Soils in Relation to Potassium Deficiency in Corn," Master's Thesis, Iowa State College, 1941.

21. Lawton, Kirk, unpublished data, Iowa State College.

22. Lawton, Kirk, The Influence of Soil Aeration on the Growth and Absorption of Nutrients by Corn Plants, *Soil Sci. Soc. Amer. Proc.*, **10**:263–268, 1945.

23. McClelland, J. E., The Effect of Time, Temperature, and Particle Size on the Release of Bases from Some Common Soil-forming Minerals of Different Crystal Structure, *Soil Sci. Soc. Amer. Proc.*, **15**:301–307, 1950.

24. McLean, E. O., and C. E. Marshall, Reciprocal Effects of Calcium and Potassium as Shown by Their Cationic Activities in Montmorillonite, *Soil Sci. Soc. Amer. Proc.*, **13**:179–182, 1948.

25. Marbut, C. F., "Atlas of American Agriculture," Part III, Soils of the United States, 1935.

26. Mehlich, A., Soil Properties Affecting the Proportionate Amounts of Calcium, Magnesium, and Potassium in Plants and HCl Extracts, *Soil Sci.*, **62**:393–409, 1946.

27. Mehlich, A., and N. T. Coleman, Type of Soil Colloid and the Mineral Nutrition of Plants, *Advances in Agron.*, **4**:67–99, 1952.

28. Mehlich, A., and J. Fielding Reed, Effect of Cation Exchange Properties of Soil on the Cation Content of Plants, *Soil Sci.*, **66**:289–306, 1948.

29. Merwin, H. D., "Release of Non-exchangeable Potassium into Exchangeable Form in Four New York Soils," Ph.D. Thesis, Cornell University, 1950.

30. Nightingale, G. T., Physiological Chemical Functions of Potassium in Crop Growth, *Soil Sci.*, **55**:73–78, 1943.

31. Olsen, S. R., and B. T. Shaw, Chemical, Mitscherlich, and Neubauer Methods for Determining Available Potassium in Relation to Crop Response to Potash Fertilization, *J. Am. Soc. Agron.*, **35**:1–9, 1943.

32. Page, J. B., and L. D. Baver, Ionic Size in Relation to Fixation of Cations by Colloidal Clay, *Soil Sci. Soc. Amer. Proc.*, **4**:150–155, 1939.

33. Peech, Michael, and Richard Bradfield, The Effect of Lime and Magnesia on the Soil Potassium and on the Absorption of Potassium by Plants, *Soil Sci.*, **55**:37–48, 1943.

34. Reitemeier, R. F., Soil Potassium, *Advances in Agron.*, **3**:113–164, 1951.

35. Reitemeier, R. F., R. S. Holmes, and I. C. Brown, Available Nonexchangeable Soil Potassium at Three Northern Great Plains Locations by a Neubauer Procedure, *Soil Sci. Soc. Amer. Proc.*, **14**:101–105, 1949.

36. Seay, W. A., O. J. Attoe, and E. Truog, Correlation of the Potassium Content of Alfalfa with That Available in Soils, *Soil Sci. Soc. Amer. Proc.*, **14**:245–249, 1949.

37. Stanford, George, Joe B. Kelly, and W. H. Pierre, Cation Balance in Corn Grown on High-lime Soils in Relation to Potassium Deficiency, *Soil Sci. Soc. Amer. Proc.*, **6**:335–341, 1941.

38. Stanford, G., and W. H. Pierre, The Relation of Potassium Fixation to Ammonium Fixation, *Soil Sci. Soc. Amer. Proc.*, **11**:155–160, 1946.

39. Truog, E., and R. J. Jones, Fate of Soluble Potash Applied to Soils, *Ind. Eng. Chem.*, **30**:882–885, 1938.

40. Volk, G. M., Significance of Moisture Translocation of Low Moisture Tension to Zone of High Moisture Tension by Plants, *J. Am. Soc. Agron.*, **33**:93–107, 1947.

41. Walker, R. K., and M. B. Sturgis, The Effects of Wetting, Drying and Treatments on the Availability of Potassium in Soils, *Proc. Assoc. Southern Agr. Workers*, **41**:79, 1940.

42. Williams, C. B., W. H. Rankin, and J. W. Hendricks, The Effects of Limestone and Fertilizers in a 4-year Rotation, *N.C. Agr. Expt. Sta. Bull.* 331, 1942.

43. York, E. T., and H. T. Rogers, Influence of Lime on the Solubility of Potassium in Soils and on Its Availability to Plants, *Soil Sci.*, **63**:467–477, 1947.

CHAPTER 12

FERTILIZERS

The use of fertilizers in the United States expanded from 2.2 million tons in 1900 to 20.5 million tons in 1954. The greatest expansion for any 10-year period came between 1940 and 1950, during which time the use of fertilizers was more than doubled. The United States is now using

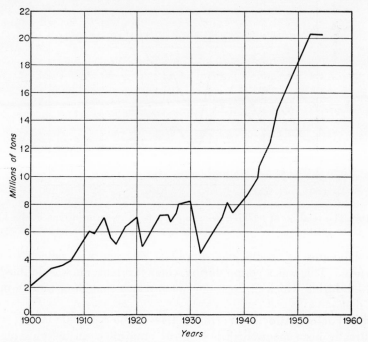

FIG. 107. The amounts of fertilizer (expressed in millions of tons) used in the United States each year since 1900 (8,14).

about twice as much fertilizer as was used in any other year prior to 1940. Figure 107 shows the trend in use of fertilizers in this country.

There were three periods between 1900 and 1950 in which the use of fertilizers dropped to a great extent. The first period was during the

First World War, when our potash source in Germany was cut off and part of our nitrate reserves were diverted to war uses. The second drop in fertilizer use came with an economic recession in 1921–1922; and the third drop, which was the big one, came in the depression years of the early thirties. Fertilizer consumption is very sensitive to price changes. Figure 108 shows the close relationship of farm income and fertilizer use from 1910 to 1954. The fertilizer consumption from 1942 to 1947 was

FIG. 108. The relation of fertilizer consumption to gross farm income in the United States since 1910.

limited because of insufficient supply of nitrogen and potash to meet demands. This was a period during which farm income was doubled and a period during which farmers did not produce enough of most crops to meet demands.

Other Factors Affecting Fertilizer Use. The economic factor, which has already been mentioned, is of great importance in determining fertilizer use. Other important factors are climate, soil fertility, nature of the crops to be grown, and education of farmers.

Soil Factor. During the period from 1940 to 1954, the increase in use of fertilizers was greatest in the Corn Belt states and in South Central and Western states. The West North Central states since 1954 have been using over eighteen times as much fertilizer as was used in the prewar years of 1935 to 1939. The soils of the West North Central states are relatively more productive without fertilizer than the soils of the Eastern states, but when prices are high farmers find the use of fertilizers quite profitable. Another important factor in fertilizer use in these states is the fact that natural fertility has gradually declined to a level where fertilizers cause profitable increases in yield.

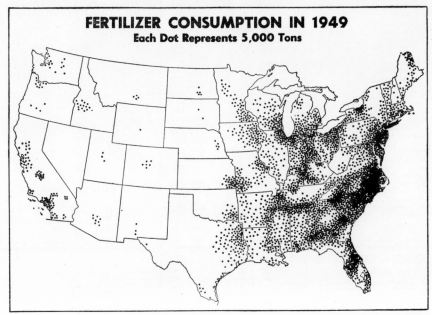

FERTILIZER CONSUMPTION IN 1949
Each Dot Represents 5,000 Tons

FIG. 109. Fertilizer consumption in 1949. (*The National Fertilizer Association.*)

The podzolized soils of the Eastern United States are much lower in fertility than the Prairie and Chernozem soils of the Central states. Figure 109 shows at a glance that the greatest amount of fertilizer is used in the Atlantic coastal states, where the soils have long been cropped and where the virgin level of fertility was lower than that found generally to the west.

Climate as a Factor in Fertilizer Use. Where the rainfall exceeds 40 in. in the eastern half of the United States, the drought expectancy is low enough so that fertilizer use is not so much of a gamble. The use of fertilizer in the 30- to 40-in.-rainfall belt has been limited to some extent by periodic droughts but increased tremendously from 1940 to 1950, when rainfall was generally favorable. At the same time, soils of the 30- to 40-in.-rainfall belt are naturally more fertile than soils receiving more than 40 in. of rainfall. The use of fertilizers in the rainfall belt with less than 25 to 30 in. is largely restricted to irrigated soils. There has been success-

TABLE 65. TONS OF FERTILIZER SOLD IN 1935 TO 1939 COMPARED WITH 1954 (8,14)

State	5-year av. 1935–1939	1954	Per cent of total consumption		Consumption ratio, 1954 to 1935–1939
			1935–1939	1954	
Maine........................	134,000	178,751			
New Hampshire..............	13,800	16,274			
Vermont.....................	17,941	40,368			
Massachusetts...............	67,022	85,917			
Rhode Island................	10,840	14,132			
Connecticut.................	57,324	87,966			
New England..............	300,927	423,408	4.14	2.06	1.41
New York...................	320,375	588,800			
New Jersey..................	163,399	265,550			
Pennsylvania................	339,874	585,947			
Middle Atlantic............	828,648	1,440,297	11.39	7.03	1.74
Ohio........................	335,135	1,008,400			
Indiana.....................	216,976	1,161,909			
Illinois.....................	33,603	897,322			
Michigan....................	131,739	575,481			
Wisconsin...................	38,505	422,268			
East North Central..........	756,018	4,065,380	10.40	19.85	5.38
Minnesota...................	12,059	313,238			
Iowa........................	8,818	609,868			
Missouri....................	74,704	649,750			
North Dakota................	750	48,643			
South Dakota................	160	31,381			
Nebraska....................	957	191,452			
Kansas......................	13,240	226,041			
West North Central.........	110,688	2,070,373	1.52	10.08	18.7
Delaware....................	38,609	89,250			
Maryland....................	169,539	309,639			
District of Columbia..........	1,520	2,700			
Virginia.....................	405,742	776,786			
West Virginia...............	44,400	73,816			
North Carolina..............	1,119,246	1,824,352			
South Carolina..............	670,205	886,654			
Georgia.....................	725,287	1,372,284			
Florida.....................	512,826	1,257,943			
South Atlantic.............	3,687,374	6,593,424	50.55	32.10	1.79
Kentucky....................	101,990	574,197			
Tennessee...................	122,744	580,206			
Alabama.....................	522,062	1,196,628			
Mississippi..................	284,592	710,298			
Arkansas....................	59,832	374,601			
Louisiana...................	135,197	328,814			
Oklahoma...................	7,029	131,390			
Texas.......................	79,251	590,023			
South Central..............	1,312,697	4,486,157	18.05	21.90	3.42
Montana....................	4,154	27,000			
Idaho.......................	5,186	75,000			
Wyoming....................	1,522	12,000			
Colorado....................	2,694	46,458			
New Mexico.................	2,112	22,475			
Arizona.....................	6,279	135,481			
Utah........................	1,990	22,379			
Nevada.....................	500	2,971			
Washington.................	24,630	125,147			
Oregon.....................	16,260	128,194			
California...................	209,123	831,570			
Western..................	274,450	1,428,675	3.76	6.95	5.19
United States.............	7,270,802	20,507,714	.....	.....	2.85

ful use of fertilizer in Iowa with 25 in. of rainfall; but 25 in. of rainfall in Texas with higher temperatures is not so effective as in Iowa, and fertilizers are not important in areas of less than 30 in. of rainfall in Texas except on irrigated soils.

Nature of the Crop to Be Grown. The use of hybrid corn has increased the demand for fertilizers. Open pollinated varieties could not make full use of available nutrients in some soils, whereas hybrid corn requires a soil that can provide an abundance of available nutrients. Furthermore, most research in and improvement of hybrid corn have been accomplished on fertile soils, and the successful use of hybrid varieties requires that farmers grow them on naturally fertile soil or on fertilized soil.

The growth of intensively farmed crops such as potatoes, tobacco, citrus, and truck crops requires tremendous amounts of fertilizers. Potatoes are an important crop in Maine, and an average of 444 lb. of fertilizers was used per acre of cropland in Maine in 1948. During the same

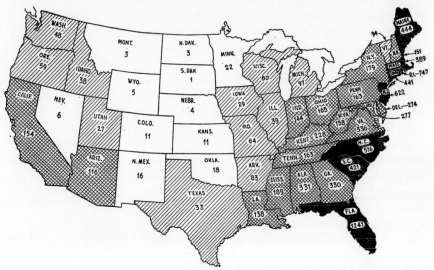

Fig. 110. Fertilizer consumption per acre of harvested cropland in the United States in 1948 (8).

year, North Carolina, a state where tobacco is a high-income crop, used 516 lb. of fertilizer per acre of cropland. Florida, with considerable acreage in citrus and truck crops, used 1241 lb. of fertilizer per acre of cropland in 1948.

Where irrigation of truck crops is practiced, the use of fertilizers may run up to a ton or more per acre. The experiment station at Weslaco, in the Rio Grande Valley of Texas, uses as much as 240 lb. of nitrogen per acre on some truck crops, which is equivalent to 1500 lb. of nitrate of soda, or 1200 lb. of sulfate of ammonia.

Factor of Education. A great deal more fertilizer could be used than is now being used in the United States. Most Iowa, Wisconsin, Illinois, and Missouri farmers are just beginning to realize that their soils will respond to fertilization. The Southern farmers are just now realizing that fertilizers pay on pasture land, and certainly we may look for a continued increase in demand for fertilizers as long as crop prices remain high.

There is much to be done in our educational program to prove the need for fertilizers on many of our soils. There is considerable prejudice on the part of some writers toward the use of chemical fertilizers. One widely circulated magazine discourages any fertilizer which has been treated with sulfuric acid. This magazine encourages the use of limestone and rock phosphate but warns against the use of superphosphate because the latter has been treated with sulfuric acid. The editors of the magazine appear to overlook the fact that sulfur is one of the six essential elements used in abundance by plants. Furthermore, they provide no scientific evidence to prove their claims against commercial fertilizers, yet they have thousands of subscribers who believe that commercial fertilizers are detrimental to soils and crops.

Another factor unfavorable to fertilizer use, which may be improved by education, is the tenant-landlord relationship. There is a residual effect from fertilizer, and if a tenant stays on a farm for only 1 year he cannot realize full value from added fertilizers. Some leases now stipulate the refund a tenant may get for added fertilizer if he has to move away at the end of the year.

Law of Diminishing Returns in Fertilizer Use. The amount of fertilizer a farmer should use is determined by the fertility level of his soil, the climate, the nature of the crop, and price relationships. He may use one rate one year and another rate another year on the same soil with the same crop, because of price trends. Yield increases will generally follow the curve of diminishing returns. Figure 111 shows the diminishing-returns curve for three crops from three different states. There are hundreds of such examples available. The significant feature of the curve is that small applications result in the greatest return on the investment. However, one may still earn a good profit on an investment in a larger application, even though the return per dollar is less than for a smaller application.

Figure 112 is a hypothetical example to illustrate this point. Each increment increase in fertilizer cost is the same, that is, $3. The value of the increase in yield falls off with the diminishing-returns curve. The $3 application brought in $11 return, while the $6 application brought in $16 return. The profit is more for the higher rate, but the return is 366 per cent for the smaller rate and 266 per cent for the higher rate of fertilizer application. The highest return per dollar invested may not give the greatest profit per acre, as indicated by Fig. 112. As a general guide one may consider the optimum range in fertilizer use to be between the point of expected greatest return and the point of expected greatest

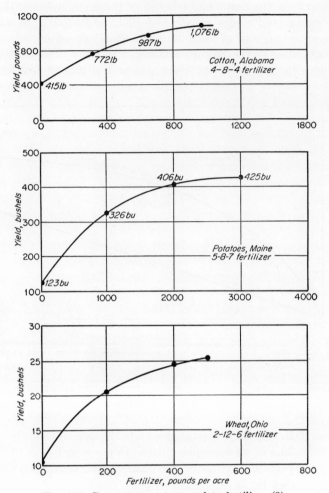

Fig. 111. Crop response to complete fertilizer (9).

profit. A farmer is speculating on prices and the weather when he uses fertilizers. Many farmers who fertilize field crops, such as corn and small grains, plan their fertilizers with the view of doubling their money invested in fertilizers during a favorable year, because an unfavorable year may mean a loss of money invested in fertilizers.

What Is in a Bag of Fertilizer? A 100-lb. bag of 4-16-8 contains the following:

4 lb. of nitrogen (total N)

16 lb. of phosphate (available P_2O_5)

8 lb. of potash (water-soluble K_2O)

Fertilizer laws, which are controlled by states, require that every bag of fertilizer bear the name and address of the manufacturer, the weight, and the guaranteed analysis, such as 3-12-12 or 10-20-0. In most states the farmer has no way of knowing what chemical compounds went into the manufacture of the bag of fertilizer. In most cases he is not concerned with the nature of the constituents, but it is well to know what goes into a bag of fertilizer, because there are times when carriers of

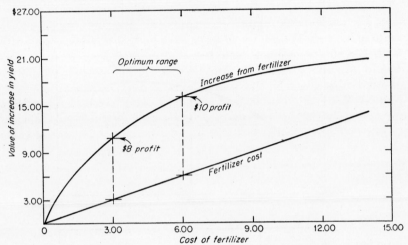

Fig. 112. A schematic diagram showing the relation of fertilizer costs to the value of the increased yields resulting from fertilizer applications. The widest point between the cost line and increased-yield curve indicates the point of greatest profit.

nitrogen, phosphorus, and potassium can be bought separately more cheaply than when mixed. A bag of 4-16-8 might contain

> 20.0 lb. of ammonium sulfate (20 per cent N)
> 35.5 lb. of superphosphate (45 per cent P_2O_5)
> 13.3 lb. of muriate of potash (60 per cent K_2O)
> ————
> 68.8 lb. of chemical carriers
> 31.2 lb. of filler
> ————
> 100.0 lb.

To figure out how much carriers are used, the following method is suggested:

Per cent N in fertilizer : per cent N in carrier $= X:100$

The same formula is used for each of the other constituents. The example above was worked as follows for the amount of sulfate of ammonia required:

$$4:20 = X:100$$
$$20X = 400$$
$$X = \frac{400}{20} = 20$$

A complete fertilizer includes nitrogen, phosphorus, and' potassium. One may buy fertilizers with only one or two of the fertilizer elements. An incomplete fertilizer is indicated by a zero for the element omitted. For example, 0-20-0 means that only phosphorus is carried in the material. In buying ammonium nitrate, one would get 33.5-0-0.

Low-analysis fertilizers are those in which the total of the percentages of N, P_2O_5, and K_2O amounts to less than 20. Ordinary or standard analysis totals 20 to 30 units.[1] High-analysis fertilizers are those with over 30 units. An 11-48-0 would be called a high-analysis fertilizer, while a 3-12-12 would be ordinary fertilizer.

Liquid Mixed Fertilizers. Considerable interest is being shown in liquid mixed fertilizers at the present time, and it is expected that liquid mixed fertilizers will grow in popularity. Liquid mixed fertilizers have been used since 1923, but it is only recently that rapid progress has been made in their production. The annual production of liquid mixed fertilizer in the United States in 1952–1953 was about 28,000 tons (17). This represents only about one-tenth of one per cent of all the fertilizers produced in that year in the United States.

The greatest handicap in the expansion of liquid mixed fertilizers has been the development of corrosion-resistant equipment. This problem is being solved satisfactorily, and there are several companies producing equipment for applying the liquids.

The most popular materials for mixing liquid fertilizers are phosphoric acid and ammonia (either aqua or anhydrous). The ammonia is usually added in quantities sufficient to neutralize the phosphoric acid.

The weight ratio of approximately 1 of nitrogen to 3 of P_2O_5 produces a salt that will remain in solution. Adding more ammonia causes some salt crystallization, therefore urea is usually added if it is desirable to increase the nitrogen content of the fertilizer, although ammonium nitrate is sometimes used. If a complete fertilizer is desired, the usual practice is to add KCl as a source of potassium. Of course the above materials are not the only ones used, but they are the most popular materials used at the present time.

Very little information is available on the relative merits of liquid and dry fertilizers. Observations made in Iowa in 1955 were that there is no appreciable difference in response to corn fertilized with either liquid or dry fertilizers.

Sources of Supply of Fertilizers in the United States. The United States has the sources and capacity to produce as much nitrogen, phosphorus, and potassium fertilizers as are needed for domestic consumption.

Nitrogen. Prior to 1939 the most important sources of nitrogen were sodium nitrate, calcium cyanamide, and sulfate of ammonia. Sodium nitrate was obtained from the nitrate deposits along the coast of Chile

[1] The average was about 27 in 1954.

and Peru. Sulfate of ammonia is a by-product of the coking industry; ammonia is liberated from coal in the coking process and is passed through sulfuric acid, where it is combined as sulfate of ammonia. Calcium cyanamide is a synthetic fertilizer in that the nitrogen is fixed from the air in the manufacturing process. Prior to 1939 the cost of nitrogen was relatively high compared to prices farmers received for their products. With the outbreak of war in Europe in 1939 the United States government constructed synthetic-nitrogen plants at many points in the interior of the country. Nitrogen is used in the manufacture of explosives, and it was recognized that a vastly larger supply of nitrogen would be needed in the event we became involved in the war. During the war years, much of the nitrogen used in fertilizers came from the synthetic sources. By 1946 about 84 per cent of the nitrogen used in fertilizers was synthetic; that is, the nitrogen was combined from atmospheric air in the manufacturing process. At the present time about 90 per cent of the nation's fertilizer nitrogen is synthetic.

Most of the government-owned nitrogen plants were sold to private industry following the Second World War. Ammonium nitrate was the principal synthetic by the end of the Second World War, but anhydrous ammonia is gaining in importance because it can usually be applied at about the lowest cost of all nitrogen fertilizers.[1] Calcium cyanamide has become more important as a defoliating material in the production of cotton and less important as a fertilizer. Sodium nitrate and sulfate of ammonia are still important fertilizers in areas where their costs are competitive with other forms of nitrogen. The liquid ammonia fertilizers produced as synthetics are used in producing a variety of fertilizers, including urea, ammonium phosphate, and mixed fertilizers, both liquid and dry. Likewise, synthetic nitrates are used in producing a variety of materials like calcium nitrate and potassium nitrate. The United States is now an exporter of nitrogen, and the price in this country is relatively low in relation to prices farmers receive for their products.

Phosphorus. The United States has been an exporter of phosphorus since the discovery of the rock phosphate deposits in Florida about a century ago. The Florida deposits are still producing a major portion of our phosphates in this country. Tennessee is an important producer of phosphate, and there is some production in Virginia and in the Western states. Our largest reserves are in the Western states, but the percentage of phosphorus in the rocks is generally lower than is found in Florida and Tennessee.

Approximately two-thirds of the phosphorus from rock phosphate is converted to superphosphate. The most common superphosphate is

[1] About 18 per cent of all nitrogen applied in 1955 was in the form of anhydrous ammonia (17).

made by treating the ground rock phosphate with sulfuric acid. This is an old process which was suggested by the great German chemist Liebig in about 1840 in a roundabout way. At that time bones were used as a source of phosphorus. Liebig suggested that treatment of the bones with sulfuric acid would increase the solubility of the phosphorus. Phosphorus in bones and in rock phosphate is in trivalent form. The reaction is as follows:[1]

$$Ca_3(PO_4)_2 + 2H_2SO_4 \rightarrow 2CaSO_4 + Ca(H_2PO_4)_2$$

This product is about half gypsum by weight and is sold with a guaranteed analysis of 20 per cent P_2O_5. It is known as "ordinary" superphosphate, or 0-20-0. During the Second World War there was plenty of ground rock phosphate available on the market, but there was an insufficient supply of sulfuric acid, consequently superphosphate was in short supply.

Treble superphosphate (sometimes called double superphosphate) is made by treating ground rock phosphate with phosphoric acid. The reaction is as follows:

$$Ca_3(PO_4)_2 + 4H_3PO_4 \rightarrow 3Ca(H_2PO_4)_2$$

This product is sold with a guaranteed analysis of 45 per cent P_2O_5. It is cheaper than 0-20-0 on a basis of price per pound of P_2O_5 and is gaining in popularity but was not as abundant as 0-20-0 in 1955.

A new product of high analysis P_2O_5 is calcium metaphosphate. It is made from metaphosphoric acid which has the formula HPO_3. Calcium metaphosphate has a guaranteed analysis of 63 per cent P_2O_5. It must hydrolyze in the soil to form the available orthophosphate form as follows:

$$Ca(PO_3)_2 + 2H_2O \rightarrow Ca(H_2PO_4)_2$$

This form of phosphorus is about equal to superphosphate on acid soils but gives less response than superphosphate on alkaline or calcareous soils.

Liquid phosphoric acid is now used to produce a number of complete liquid fertilizers available on the market.

Potassium. The United States imported from Europe the greater part of the potash used in this country prior to 1933. Since that time our deposits in Utah, California, and New Mexico have been developed to a point where we are now able to produce as much potash as is required to meet demands in this country. European potash became available at competitive prices in the United States soon after the Second World War.

---

[1] The phosphorus in rock phosphate is primarily in apatite form and may be fluoroapatite or carbonate apatite. The former is $[Ca(PO_4)_2]_3CaF_2$, and the latter is $[Ca(PO_4)_2]_3CaCO_3$.

TABLE 66. COMPOSITION OF FERTILIZER MATERIALS

Nitrogen carriers	Per cent nitrogen
Sulfate of ammonia	20*
Nitrate of soda	16
Ammonium nitrate	33.5
Calcium cyanamide	20.5
Potassium nitrate	13
Calcium nitrate	15
Urea	46
Ammonium phosphate (11-48-0)†	11
Anhydrous ammonia	82
Dried blood	13
Guano	13
Ammoniated superphosphate	3–9

Phosphorus carriers	Per cent available P_2O_5
Superphosphate	20
Treble superphosphate	45
Ammonium phosphate (11-48-0)†	48
Calcium metaphosphate	63
Basic slag	10
Ammoniated superphosphates	16–20

	Per cent total P_2O_5
Fused tricalcium phosphate	25
Rock phosphate	32

Potassium carriers	Per cent K_2O
Muriate of potash	60
Potassium sulfate	48
Sulfate of potash-magnesia	26
Manure salts	30
Kainite	20
Potassium nitrate	44

* The percentage of nitrogen can be calculated from the chemical formula. $(NH_4)_2SO_4$ has a molecular weight of 132. There are two atoms of nitrogen, each with an atomic weight of 14. By dividing 28 by 132 one gets about 21 per cent nitrogen in pure material.

† There are several grades of ammonium phosphate.

The most abundant source of potash is KCl, known as muriate of potash.[1] The potash salts from Germany, chiefly KCl, are derived from salt mines. The deposits from New Mexico are also mined. The principal potash salts produced in this country, however, are from the salty old lake beds in Utah and in the desert area of California.

[1] From the commercial name (muriatic acid) for HCl.

Some Factors Affecting Fertilizer Use. *Nitrogen.* A soil with 4 per cent organic matter contains about 0.2 per cent nitrogen or about 4000 lb. of nitrogen per acre furrow slice. Yet only a few pounds of nitrogen is available to plants. About 99 per cent of the nitrogen is tied up in organic matter. The longer the soil has been in cultivation and the longer it has been since a legume was grown, the greater is the response to nitrogen added to corn. This is illustrated in Table 67.

TABLE 67. EFFECT OF NITROGEN ON YIELD OF CORN (6)

40 lb. nitrogen applied as side-dressing in 50 experiments in Iowa

Cropping sequence	Check yield, bu.	Yield increase, bu.
Second-year corn after legume...............	70.1	8.9
Third-year corn after legume or sod..........	52.1	18.1

Since nitrogen is released through decomposition of organic matter, one can expect more available nitrogen during moist warm weather than during cool or dry weather. During cool weather there is little available nitrogen because of the slow rate of decomposition of organic matter. This is one of the reasons why we almost invariably get response from addition of nitrogen to oats, barley, and wheat in the spring in the Corn Belt.

All nitrogenous fertilizers cannot be used in the same manner. Some of the more important carriers of nitrogen are discussed below.

Organic carriers of nitrogen must go through a period of decomposition before the nitrogen is released to plants. Best response is obtained from organic nitrogen during moist warm weather. Organic nitrogen is more expensive than inorganic nitrogen and is not generally used on field crops. Organic nitrogen is particularly well adapted for use on lawns, where the nitrogen is slowly released throughout the growing season.

The nitrogen in calcium cyanamide is not immediately available, and this material should be put on the soil 1 or 2 weeks in advance of planting. If calcium cyanamide is put on at the time of planting, there is a risk of injury to the seedlings.

Urea is quickly converted into ammonia and then to nitrate in the soil, so that it can be used in about the same way as ammonium and nitrate salts.

Anhydrous ammonia is the cheapest form of fertilizer nitrogen. Special equipment is needed for its application to the soil. The anhydrous ammonia exists as a liquid while under pressure. It is distributed from a tank which is placed on the plow or cultivator. When the pressure is released, the anhydrous ammonia volatilizes and is run through a tube into the soil immediately behind a special furrow opener. The gaseous ammonia is placed deep enough in the soil so that no loss to the atmosphere is expected.[1] The gaseous ammonia combines readily with soil moisture and forms ammonium salts, or combines with clay and organic matter in the soil, or is converted to nitrate.

Fig. 113. Anhydrous ammonia distributor mounted on a tractor.

Nitrate and ammonium salts are by far the best-known and most widely used nitrogenous fertilizers. Both forms are water-soluble and immediately available. The ammonium ions are not lost by leaching to any great extent, however, since they are adsorbed by clay and organic matter. In well-aerated, moist, warm soils the ammonia is readily converted to nitrates by nitrifying bacteria of the soil. The nitrate form is easily lost by leaching, since the ion is not adsorbed by the clay and organic colloids.

It is frequently advisable to split the applications on soils of low fertility where considerable nitrogen is used by applying a small part at planting time, usually as part of a mixed fertilizer containing phosphorus and potassium, and the remainder either as a side-dressing after the crop has a good start or by plowing under the greater part of it ahead of planting.

Ammonia or nitrate nitrogen may be "plowed down" with cornstalks or other carbonaceous residues in the spring in preparation for planting corn. Some of the nitrogen would be converted to organic form, and leaching losses would be reduced or prevented. If nitrate nitrogen is

[1] Losses may be expected if applied to soils which are dry to the wilting point or if the ammonia is applied too shallow. If applied to a depth of 6 in. or deeper in moist soil below pH of 7, no losses of ammonia should be expected. In calcareous or alkaline soils one may have some losses of ammonia when moist and especially when dry.

applied ahead of planting when there are very small amounts of residues in the soil, part of the nitrates may be lost by leaching before the crop is planted. Under the same conditions, ammonia nitrogen may be applied in the bottom of the furrow when the soil is plowed in the spring, with much smaller losses by leaching. By applying the ammonia at this depth, the rate of nitrification would be somewhat restricted by the higher CO_2 concentration and cooler temperature as compared with nitrification in the surface inch or two of the soil.

FIG. 114. Extra nitrogen should be side-dressed when corn is about knee-high or at second cultivation. (*Iowa State College.*)

The plowing under of nitrogen fertilizers in the spring ahead of planting appears to give about as good results as side-dressing of corn in Iowa. Scarseth and coworkers (16) have shown that plowing under of ammonia nitrogen in the spring was superior to side-dressing of corn in Indiana. Krantz (11) found that corn starved for nitrogen late in the season when the nitrogen was plowed under ahead of planting. Krantz believed that some of the nitrogen might have been lost by leaching. The sandy soils of the Southeastern states are probably subject to greater leaching losses in the spring than are the "heavier" loam and silt loam soils of the Corn Belt. Where farmers are accustomed to side-dressing and have the equipment, there is apparently no reason why they should abandon this method in favor of plowing down of nitrogen.

Phosphorus application has already been discussed in Chap. 10. Aside from phosphorus in mixed fertilizers, one may purchase raw-rock phosphate, superphosphate, or metaphosphate. The limitations of raw-rock phosphate were discussed in Chap. 10. Where this material is used, it is applied broadcast at a rate of 800 to 1000 lb., sometimes as high as 1 ton per acre. The material contains about 32 per cent P_2O_5. Such a large application would be made only once in about 10 to 20 years. It represents a long-time investment, and such a practice would not appeal to a tenant operator. Even with the large application of rock phosphate periodically, it may prove profitable to use superphosphate as a starter fertilizer or use a starter fertilizer containing water-soluble phosphorus.

Practically all of the phosphorus in superphosphate is water-soluble. It exists as the readily available $H_2PO_4^-$ ion although it combines readily with clay minerals, calcium, iron, and aluminum compounds. Superphosphate is especially useful as a starter for young plants. It should be applied so that the concentration of phosphorus will be high in the immediate vicinity of the roots of the seedling. As the roots extend themselves and come in contact with a greater and greater total soil surface, there is less demand for the starter phosphate. Soils of medium- to high-fertility level, with respect to phosphorus, usually respond to starter phosphate. Soils of low fertility need starter phosphate plus an additional amount distributed in the soil to satisfy the needs of the plant as it extends its root system. Phosphate needs beyond that required in a starter should be plowed into the soil before planting the crop.

Calcium metaphosphate may be used like superphosphate on acid soils. It is not as available as superphosphate on calcareous soils.

Fused tricalcium phosphate is more available than raw-rock phosphate but is not recommended on calcareous soils. It is not recommended as a starter fertilizer on slightly acid soils but is useful as a plow-down phosphate on slightly acid soils (meaning acid soils limed to a pH of approximately 6.5, or naturally slightly acid).

Basic slag contains phosphorus in the tricalcium phosphate (PO_4^{---}) form and is used like raw-rock phosphate.

Potassium. Potassium fertilizers are generally water-soluble and are immediately available to plants. Potassium does not leach downward as readily as nitrate because of the tendency for the positively charged K^+ ion to be adsorbed by the negatively charged clay crystals and organic anions.

Potassium will leach down faster than phosphate, however, and may be applied to the surface as a top-dressing where potash-starvation signs are shown by the crop. Potassium salts should be applied at planting time, however, like phosphorus.

The need for potash is correlated with lime requirement and pH, but with one important exception. Some humid-region soils that have an excess of lime, such as the high-lime soils of Iowa and Illinois, require considerably more fertilizer potassium for production of corn than do neutral or slightly acid soils containing the same amount of exchangeable potassium.

Except for high-lime soils, the greatest response to potash is in areas of highest lime requirement. Soils that have been strongly leached are acid because of the replacement of bases (Ca^{++}, Mg^{++}, K^+, and Na^+) by hydrogen. On the other hand, the soils of subhumid regions which have not been leached of lime are also generally high in potassium.

Moisture and aeration in the soil affect the response to potash. One can expect more response to potash during wet years than in dry years on the same soil. Or, stating it another way, a poorly drained soil responds more to potash than a similar well-drained soil.

Determining the Need for Fertilizer. There is probably no decision a farmer makes which is more difficult than choosing the right kind and amount of fertilizer. Soils and crops are so variable in their fertilizer requirements that considerable care should be taken in deciding on the fertilizer to be used. Expert advice should be sought by every farmer who expects to use fertilizer, unless he is well trained in soils and soil fertility.

Soil Tests. Most states have soil-testing laboratories under the direction of the state agricultural college. These laboratories provide the best means of choosing the right kind and amounts of fertilizer. There are several reasons why these laboratories are the most reliable source of information. The techniques used in testing the soils are carefully controlled and are much more accurate than the commercial quick-test kits. The tests used by the laboratories are correlated with experimental results in the field, and the laboratory operator's recommendations are backed by experimental evidence. Most important of all is the fact that the farmer receives expert recommendations as to the kind and amount of fertilizer to use on the crops he expects to grow on the soils which he has tested.

The most important limitation in testing soils is the soil sample. If the soil is not representative of the area tested, the test data are practically worthless. Even on uniform topography, a sample should represent no more than 10 acres. The sample should represent only one soil type and only one topographic condition. In other words, a soil sample should not be a composite of two soil types. Neither should one sample be a composite of material collected on two different kinds of slope. In collecting the sample one should use a soil auger, or some soil-sampling tool, and collect many small samples to a depth of 6 in. over a uniform-appearing area. Notes should be taken as to the soil type (if known), percentage of slope, drainage relations (surface and subsoil), liming history, fertilizer history, and crop history, as well as the date of sampling.

The cost of having the soils tested is small compared with the cost of fertilizer, and the soils do not have to be tested every year. It is a good plan, however, to have soils tested every 4 to 6 years.

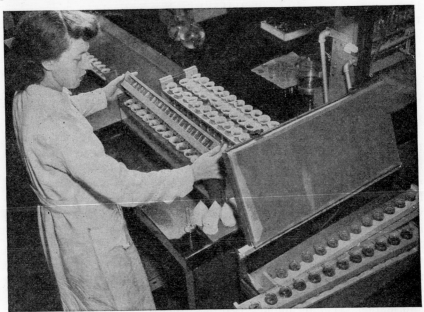

Fig. 115. A view of activities in a modern soil-testing laboratory. (*Soil Testing Laboratory, Iowa State College.*)

Use of Quick-test Kits. The use of quick tests for pH or lime requirement is considered practical for use by people with very little training. The tests for phosphorus and potassium may be used by an individual who is skilled in their use, who knows their limitations, and who has a good general knowledge of the response of different soils of his area to different fertilizers for different crops. These restrictions on the use of quick tests may appear somewhat rigid but are in accord with the thinking of most agronomists.

The greatest value of commercial quick-test kits is that they stimulate interest in soil testing and fertilizer use. They are excellent teaching aids in vocational agriculture classes and in farmer meetings. But the tests should not be used as a basis for recommending the purchase of $500 to $1000 worth of fertilizer a year by a farmer. The farmer might save hundreds of dollars by spending a few dollars with a state-college soil-testing laboratory.

Detecting Hunger Signs in Crops. The author once asked a leading soil-fertility investigator what item of equipment he would use if he were limited to one item for judging fertilizer needs. His answer was "a ladder." He said he would climb over the fence and look at the crop.

There is an almost endless list of suggestions one might make in advising farmers how to watch their crops in order to predict fertilizer needs. One should keep in mind, however, that yields may be greatly depressed because of a need for a particular element, yet the crop may never show a hunger sign. Hunger signs appear in cases of severe shortage of an element.

Crops well fed with nitrogen have a dark-green color. When nitrogen is deficient, the lower leaves of corn turn yellow at the tips and along the midrib. Continued nitrogen starvation causes the lower leaves to die. Another indication of nitrogen shortage is many barren stalks.

Phosphorus starvation in corn is indicated by a purpling of the leaves and a stunted growth. Potash starvation in corn is indicated by firing of the edges of the leaves.

Potash starvation in alfalfa is shown by white specks appearing along the margin of the leaves; after a few days the leaves turn yellow along the edges. Boron deficiency is shown by a yellowing of the terminal leaves in alfalfa.

Space does not permit a description of more than a few hunger signs in crops. The most comprehensive list of hunger signs, with many color photographs, is found in "Hunger Signs in Crops," published jointly by the American Society of Agronomy and American Fertilizer Association. Another list has been published recently in "Diagnostic Techniques for Soils and Crops," published by The American Potash Institute.

In diagnosing poor crop growth, one must always recognize the possibility of insect or disease damage. It is true that a great many hunger signs were once thought to be diseases, but the reverse may be true in some cases.

The tops and roots of plants should be examined very thoroughly before attributing abnormalities to nutrient deficiencies. Usually the damage done by diseases or insects can be located in a badly infected plant. In case of nutrient deficiency, there is a characteristic symmetrical pattern in the starvation symptom. Furthermore, all the plants suffering from the deficiency will have somewhat similar characteristics.

It is not the intent of this section to teach the technique of distinguishing between nutrient deficiencies and disease or insect damage. The point is that the enthusiast in soil fertility and soil testing should be aware of the limitations on increasing yields by adding more and more fertilizer. Fertility may not be the limiting factor.

Proper Balance in Fertilizers. One may usually expect some increase from the use of nitrogen, phosphorus, or potassium alone on a field crop where the elements are deficient. This is not always true, however, and sometimes yields are decreased by the application of only one or two of the three fertilizer elements. Sometimes the addition of all three is necessary before a substantial increase in yield is realized.

The use of factorial experiments has greatly increased our information in regard to fertilizer needs on different soils. A simple factorial is shown as follows:

	P_0	P_1
N_0	N_0P_0 40	N_0P_1 45
N_1	N_1P_0 45	N_1P_1 65

where N_0 = no nitrogen, N_1 = nitrogen fertilizer, P_0 = no phosphorus, and P_1 = phosphorus fertilizer.

Nitrogen without phosphorus increased the yield 5 bu., and phosphorus without nitrogen increased the yield 5 bu. The addition of both nitrogen and phosphorus increased the yield not by 10 bu. but by 25 bu. This extra increase is known as *interaction* of two or more factors in an experiment. Sometimes the interaction is negative. The data in Table 68 show both positive and negative interactions.

TABLE 68. EFFECT OF N, P, AND K (ALONE AND IN ALL COMBINATIONS)
ON THE YIELD OF CORN (7)

Fertilizer treatment*	N_0		N_1	
	P_0	P_1	P_0	P_1
K_0	46	47	65	76
K_1	47	39	65	88

* N_0, P_0, and K_0 indicate no nitrogen, phosphorus, or potassium added. N_1, P_1, and K_1 are 60 lb. of N, P_2O_5, and K_2O, respectively. Yield is in bushels of corn per acre.

In the no-nitrogen block there was negative interaction. Phosphorus and potassium each increased the yield by 1 bu., but when these two elements were added without nitrogen they decreased the yield from 46 to 39 bu. per acre.

In the nitrogen block there was no effect of potassium alone but an increase of 11 bu. by the addition of phosphorus alone. When both potassium and phosphorus were added in the presence of nitrogen, the increase was 23 bu.

In the total effect of fertilizers, nitrogen, phosphorus, and potassium practically doubled the yield, by raising the yield from 46 to 88 bu. per acre.

Such experiments as shown in Table 68 are being run on many farms in several states of this country. By having experiments of this kind on the major soil types of each state it is possible to make sound recommendations to the farmer based on both his soil-test data and experimental evidence from soils similar to his own.

Placement of Fertilizer. The idea behind the application of fertilizer in bands or in the hill is that plants may take up a sufficient amount of a nutrient by having only a part of the root system absorbing the nutrient,

FIG. 116. Planting corn and applying starter fertilizer in hills for "check-row" cultivations. (*Iowa State College.*)

and the concentration of a fertilizer element will reduce the fixation or immobilization.

The more superphosphate and potassium fertilizers are mixed with the soil, the lower the percentage recovered by crops during the first year. As a general recommendation, about 50 per cent more starter fertilizer should be used when the fertilizer is drilled in the row than when it is applied near the hill for corn. Furthermore, if the starter fertilizer is being broadcast for corn, twice as much should be used as when it is placed near the hill.

There is a limit to the number of pounds of soluble salts that can be applied per acre to the hill for corn. Too much soluble salts may reduce germination or kill seedlings, thereby reducing the stand. As a general recommendation, the pounds of N, P_2O_5, and K_2O added together should not exceed 50 lb. per acre for hill applications.   An application of 150 lb. of 4-16-8 will contain 42 lb. of N, P_2O_5, and K_2O.

Where more than 50 lb. of N, P_2O_5, and K_2O is needed, the additional fertilizer may be applied in several different ways.   If extra nitrogen is the only need, the application may be plowed down ahead of planting or made as a side-dressing at the second or third cultivation when the corn is about knee-high.   If the soil is at a low level of fertility, there is need for

Fig. 117. A farmer should leave an untreated strip of two to four rows in order to determine whether his fertilizer practices are providing a profitable increase in yield. (*Iowa State College.*)

more than just a starter application of fertilizer; that is, extra amounts of nitrogen, phosphorus, and potash may all be needed.   Additional phosphorus and potash should be applied just before or at planting time and applied deeper than a starter fertilizer is ordinarily applied.

Where more than starter amounts of phosphorus and potash are needed, it has long been the practice to broadcast the extra fertilizer just before planting time.   The advisability of broadcasting phosphorus and potassium fertilizer has been questioned by a number of investigators because of the problem of fixation and the fact that broadcasting and subsequent disking leaves the fertilizer mixed in the top 2 in. of soil, where drying occurs rapidly.   Broadcasting of fertilizer for oats and legume seedings is the general practice in the Middle West, but it has been shown that drilling the fertilizer with a grain drill attachment is a more desirable practice (4,12).

The planting of corn follows plowing of the soil. If the fertility level is low, the extra amount of fertilizer (over and above the starter application) can be placed in bands in the plow sole. This practice has been given the popular name of "plow-sole" application. The plow-sole application has several desirable features, which have been pointed out by Chapman (3) and Scarseth *et al.* (16). The deeper placement of fertilizer helps to keep the plant going after the roots are feeding below the depth of the starter fertilizer. The fertilizer is concentrated in bands, which reduces fixation. The plow-sole application is below the top 2 in. which dry so rapidly.

Fig. 118. A corn planter with a two-level fertilizer applicator. A part of the fertilizer is applied as a "starter" at a depth of 2 in., and a part of the fertilizer is applied at a depth of 6 in. (*Farmcraft Manufacturing Company.*)

The depth of placement of fertilizer in the hill has been studied under various conditions, and because of the variation in soil and climatic conditions, the experimental results may appear to be contradictory throughout the country. It is well to consider some of the factors that affect depth of placement. If the soil dries out quickly after a rain, the fertilizer should be applied deeper than the level of the seed. If the fertility level is low and the applied fertilizer is going to affect nutrient uptake later in the growth stages of the crop, the fertilizer should be below the level of the seed. On the other hand, if the soil holds moisture well and starter effect is the main effect, the fertilizer should be applied at the seed level or only slightly below for corn.

TABLE 69. EFFECT OF DEPTH OF PLACEMENT ON RECOVERY BY CORN OF RADIOACTIVE PHOSPHORUS (19)

Methods of phosphate placement	P_2O_5 applied, lb./acre	Corn yield, bu./acre	Phosphorus in plant derived from fertilizer, per cent		
			Plants 4–10 in. high	Plants 30–40 in. high	Roasting ear
None............	0	77.5			
1 band, ½ in. deep..	30	80.7	12.7	21.8	11.3
1 band, 2 in. deep (seed depth).....	30	80.5	27.5	25.5	9.2
1 band, 3 in. below seed...........	30	83.4	1.4	13.5	8.6
2 bands, seed depth	30	85.2	25.1	30.5	11.8
1 band, seed depth..	60	87.9	57.9	32.6	10.8

Stanford and Nelson (19), using radioactive phosphorus, found that, during early stages of growth, greater utilization of phosphorus occurred when it was placed at the seed level than when it was banded above the seed or 3 in. below the seed.

The usual recommendation for cotton is to apply the fertilizer about 2 in. to the side and 2 in. below the seed level. Table 70 shows that, on

TABLE 70. EFFECT OF FERTILIZER PLACEMENT ON YIELD OF COTTON ON NORFOLK FINE SANDY LOAM (5)

Fertilizer placement (800 lb./acre of 4-8-4 on Apr. 16)	Soluble salts in seed zone, Apr. 30, p.p.m.	Seedlings above soil, May 6	Yield, lb./acre
No fertilizer.........................	71	186	760
Direct contact with seed...............	11,819	...	95
Mixed with soil below seed............	1,202	129	835
1¾ in. band:			
1 in. below seed	1,335	19	122
2 in. below seed....................	1,173	121	371
3 in. below seed.....................	621	173	735
4 in. below seed.....................	337	215	1,062
Bands 1½ in. each side:			
1 in. below seed level...............	283	203	1,057
2 in. below seed level...............	123	211	1,147
4 in. below seed level...............	99	210	1,143

Norfolk fine sandy loam, the best yield of cotton was obtained by applying the fertilizer 2 in. below the seed level.

Relation of Stand to Response from Fertilizers. Dumenil and Stanford (6) observed during 1948 that hill application of fertilizer improved the stand of corn. It is quite likely that even on soils of high fertility level, starter fertilizer will increase yields sufficiently to make the applications economical.

Data in Table 70 show that, where the fertilizer was applied too close to the seed, the stand was injured. A very significant feature of the data is that the fertilizer actually increased the stand compared to the plots

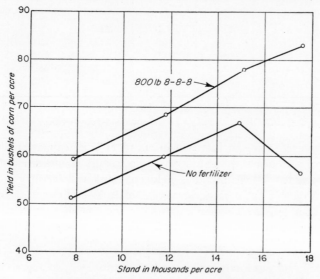

Fig. 119. The relation of stand to yield and fertility level (13).

receiving no fertilizer, and the increased stand is reflected in the increased yield of cotton. The data show that fertilizer salts applied 2 in. below the seed level and 1½ in. to the side of the seed gave the best results. Cotton is a tap-rooted plant and appears to respond better to application of fertilizer from 1 to 2 in. below the seed level.

Recent experiments in Iowa (13), Ohio (20), Pennsylvania (18), North Carolina (11), and Mississippi have proved rather conclusively that high yields of corn require a higher number of plants per acre than are normally obtained by ordinary farming methods. At the same time, it should be recognized that increasing the stand on soils of low fertility *without* fertilizer may actually reduce the yield of corn. Figure 119 shows at a glance that thick stands of corn require high fertility.

Table 71 shows the relation of stand to various levels of fertility on a

Mississippi soil. The data also show the importance of supplying adequate amounts of nitrogen, phosphorus, and potassium rather than only one of the three elements when all three are needed.

TABLE 71. YIELD OF CORN IN A FERTILIZER-SPACING EXPERIMENT IN MISSISSIPPI IN 1948 (10)

Nitrogen, lb./acre	Corn yield, bu., with plant populations per acre of					
	4,000 stalks		8,000 stalks		12,000 stalks	
	P_0K_0*	P_1K_1†	P_0K_0*	P_1K_1†	P_0K_0*	P_1K_1†
0	14.1	19.8	15.3	22.0	9.7	18.0
30	28.3	34.0	27.9	31.8	29.0	31.2
60	48.2	48.0	44.9	61.9	49.8	57.6
90	41.5	62.6	54.3	72.5	55.9	72.3
120	44.9	60.4	55.7	78.2	63.2	95.8

* P_0K_0 = no phosphorus or potassium added.
† P_1K_1 = 280 lb. of P_2O_5 and K_2O added over a 4-year period.

As a general rule, an increase in stand of corn causes an increase in number of ears of corn, but a decrease in weight of ears where fertility is held constant. Where stand is held constant and fertility is increased we would expect an increase in weight of ears. These relationships are shown in Table 72. The ear weights are small compared to weights normally expected in the Corn Belt. Weights of 0.5 lb. and higher are more common in the Corn Belt (18).

TABLE 72. RESULTS OF FERTILIZER-SPACING EXPERIMENTS IN MISSISSIPPI IN 1946 (10)

Treatment*		Yield of corn, bu./acre	Weight per ear, lb.	Ears per plant
Nitrogen, lb./acre	Plants per acre			
0	4,000	21.0	0.31	1.11
60	4,000	55.5	0.40	2.31
120	4,000	67.1	0.44	2.53
0	12,000	14.3	0.12	0.64
60	12,000	52.8	0.29	1.01
120	12,000	81.8	0.35	1.31

* In addition to nitrogen, all these plots received 80 lb. each of P_2O_5 and K_2O.

The data in Table 72 and the data of Krantz (11) show that additional amounts of nitrogen tend to increase the number of ears per plant where the plant is adequately supplied with other nutrients. One will almost invariably find a large proportion of barren stalks (without ears) in a field of corn showing nitrogen-starvation symptoms.

Moisture must always be considered as a potential limiting factor when we increase fertility and increase stands of corn. For this reason recommendations must be somewhat conservative. Under Iowa conditions, with high fertility, it is recommended that farmers plant about 15,000 stalks per acre. This stand is obtained by planting 4 stalks per hill in 42- by 42-in. hills or by drilling corn about every 10 in. in 40-in. rows.

TABLE 73. RELATION OF RATE OF PLANTING TO NUMBER OF STALKS OF CORN PER ACRE* (13)

Stalks per 40- × 40-in. hill	Distance apart of stalks in 42-in. drilled rows, in.	Stalks per acre
2	19	7,800
3	12½	11,760
4	9½	15,680
5	7½	19,600

* Ordinarily 10 to 15 per cent more than this amount is needed to get the desired stand.

Krantz (11) recommends 14,000 stalks per acre on soils of high fertility in North Carolina when single-eared hybrid corn is grown. He recommends 10,000 stalks per acre under the same conditions when multiple-eared hybrid corn is grown.

Based on studies in Ohio, published in 1947, Stringfield and Thatcher (20) made the following recommendation:

Estimate the yielding capacity of the field in question for a reasonably good season. If this estimate is 60 bushels or less of grain per acre, plant three viable seeds per hill or 42 inches of row-space. For higher estimated yields plant the number obtained by dividing the estimated yield by 20. A divisor of 25 is suggested for the later, larger hybrids of Southern Ohio.

Stringfield and Thatcher have provided further good evidence that yields are practically the same in hill-planted and drilled corn where total populations of plants per acre are the same.

Adaptation of Species or Variety. Plants differ greatly in their response to light intensity, length of day, temperature, soil conditions, moisture conditions, and competition with other plants. There are many factors that affect growth response in plants, and great care should be taken to plant adapted varieties. Soil fertility can never overcome the effects of climate on a nonadapted species. In other words, one cannot move Iowa corn varieties to Oklahoma and expect them to grow normally regardless of fertility.

A very interesting feature in varietal difference is brought out in the data in Table 74. The two varieties of barley were grown on the Wesemann farm in O'Brien County, Iowa, in 1948. The Kindred variety responded more to small applications of fertilizers than the Moore variety. On the other hand, the Moore variety responded more to large applications of fertilizers than the Kindred. This would indicate that there are varieties that are more suitable for growing on soils of high fertility level.

TABLE 74. EFFECT OF FERTILIZER APPLICATION ON RESPONSE OF BARLEY ON LOW-FERTILITY SOIL (12)

Fertilizer	Yield, bu./acre	
	Moore variety	Kindred variety
Check	30.2	33.9
P_1	38.4	42.5
P_2	47.9	45.9
N_1	28.6	33.3
N_1P_1	46.7	47.4
N_1P_2	50.7	48.6
N_2	32.6	35.0
N_2P_1	49.6	41.1
N_2P_2	58.3	50.8
Average	42.6	42.1

$P_1 = 40$ lb. P_2O_5; $P_2 = 80$ lb. P_2O_5; $N_1 = 20$ lb. N; $N_2 = 40$ lb. N.

It should be kept in mind that crop variety differences may be as important as soil-fertility practices in explaining differences in yields on similar soils.

High Yields Are Dependent on Many Factors. The discussion of the factorial experiment with nitrogen, phosphorus, and potassium, the relation of stand and fertility, and the relation of crop variety to fertility indicate that high yields are the result of interaction of a great many factors. We have observed only a few of those factors in this chapter.

High yields require favorable weather; good physical condition of the soil; freedom from insects, diseases, and weeds; and good stands, high fertility, and good varieties.

Fertilizers are not cure-alls, and while they are very important to sustained high yields, they cannot compensate for other limiting factors.

Every once in a while one hears of a farmer who has tried fertilizers and will not use them any more because they "burned up" his crop. It is true that fertilizers may reduce yields because of negative interaction of certain factors (see, for example, the data in Table 68), and this frequently occurs when only starter fertilizer is used on corn on a nitrogen-deficient soil. The starter fertilizer contains just enough nitrogen to give the corn a good start, and if there is not enough nitrogen made available by the decomposition of organic matter later in the season, one would expect the corn to fire badly.

All these important factors in fertilizer use make it advisable that farmers be well trained in soils and soil fertility or that they seek expert advice from their state college, particularly with their soil testing.

REFERENCES

1. Annual Report, Western Iowa Experimental Farm, 1948.
2. Bauer, F. C., and Associates, Effect of Soil Treatment on Soil Productivity, *Ill. Agr. Expt. Sta. Bull.* 516, 1945.
3. Chapman, C. J., What about Plow-sole Fertilizing? *Am. Fert.*, **10**:7–8, 1945.
4. Coe, Dana G., Effects of Various Methods of Applying Fertilizers on Crops and on Certain Soil Conditions, *Soil Sci.*, **21**:7–21 and 127–141, 1926.
5. Cumings, G. A., A. L. Mehring, J. J. Skinner, and Ward H. Sachs, Mechanical Application of Fertilizers to Cotton in South Carolina, 1931, *U.S. Dept. Agr. Cir.* 264, 1933.
6. Dumenil, Lloyd, and George Stanford, unpublished data.
7. Dumenil, Lloyd, Don't Starve Your Corn, *Iowa Farm Sci.*, April, 1951.
8. *Fertilizer Review*, May-June, 1949; April-May-June, 1950; April-May-June, 1951.
9. Fertilizers and Lime in the United States, *U.S. Dept. Agr. Misc. Pub.* 586, 1946.
10. Jordan, Howard V., Kermit D. Laird, and D. D. Ferguson, Growth Rates and Nutrient Uptake by Corn in a Fertilizer-spacing Experiment, *J. Am. Soc. Agron.*, **42**:261–268, 1950.
11. Krantz, B. A., Fertilize Corn for Higher Yields, *N.C. Agr. Expt. Sta. Bull.* 366, 1949.
12. Nelson, L. B., unpublished data.
13. Nelson, L. B., and Lloyd Dumenil, Plant to Fit Fertility, *Iowa Farm Sci.*, April, 1947.
14. *Plant Food Rev.*, Vol. 1, No. 1, 1955.
15. Report Prepared by the Agronomy Department, Iowa State College, *Proc. Corn Belt Section Am. Soc. Agron.*, 1940.
16. Scarseth, George D., Harry L. Cook, Bert A. Krantz, and Alvin J. Ohlrogge, How to Fertilize Corn Effectively in Indiana, *Ind. Agr. Expt. Sta. Bull.* 482, 1944.
17. Slack, A. V., Production and Use of Liquid Fertilizers, *Agriculture and Food Chem.*, **3**:568–574, 1955.
18. Seem, B. L., and L. L. Huber, Corn Planting Rates, Soil Productivity, and Yield, *Penn. Agr. Expt. Sta. Bull.* 480, Suppl. 3, 1947.
19. Stanford, G., and L. B. Nelson, Utilization of Phosphorus as Affected by Placement. I. Corn in Iowa, *Soil Sci.*, **68**:129–135, 1949.
20. Stringfield, G. H., and L. E. Thatcher, Stands and Methods of Planting for Corn Hybrids, *J. Am. Soc. Agron.*, **39**:995–1010, 1947.

CHAPTER 13

THE UTILIZATION OF FARM MANURE

About 1 billion tons of manure is produced on American farms each year, and the value of this manure in crop-producing power is worth more than the nation's wheat crop. The nutrients contained in this much manure are equivalent to three times the nutrients sold in commercial fertilizers in 1955. The organic matter contained in 1 billion tons of

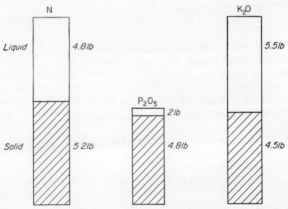

Fig. 120. The distribution of plant nutrients between liquid and solid portions of a ton of manure (14).

manure amounts to twice the annual depletion of humus in the soil. Unfortunately, a large part of the crop-producing value of manure is never realized by the farmer because of unavoidable losses or those due to carelessness.

A ton of manure contains an average of 10 lb. of N, 5 lb. of P_2O_5, and 10 lb. of K_2O, worth 12, 10, and 7 cents per pound, respectively. According to these prices a ton of manure is worth $2.40 in fertilizer value. Based on 1955 prices, the ability of manure to increase crop yields is worth about $4.80 per ton as indicated by studies in Iowa (2) and over $5 per ton as indicated by studies in Indiana (7).

Time and Rates of Application of Manure. Turk and Weidemann
(14) reported on experiments conducted in Michigan. Their data show
that the smaller applications of manure gave a greater return per ton of
manure applied. This was particularly true of corn.

TABLE 75. EFFECT OF VARYING AMOUNTS OF MANURE ON CROP YIELDS IN A
3-YEAR ROTATION* (14)

Treatment	Corn (9-year av.)		Barley (8-year av.)		Wheat (7-year av.)	
	Bu./acre	Increase	Bu./acre	Increase	Bu./acre	Increase
5 tons/acre....	45.8	11.0	18.7	5.8	24.4	2.6
10 tons/acre..	49.4	14.6	22.8	9.9	27.4	5.6
15 tons/acre..	51.0	16.2	26.4	13.5	28.1	6.3
Check.........	34.8	....	12.9	....	21.8	

* Manure was hauled directly from the stable to the field, applied broadcast, and
plowed under before corn in a rotation of corn, barley, and wheat on a Hillsdale sandy
loam soil.

Data in Table 76 are from experiments conducted at Ames, Iowa, on
the agronomy farm. These data show that second-year corn was benefited by the application of manure ahead of the first-year corn in rotation. These data show that the residual effect of the manure was carried over into the fourth year.

TABLE 76. EFFECT OF MANURE ON YIELD OF CROPS IN 4-YEAR ROTATION ON
WEBSTER SERIES (2), 1915–1938

Crop	Yield		Increase when manured		
	Check	8 tons manure*	Yield	Per cent	Value†
First-year corn, bu./acre......	56.1	67.9	11.8	21.1	$14.16
Second-year corn, bu./acre....	51.4	61.1	9.7	19.1	11.64
Oats, bu./acre...............	60.0	63.7	3.7	6.2	2.58
Clover, tons/acre............	2.12	2.70	0.58	27.3	9.86

* Applied to clover sod.
† Based on average farm prices of 1955. Corn $1.20 per bushel, oats 70 cents per
bushel, clover $17 per ton.

The Purdue University Agricultural Experiment Station carried on
some studies to determine the place in the rotation at which manure
should be applied. The largest total crop increase was obtained from
the application of 4 tons of manure to the corn and 2 tons of manure top-
dressed on wheat following corn in a corn-wheat-clover rotation. Table

77 shows the results of the study. One may see from the data that manure anywhere in the rotation was profitable, without too much difference in yields with the different times of application. The most important point is that 4 tons was about as much as it was profitable to apply at any one time.

TABLE 77. EFFECT OF PLACE IN ROTATION AT WHICH MANURE IS APPLIED (7)

Time of application of 6 tons manure	Acreage yields, 1919–1936			Financial statement*	
	Corn, bu.	Wheat, bu.	Hay, lb.	Total value of grain and hay	Value of increase per ton of manure
Check†..................	44.0	24.5	3741	$133.59	
Plowed under for corn.....	57.7	30.3	4215	165.67	$5.39
Top-dressed for corn after planting...............	53.5	31.7	4396	164.96	5.23
4 tons plowed under for corn, 2 tons on wheat in winter	57.8	31.2	4742	172.06	6.41
Top-dressed on wheat in winter.................	51.8	29.4	4720	161.08	4.58
Top-dressed on young clover after wheat.......	54.9	29.0	4730	164.25	5.11
Top-dressed on second-growth clover..........	57.7	30.0	4204	164.97	5.23

* Based on $1.20 per bushel for corn, $2 per bushel for wheat, and $17 per ton for hay.
† Average of three plots.

Corn gives better response to manure than other crops commonly grown in Corn Belt rotations. There are several reasons for this fact. Corn needs most of its nitrogen from the latter part of June through July and in August. During this period the soil temperatures are high enough to cause rapid release of nitrogen from the manure. Legume crops do not respond so much to manure because they are able to induce nitrogen fixation by the symbiotic bacteria. Small grains do not respond so much to manure because they are grown during the cooler part of the season when decomposition of the manure is slow. Still another factor in the response of corn to manure is that the potash in manure is readily available, and it has been pointed out in previous chapters that corn responds more to potash than do most other field crops in Corn Belt rotations.

In Corn Belt rotations, the usual practice is to apply manure that accumulates in spring, summer, and fall to the meadows or pastures. The manure that accumulates in the winter is applied in the spring to land which is to be planted to corn. Where second-year corn is planted, the manure should be applied to the second-year-corn ground in the spring.

Composition of Farm Manure. It has already been pointed out that a ton of average farm manure contains about 10 lb. of N, 5 lb. of P_2O_5, and 10 lb. of K_2O. About half the nitrogen and over half the potash is in the liquid excrement. By the use of straw, peat, or some other organic material as a bedding, the liquid excrement can be preserved against leaching losses in the barn. The average farm manure is assumed to include the bedding.

The amounts of nitrogen, phosphorus, and potassium excreted by animals from a given amount of feed consumed is determined primarily by whether or not the animal is growing. Young livestock will excrete a smaller percentage of the nitrogen, phosphorus, and potassium consumed than will mature animals. Work horses excrete nearly all the nitrogen, phosphorus, and potassium consumed, since their principal need from food is the energy material. Mature animals which are producing milk will excrete less nitrogen, phosphorus, and calcium than when they are dry.

The data in Table 78, indicate that there is considerable variation in the composition of manure from different kinds of livestock. The values are based on excrement without bedding. With the addition of bedding and the combination of the solid and liquid excrement, the percentages of N, P_2O_5, and K_2O will average about 0.5, 0.25, and 0.5, respectively.

TABLE 78. AVERAGE COMPOSITION OF SOLID AND LIQUID EXCREMENT OF MATURE ANIMALS* (9)
Percentage basis

Class of livestock	Nitrogen		P_2O_5		K_2O		CaO	
	Solid	Liquid	Solid	Liquid	Solid	Liquid	Solid	Liquid
Horses....	0.50	1.20	0.30	trace	0.24	1.50	0.15	0.45
Cattle....	0.32	0.95	0.21	0.03	0.16	0.95	0.34	0.01
Sheep.....	0.65	1.68	0.46	0.03	0.23	2.10	0.46	0.16
Hogs.....	0.60	0.30	0.46	0.12	0.44	1.00	0.09	0.00
Hens.....	1.00	....	0.80	....	0.40			

* Data of Ames and Gaither, Ruschmann, and Van Slyke quoted by Salter and Schollenberger.

From the data in Table 78 one may see that sheep manure is a rich manure if the liquid is saved. If only the solid material is saved, sheep manure is not much richer than the manure of cattle, hogs, and horses. The mechanical condition of sheep manure makes it very desirable for use in gardening, and one may purchase sacks of sheep manure from several fertilizer companies.

Poultry manure is considerably richer in nitrogen, phosphorus, and potassium than the average farm manure. Poultry manure which has been collected from dropping boards under roosts, without litter, will contain about 20 lb. of N, 16 lb. of P_2O_5, and 8 lb. of K_2O per ton of moist manure.

Estimating the Amount of Manure Produced on a Farm. Salter and Schollenberger (9) compiled data from various sources and estimated the amount of manure that would be produced annually from different classes of livestock. Their data, shown in Table 79, are based on the assumption that the animals are housed continuously and that the manure contains a normal amount of bedding material.

TABLE 79. MANURE PRODUCED ANNUALLY BY DIFFERENT CLASSES OF LIVESTOCK OF MIXED AGES ON COMMON RATIONS (9)

Class of livestock	Manure, tons per 1000 lb. of liveweight
Horses	9.0
Steers	8.5
Cows	15.0
Sheep	7.5
Hogs	18.0
Poultry	4.5

Ross (8) made a study of 224 dairy farms in Illinois and determined the number of loads of manure (approximately 1 ton per load) that was actually hauled out to the fields. He considered one mature horse, cow, or steer as being one animal unit (two young animals as one unit) and 5 hogs, 7 sheep, or 100 hens as being one animal unit.

TABLE 80. AVERAGE ANNUAL AMOUNTS OF MANURE RECOVERED PER ANIMAL UNIT ON 224 DAIRY FARMS IN ILLINOIS (8)

Animal	Manure, loads per animal unit*
Dairy cattle	6.6
Work animals	5.5
Steers	1.2
Hogs	1.7
Poultry	1.9
Sheep	0.8

* There is approximately 1 ton of manure per load.

In comparing Tables 79 and 80, it may be readily recognized that not more than half the total manure produced on the average farm in Illinois is actually hauled out to the fields. Part of the manure is dropped on pastures, in fields, and on roads. Part of the manure is wasted, and there is considerable shrinkage in the manure that accumulates around barns and lots.

Conservation of Manure That Accumulates in Barns and Lots.   The best possible practicable method of storing manure would be to treat it in the same manner that ensilage is preserved.   Manure should be kept under anaerobic conditions without drying, in order to minimize nitrogen losses.

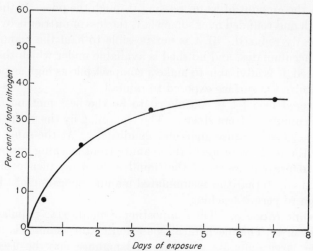

Fig. 121. The rate of nitrogen loss upon exposure of manure at 67°F. (3).

If manure is kept under a shed and protected from leaching losses, the only loss is in decomposition of organic matter and volatilization of nitrogen.[1]   On the other hand, if manure is subjected to leaching losses, the greater part of the potassium may be lost, as well as some phosphorus and the greater part of the nitrogen.   Nitrogen may be lost by both leaching and volatilization, while phosphorus and potassium are lost by leaching.

If manure must be removed from the barns and cannot be protected from leaching losses, it should be hauled to the field as soon as it is removed from the barn.   Nitrogen losses will be high in the field if the manure cannot be plowed under immediately.   The phosphorus and potassium will be conserved, however, since they will leach into the ground.   If the manure is piled up around the barn without protection there will be loss of nitrogen, phosphorus, and potassium.

No matter how careful one may be in handling manure around the barn, there may be serious loss of nitrogen after it is applied to the field if it is not turned under immediately.   Midgley and Weiser (4) found that 48 per cent of the ammonia nitrogen in samples of manure was lost after 2 days of exposure out of doors at 23°F.   Heck (3) exposed cow manure

[1] In so far as N, P_2O_5, and K_2O are concerned, of course there is loss of sulfur as H_2S.

for different periods of time at 20°C. (67°F.).   He found that 7.7 per cent of the total nitrogen was lost in 12 hours, 23.4 per cent in 36 hours, and 36.2 per cent in 7 days.

Ames and Gaither (1) show that about half the nitrogen, about half the phosphorus, and about 95 per cent of the potassium in manure (including bedding from horses, cattle, and sheep) are water-soluble.   Of course, the amount of nitrogen, phosphorus, and potassium leached from manure will depend on the amount of water passing through the pile.   If the manure is piled high and rounded over somewhat, the loss of nutrients by leaching will be greatly reduced.   If it is not possible to haul the manure to the field as it accumulates, and no shed is available under which the manure can be stored, it is advisable to make a compact pile as high as possible so as to minimize the surface exposed to rainfall.

The covered feed lot is considered to be the best method of storing manure accumulated from steers.   The trampling by the steers compacts the manure so as to cause anaerobic conditions.   At the same time, the shed over the feed lot protects the manure from leaching action of rain. In order to prevent losses of the liquid excrement, plenty of bedding should be used, so that the accumulated manure appears moist but is not wet enough to permit leaching.

Composting Manure.   The composting of manure is a popular practice with gardeners.   The mechanical condition of the manure is improved, and rather large amounts of composted manure may be used around plants without "burning" them.

The composting of manure causes a shrinkage in organic matter and a loss of nitrogen but an increase in percentage of nitrogen.   In other words, the loss of carbohydrate material is greater than the loss of nitrogenous material, and therefore the nitrogen percentage is increased.   The loss in organic matter with little loss of phosphorus and potassium will mean a considerable gain in percentage of phosphorus and potassium.

Data from Shutt (10) in Table 81 show the effect of rotting of manure on the change in percentage of the fertilizer elements.

TABLE 81. COMPOSITION OF FRESH VERSUS ROTTED MANURE
Mixed horse and cow manure rotted 3 months under cover, expressed in pounds per ton (10)

Manure	Organic matter	Nitrogen	P_2O_5	K_2O
Fresh............	485	12.0	6.2	15.5
Rotted..........	590	26.8	16.7	43.5

Shutt observed that a protected pile of manure contained the same amount of phosphorus after 12 months, but the percentage of phosphorus had increased 26 per cent.

Peperzak (6) made a very interesting study of the effect of decomposition on the nature of the phosphorus compounds in manure. He took samples of manure from various depths in a manure heap at the Sioux City, Iowa, stockyards. The samples were presumed to represent different ages of manure which had been accumulating for about 20 years. His data show an increase in percentage of total phosphorus up to 10 years. Beyond 10 years in age there was a decrease in phosphorus, believed to be due to leaching. The data for the last 10 years of accumulated manure are shown in Table 82.

TABLE 82. PHOSPHORUS FRACTIONS IN SAMPLES OF MANURE OF DIFFERENT AGES (6)
From Sioux City, Iowa, stockyards

Approximate age of manure	Organic phosphorus*	Inorganic phosphorus*	Total
1 week..................	1.36	1.44	2.80
	(49)	(51)	(100)
2 months...............	1.61	2.32	3.93
	(41)	(59)	(100)
6 months...............	1.46	3.49	4.95
	(30)	(70)	(100)
2 years.................	1.96	3.74	5.70
	(34)	(66)	(100)
10 years................	1.99	6.20	8.19
	(24)	(76)	(100)

* Upper figure is in parts per thousand.   Lower figure shows percentage of total.

Peperzak's study shows that as decomposition takes place in the manure heap, the percentage of total phosphorus increases because of the shrinkage of the total organic matter through decomposition.

Figure 122 shows that as organic material undergoes decomposition, the readily decomposable materials like cellulose and hemicellulose disappear, while lignin, protein, and mineral constituents increase in percentage. The mineral constituents provide a good base for gauging the disappearance or accumulation of other constituents.   There is three times the percentage of mineral constituents in the compost, which means that only about one-third of the original organic matter remains.   Lignin accumulates because it decomposes more slowly than cellulose and hemicellulose. The percentage of protein increases with composting.   The protein material is made up largely of living and dead microbial tissue in the composted material.

The composting of manure is a process of humus formation.   An old compost is made up largely of lignin and microbial tissue.   There have been many overly enthusiastic claims as to the value of compost.   There is no doubt that a gardener who uses large amounts of manure will have better results with composted manure than with fresh manure.   There is no basis for claims that composting improves the nutritive value of manure. On the contrary, composting results in loss of organic matter and nitrogen. The advantage for composted manure lies in its improved physical condition. Gardeners especially prefer to work with composted manure, but it would be wasteful for a farmer to compost manure for use on field crops.

Experiments conducted in our laboratory show that nitrogen and phosphorus release from microbial tissue are highly correlated (13). Because of the large amount of microbial material in compost, the release of nitro-

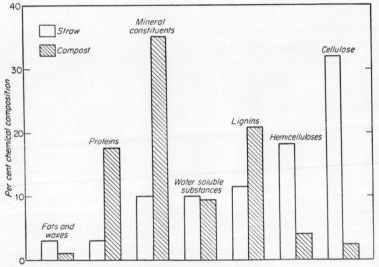

Fig. 122. Comparative chemical composition of oat straw and of a compost prepared from oat straw (15).

gen and phosphorus on further decomposition of compost should result in the release of nitrogen and phosphorus in about the ratio in which they are taken up by plants. This point is significant where plants are grown in a soil which may have large amounts of compost turned under, such as in gardens and flower beds.

The use of large amounts of fresh manure containing bedding in a garden may result in burning of the plants. The burning may be due to competition between the decomposing organic matter and the plant for nitrogen or even phosphorus. Phosphorus-starvation symptoms have been induced in tomatoes by use of fresh manure when transplanting tomatoes. The rapid decomposition of manure in the soil causes phosphorus immobilization by microorganisms.

In summary, composting results in the following changes:

1. A decrease in organic matter and nitrogen but an increase in percentage of nitrogen

2. A decrease in carbon to nitrogen ratio, which should result in almost immediate mineralization of nitrogen upon incorporation in the soil

3. An increase in percentage of mineral constituents

4. An increase in inorganic phosphorus as percentage of total phosphorus

5. An increase in percentage of lignin and decrease in percentage of cellulose and hemicellulose, which means a low level of microbial activity when the compost is added to the soil, as compared to fresh manure

6. An improvement in mechanical condition of the manure, which is of particular value in gardening

Nitrogen-Carbon Relationships in Farm Manure. A ton of average farm manure contains about 500 lb. of dry matter. The average proportion of carbon is about 45 per cent. On this basis, a ton of manure contains about 225 lb. of carbon, and it has already been pointed out that manure containing bedding has about 10 lb. of nitrogen on the average. This means an average carbon to nitrogen ratio of about 22.5 to 1. This is about the same ratio one expects in residues of mixed grass and legume hays.

It is pointed out in Chap. 9 that if the carbon to nitrogen ratio is between 17 and 33, no immobilization of nitrogen is expected, yet no mineralization of nitrogen is expected until the carbon to nitrogen ratio becomes as narrow as about 17 to 1.

All this means that ordinary farm manure can be applied just before planting without causing nitrogen starvation by the new seedlings. On the other hand, it is desirable that the manure be given sufficient time to decompose, so that some nitrogen will be mineralized to help give the crop a good start.

Table 83 shows the data of Stevenson and Brown (11), which illustrate the advantage of applying manure before planting the crop. The data

TABLE 83. EFFECT OF DIFFERENT METHODS OF INCORPORATING MANURE FOR CORN* (11)

Method of incorporating manure	Increase in yield for 6 tons of manure		
	Corn, 5-yr. av., bu.	Oats, 5-yr. av., bu.	Clover, 5-yr. av., lb.
Plowed under................	6.4	5.1	820
Disked in after plowing.......	7.1	5.4	940
Cultivated in after corn was up	3.1	1.0	660

* In a corn-oats-clover rotation on Carrington silt loam.

are not entirely conclusive. The fact that very little residual effect occurred to increase the yield of oats indicates that some nitrogen might have been lost by not getting the manure deep enough in the soil with shallow cultivation. Nitrogen may be lost from manure left on the surface.

Use of Chemicals in Preserving Nitrogen in Manure. Gypsum has been used to reduce ammonia losses from manure. The reaction that occurs is as follows:

$$CaSO_4 + (NH_4)_2CO_3 \rightarrow CaCO_3 + (NH_4)_2SO_4$$

The effectiveness of gypsum is limited by its solubility. Furthermore, the effectiveness is partially determined by how well the powdered gypsum is mixed with the manure. While the reaction shown looks simple enough, not all the ammonia is conserved by the gypsum, since the reaction occurs slowly.

The most widely used material is ordinary superphosphate, which is about half gypsum. The reactions probably occur as follows:

$$CaSO_4 + (NH_4)_2CO_3 \rightarrow CaCO_3 + (NH_4)_2SO_4$$
$$CaH_4(PO_4)_2 + (NH_4)_2CO_3 \rightarrow CaCO_3 + 2NH_4H_2PO_4$$
$$2CaCO_3 + CaH_4(PO_4)_2 \rightarrow 2H_2O + 2CO_2 + Ca_3(PO_4)_2$$

The significance of the third reaction is that for every pound of ammonia preserved there will be over 4 lb. of monocalcium phosphate reverted to tricalcium phosphate.[1] In other words, the preservation of ammonia with superphosphate may reduce the effectiveness of the superphosphate during the first crop year after it is applied. It is shown in Chap. 10 that tricalcium phosphate has low efficiency on soils with a pH of greater than 6.5.

The higher analysis superphosphate, such as 0-45-0, is practically all monocalcium phosphate. The reactions that occur are the same as the last two above, since no gypsum is present. Again, the preservation of ammonia may reduce the effectiveness of the superphosphate (although this statement lacks direct proof).

The most important aspect of using superphosphate with manure is that manure is deficient in phosphorus compared to nitrogen and potassium. This factor is discussed under the next heading. In summary, we may say that preservation of nitrogen by use of chemicals is overshadowed by the use of phosphorus as a reinforcement for manure.

Reinforcing Farm Manure with Superphosphate. A ton of farm manure is about equal to 100 lb. of 10-5-10 fertilizer. Due to the fact that less than half the nitrogen is recovered the first year, the fertilizer value is closer to 100 lb. of 4-5-10. Even so, the ratio of nitrogen to phosphorus to potash is still out of balance with the usual starter fertilizer recommendation, which is more nearly a 1-4-2 for corn on Middle Western soils.

[1] Where the ammoniated phosphate contains less than about 3 per cent ammonia, the reversion is only to dicalcium phosphate.

In order to raise the phosphorus content of manure to the desired level in relation to nitrogen and potash, it is frequently recommended that 50 lb. of 0-20-0 be used per ton of manure, if no other fertilizer is to be used in the management program.

The reinforcing of manure is probably more popular in the Northeastern states than in any other part of the country.   In Vermont, for example, dairying is the major farm enterprise, and health regulations require the daily removal of manure from dairy barns.   Dr. Midgley, head of the agronomy department at the State Agricultural College, has been a strong advocate of reinforcing manure with superphosphate as the manure is hauled to the fields, or better still, by adding the phosphate in the gutters behind the stalls in the dairy barns.   The manure is used for the benefit of hay or pasture, and if the phosphate were not mixed with the manure it would be broadcast or drilled.   Under such conditions, there is no doubt that the most desirable practice is to mix the phosphate and the manure together.

Salter and Schollenberger (9) discouraged superphosphate as a preservative.   They compared the reverted phosphate in phosphated manure to ordinary tricalcium phosphate.   Midgley and Dunklee (5) felt that Salter and Schollenberger might have overemphasized the factor of reversion of superphosphate if the material were mixed with manure.   Midgley and Dunklee carried out a rather extensive study to determine the merits of mixing phosphate with the manure or applying them separately.   They used tomatoes in a greenhouse study and selected a soil which had a high capacity for fixing phosphorus.   They found that all forms of phosphate were more effective when added with the manure, as a mixture, than when added separately from the manure.   After learning that soils with a high

TABLE 84. EFFECT OF MANURE* AND SUPERPHOSPHATE ON YIELD OF TOMATOES (5)

Soil type	Total yields per pot, g.†		Difference in favor of applying together, g.
	Materials applied separately	Materials applied together	
Woodbridge loam..........	8.6	29.7	21.1
Vaiden clay...............	14.1	27.0	13.9
Worthington loam.........	29.9	38.3	8.4
Vergennes clay loam.......	40.4	47.6	7.2
Addison clay loam.........	47.1	51.6	4.5
Merrimac sandy loam......	54.0	58.5	4.5
Kaolinite and sand........	30.1	27.3	−2.8
Quartz sand..............	10.2	8.0	−2.2

* A rate of 10 tons of manure per acre with 500 lb. of 0-20-0.
† Data represent the total of two crops of tomato plants.

fixing capacity for phosphorus responded much better to mixed phosphorus and manure, they used soils of variable fixing capacities. Table 84 shows their data where several soils were used.

The question at this point is whether the manure should be reinforced with phosphorus when applied to corn ground in the Corn Belt. The real question is, "Should the starter phosphate be placed in the hill or mixed with the manure?" The most important effect of phosphate on corn is the starter effect, and for this reason it is expected that the greatest return will come from applying the manure and phosphate separately and applying the phosphate in the hill at planting time.

In the light of the findings of Midgley and Dunklee (5), one could predict that mixing of manure and phosphate before broadcasting on oat ground would increase the effectiveness of the phosphate. The idea is supported by the work of Professor Swenson and his associates in Massachusetts, cited in Chap. 10. They found that addition of organic matter increased the solubility of phosphorus in a solution containing precipitated ferric phosphate (12).

In summary, as a general recommendation, manure should be applied for the primary benefit of corn, and the starter phosphate should be applied in the hill or row at planting time. Another consideration is that the starter value of superphosphate might be reduced by mixing manure with it, because of the conversion of some of the monocalcium phosphate to tricalcium phosphate.

REFERENCES

1. Ames, J. W., and E. W. Gaither, Barnyard Manure: Production, Conservation, Reinforcement and Value, *Ohio Agr. Expt. Sta. Bull.* 246, 1912.
2. Cheney, H. B., and A. J. Englehorn, Manure, *Farm Science Reporter* (Ames), Vol. 6, No. 4, 1945.
3. Heck, A. Floyd, Conservation and Availability of the Nitrogen in Farm Manure, *Soil Sci.*, **31**:335–359, 1931.
4. Midgley, Alvin R., and V. L. Weiser, Effect of Superphosphates in Conserving Nitrogen in Cow Manure, *Vt. Agr. Expt. Sta. Bull.* 419, 1937.
5. Midgley, Alvin R., and David E. Dunklee, The Availability to Plants of Phosphates Applied with Cattle Manure, *Vt. Agr. Expt. Sta. Bull.* 525, 1945.
6. Peperzak, Paul, "Phosphorus Compounds in Manures," Master's Thesis, Iowa State College, 1948.
7. "Progress Report 1915–1936," Purdue University Agricultural Experiment Station, 1936.
8. Ross, H. A., The Production and Utilization of Manure on Illinois Dairy Farms, *Ill. Agr. Expt. Sta. Bull.* 240, 1922.
9. Salter, Robert M., and C. J. Schollenberger, Farm Manure, *Ohio Agr. Expt. Sta. Bull.* 605, 1939.
10. Shutt, Frank T., Barnyard Manure, *Canada Dept. Agr. Central Expt. Farm Bull.* 31, 1898.

11. Stevenson, W. H., and P. E. Brown, Rotation and Manure Experiments on the Wisconsin Drift Soil Area, *Iowa Agr. Expt. Sta. Bull.* 167, 1916.

12. Swenson, Richard M., C. Vernon Cole, and Dale H. Sieling, Fixation of Phosphate by Iron and Aluminum and Replacement by Organic and Inorganic Ions, *Soil Sci.*, **67**:3–22, 1949.

13. Thompson, L. M., C. A. Black, and F. E. Clark, The Accumulation and Mineralization of Microbial Organic Phosphorus, *Soil Sci. Soc. Amer. Proc.*, **13**:242–245, 1948.

14. Turk, L. M., and A. G. Weidemann, Farm Manure, *Mich. Agr. Expt. Sta. Cir.* 196, 1945.

15. Waksman, Selman A., and F. C. Gerretson, Influence of Temperature and Moisture upon the Nature and Extent of Decomposition of Plant Residues by Microorganisms, *Ecology*, **12**:33–60, 1931.

CHAPTER 14

SULFUR AND THE MINOR ELEMENTS

Nitrogen, phosphorus, and potassium are the primary fertilizer elements, and fertilizer laws require a guaranteed analysis of percentages of N, P_2O_5, and K_2O. On the other hand, many fertilizers are advertised to contain certain other elements which are known to be needed in certain localities. For example, a certain fertilizer is sold for alfalfa in Wisconsin which contains boron, and certain fertilizers are advertised to contain sulfur in California. One particularly popular garden fertilizer is advertised to contain all the minor elements.

Sulfur. Sulfur is one of the six macronutrients. Thus far we have considered five of the macronutrients in detail: calcium and magnesium under lime, and nitrogen, phosphorus, and potassium under fertilizers.

Occurrence of Sulfur in Soils. In humid regions, all but a few pounds of sulfur per acre occur in organic combination. Soils of humid regions usually contain from 200 to 1000 lb. of sulfur per acre furrow slice. In terms of SO_3, this is about 500 to 2500 lb. per acre.

In subhumid, semiarid, and arid regions the amount of sulfur in the topsoil is comparable to that in humid-region soils, because the amount of sulfur is correlated with the amount of organic matter. Sulfates accumulate at the bottom of the B horizon of soils in subhumid and drier climates, so that the sulfur content of the profile of a representative subhumid soil is greater than that of a representative humid-region soil.

Utilization of Sulfur by Crops. Mehring and Bennett (20) estimate that the ratio of the N, P_2O_5, K_2O, and SO_3 contents of all crops harvested in the United States is 1 to 0.4 to 0.6 to 0.3.

Table 85, prepared from data of Lipman and Conybeare, shows the relative amounts of P_2O_5 and SO_3 in several crops.

Thomas *et al.* (33) analyzed nearly 1000 leaf samples and found great variation in percentage of total sulfur. Yet they observed a remarkably narrow range in per cent (0.2 to 0.4 per cent) of organic sulfur in leaf samples. Plants high in total sulfur contain a considerable amount of inorganic sulfur or sulfate. Sulfur is one of the important elements which readily enter into synthesis of organic compounds. It is a constituent of protein and appears to be related to nitrate reduction (23). Plants which are deficient in sulfur tend to accumulate nitrate nitrogen, which may be due to insufficient sulfur amino acids, which are essential to protein synthesis.

TABLE 85. AMOUNTS OF P_2O_5 AND SO_3 REMOVED BY DIFFERENT CROPS (17)

Crop	Yield	Pounds removed per acre	
		SO_3	P_2O_5
Corn.............	100 bu.	40.0	52.5
Wheat............	50 bu.	25.5	36.5
Potatoes..........	400 bu.	81.5	38.8
Alfalfa...........	4 tons	57.5	41.0
Tobacco..........	5000 lb.	21.0	16.0

Legumes use more sulfur than nonlegumes, and nodulation is improved in legumes by adding sulfur to sulfur-deficient soils. Starkey (31) is of the opinion, however, that sulfur serves the same function in legumes as in nonlegumes and that nodulation is not directly related to sulfur. A possible explanation is that lack of sulfur reduces the assimilation of nitrogen by a legume and decreases the ratio of carbohydrate to nitrogen inside the plant, thereby reducing the activity of symbiotic organisms.

Plants may take up sulfur directly from the soil, chiefly as sulfate, or may absorb SO_2 directly from the air. While the CO_2 content of the atmosphere averages 315 p.p.m., the SO_2 concentration is only about 0.05 p.p.m. The ratio of carbon to sulfur in the atmosphere is about 2400 to 1 on a weight basis, and in alfalfa about 150 to 1. On the basis of these ratios it would be possible for alfalfa to secure about 6 per cent of its sulfur from the air (1,5).

Sulfur Cycle. The sulfur cycle is much more complicated than the carbon or nitrogen cycle. In a general way, however, organic sulfur accumulates in the soil from plant residues. The decomposition of organic sulfur is brought about by many different organisms. The popular opinion is that sulfur is released initially as H_2S, which is oxidized to the sulfate form. Starkey (31) points out, however, that while the sulfide is a product of decomposition, it may not be the principal intermediate compound because an organic acid like sulfinic acid ($R-SO_2H$) may be transformed to sulfuric acid. At any rate, the principal inorganic form of sulfur is the sulfate under aerobic conditions, and the absorption of sulfur by plants, therefore, is largely from the sulfate form.

Losses of Sulfur from the Soil. Sulfate salts are generally quite soluble and leach from the soil in humid regions. Sulfur losses are much like nitrogen losses, because conditions favoring decomposition of organic matter cause the accumulation of sulfates and nitrates, which may leach out of the soil if they are not removed by plant absorption. Leaching losses of sulfur, therefore, should be considered in the same manner as leaching losses of nitrogen. Lipman and Conybeare (17) estimated that the average loss of sulfur was 41.8 lb. in soils of the United States. Lyon and Bizzell (18) found an average loss of 37 lb. of sulfur per acre in lysimeter studies in New York.

Erosion removes sulfur like any other nutrients. The losses again may be compared to nitrogen, since the profile distribution of sulfur in the humid region is similar to that of nitrogen and organic matter.

Additions of Sulfur to Soils. Bertramson *et al.* (5) reported the amounts of sulfur accumulated from rainfall at different locations in Indiana in 1 year. Their data are shown in Table 86. Omitting the figure for Gary,

TABLE 86. SULFUR IN PRECIPITATION AT 11 LOCATIONS IN INDIANA IN 1 YEAR
SEPT. 1, 1946, TO AUG. 31, 1947

Location	Total sulfur, lb./acre	Total rainfall, in.
Nashville	20.0	39.1
Gary (industrial city)	127.1	31.9
Monterey	27.4	34.2
Orland	25.8	37.1
Indianapolis	32.6	36.6
Rising Sun	29.7	40.7
Evansville	29.0	40.6
Larwill	23.2	35.6
Branchville	30.4	41.5
Lafayette	21.7	37.9
Montgomery	27.7	42.1

the average amount of sulfur added in rainfall was about 27 lb. (this is about 67.5 lb. of SO_3), which is as much sulfur as is removed by field crops in Indiana.

Ordinary superphosphate (which amounts to nearly 90 per cent of superphosphate fertilizer) contains about 50 per cent gypsum; therefore, in terms of SO_3 and P_2O_5, ordinary superphosphate contains 30 per cent SO_3 and 20 per cent P_2O_5.

Sulfate of ammonia (which amounts to about 15 per cent of the domestic production of chemical nitrogenous fertilizers) contains 60 per cent SO_3 and 20 per cent N.

Other fertilizers, such as kainite, sulfate of potash, and sulfate of potash-magnesia, contain a considerable amount of sulfur. Mehring and Bennett

(20) calculated that we are now applying more sulfur in fertilizers every year than is removed by crops.

Farm manure contains about 4 lb. of SO_3 per ton, and a 4-ton application of manure adds as much sulfur as is removed in 40 bu. of corn.

Need for Sulfur as a Fertilizer. The amount of sulfur added in fertilizer plus rainfall exceeds that removed by leaching plus crop removal. Such statements are based on averages and can be misleading. Conrad (8) recently published a map showing 46 different locations scattered all over California where sulfur-deficient soils have been located. Washington and Oregon also have sulfur-deficient soils.

Yields of alfalfa and forage crops are frequently doubled or tripled by addition of sulfur to the deficient soils (8).

On well-drained soils where high-analysis fertilizers (not containing sulfur) are used, one may expect to run into sulfur deficiencies eventually.

Available data indicate that, except in industrial areas, leaching losses about equal income of sulfur by rainfall. From a management point of view, a farmer should plan to use fertilizers containing sulfur or to add sulfur or gypsum if he uses high-analysis (sulfur-free) fertilizers.

Use of Sulfur on Alkaline Soils. The use of sulfur on alkaline soils is discussed in Chap. 7

Difficulties in Establishing Essentiality of Minor Elements. In 1910, when Cyril G. Hopkins published his classic textbook, "Soil Fertility and Permanent Agriculture," there were 10 elements recognized as essential to plants. The following expression became popular in Hopkins's time to help students remember the essential elements:

C   HOPKNS   CaFe   Mg

(See Hopkins Cafe, mighty good)

It was known as early as 1910 that plants contained many more elements than those listed as essential. The techniques used in solution culture work were too crude at that time to establish conclusively the indispensability of a minor element. Salts which were refined and sold as C.P. (chemically pure) grade contained trace amounts of minor elements which were ample for plant growth. The early studies with copper were of no value if distilled water was obtained from a still constructed of copper, since enough copper was dissolved from the walls of the coils to supply the needs of the plants. It was necessary to use water redistilled through pyrex before copper was determined to be essential.

The addition of boron was known to stimulate plant growth, and the belief was held up to 1915 (and even later by many scientists) that boron and perhaps other minor elements served primarily as stimulants and were probably not essential.

Because of the occurrence of so many elements in plants, there has been a continuous study by plant physiologists to determine the essentiality of minor elements. McHargue (22) began publishing his studies on manganese in 1914 and is given credit for establishing manganese as essential to plant life. While Mazé (19) published work in 1915 to show the need of corn for boron and zinc, it was not until 1923 that Warrington (34) definitely proved the necessity of boron. In 1926 Sommer and Lipman (30) confirmed Warrington's work with boron and proved also the essentiality of zinc. Sommer (28) proved the indispensability of copper in 1931, and as recently as 1942 molybdenum was added to the list of essential elements by Arnon and Stout (3).

At the present time there are fifteen elements that are widely known to be essential to plant life, but the list may not be complete. There is an increasing amount of evidence in favor of grouping chlorine with the list of essential minor elements. It is now listed with sodium as beneficial.

TABLE 87. ELEMENTS FOUND IN PLANTS (24)

Elements occurring in plants in abundance	*Elements occurring in plants in microquantities*	
ESSENTIAL	ESSENTIAL	
Nitrogen	Iron	
Phosphorus	Manganese	
Potassium	Copper	
Calcium	Zinc	
Magnesium	Boron	
Sulfur	Molybdenum	
Oxygen		
Carbon	NOT ESSENTIAL*	
Hydrogen	Lithium	Iodine
	Beryllium	Cesium
BENEFICIAL	Fluorine	Barium
Sodium	Aluminum	Lanthanum
Chlorine	Silicon	Praseodymium
	Titanium	Neodymium
	Vanadium	Samarium
	Chromium	Europium
	Cobalt	Gadolinium
	Nickel	Terbium
	Gallium	Dysprosium
	Germanium	Erbium
	Arsenic	Ytterbium
	Selenium	Gold
	Bromine	Mercury
	Rubidium	Thallium
	Strontium	Lead
	Yttrium	Radium
	Silver	Thorium
	Tin	Uranium

* Reading vertically, arranged in order of ascending atomic weights.

Boron.   Boron first came into prominence during the first decade of this century because of recognition of its toxicity.   During the Second World War the potash salts from domestic sources were found to cause toxicity, and the trouble was soon traced to boron impurities.

Prior to establishment of boron as an essential element there were many nonparasitic diseases recognized which were later found to be caused by boron deficiency.   Some of the diseases are top sickness of tobacco, heart rot of beet, cork disease of apple, brown rot of cauliflower, and cracked stem of celery (26).

Occurrence of Boron in Soils and Plants.   Whetstone, Robinson, and Byers (35) made a comprehensive study of the boron status of American soils, which was published in 1942.   They point out that there are three areas where boron deficiencies are most likely to occur: the Atlantic Coastal Plain; a region across Michigan, Wisconsin, and Minnesota; and the Pacific coastal region along with the Pacific Northwest.   They found that soils developed under normal rainfall contained from 8 to 176 lb. of boron per acre furrow slice.   The available boron ranged from 0.8 to 129.6 lb. per acre and averaged 34.2 lb. per acre in over 300 samples, which was about half the average amount of total boron.

As a rule, boron does not exceed 70 p.p.m. in naturally grown plant leaves (24); however, Eaton (10) reported 3875 p.p.m. boron in musk-melon, 3080 p.p.m. in zinnia, and 2245 in sweet clover.   These are exceptional cases, and concentrations over 70 p.p.m. are usually associated with toxicity.   A 3-ton crop of alfalfa with 60 p.p.m. boron would remove only about 0.3 lb. of boron.

In areas where alfalfa is grown, this crop is a good indicator.   The yellowing of terminal leaves of alfalfa indicates boron deficiency.   Applications of borax should be made in small plots in fields wherever alfalfa is observed to turn yellow, in order to determine if the soil is deficient in boron.   On the other hand, yields may be affected before the yellowing is evident.   It is necessary for experiment stations to continue their search for areas where boron fertilization may now, or will soon, be required.

Relation of Boron Uptake to Other Elements.   Branchley and Warrington (6) observed that calcium uptake by plants was retarded by lack of boron. It is also known that boron availability decreases as the pH rises above neutrality, so the effective utilization of calcium and boron would be reduced by overliming a soil.   Jones and Scarseth (15) point out that normal plant growth requires a proper balance between boron and calcium.   They also observed that high potash uptake caused higher boron uptake, which was associated with low calcium uptake and also lower limits of boron toxicity.

Use of Boron as a Fertilizer.   Boron is subject to leaching losses in the humid part of the United States, and leaching losses coupled with crop

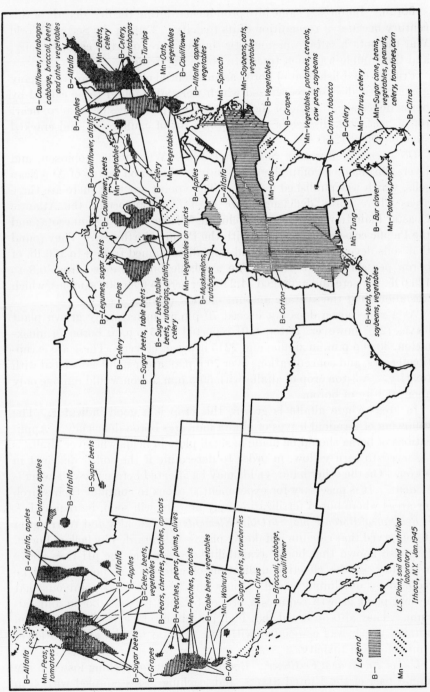

B—Cauliflower, rutabagas
cabbage, broccoli, beets
and other vegetables

Mn—Beets,
celery

B—Celery,
rutabagas

B—Turnips

Mn—Oats,
vegetables

B—Cauliflower

B—Alfalfa, apples,
vegetables

Mn—Soybeans, oats,
vegetables

Mn—Vegetables, potatoes, cereals,
cow peas, soybeans

Mn—Sugar cane, beans,
vegetables, peanuts,
celery, tomatoes, corn

B—Alfalfa

B—Apples

B—Cauliflower, alfalfa

Mn—Spinach

B—Vegetables

B—Grapes

B—Cotton, tobacco

B—Celery

Mn—Citrus, celery

B—Citrus

B—Cauliflower; beets

B—Celery

B—Cauliflower; beets

Mn—Vegetables

B—Celery

Mn—Vegetables

B—Apples

B—Alfalfa

Mn—Oats

Mn—Tung

B—Bur clover

Mn—Potatoes, peppers

B—Legumes, sugar beets

B—Peas

Mn—Vegetables on mucks

B—Muskmelons,
rutabagas

B—Sugar beets, table
beets, rutabagas, alfalfa
celery

B—Cotton

B—Vetch, oats,
soybeans, vegetables

B—Celery

B—Sugar beets, table beets

B—Sugar beets, table
beets, rutabagas, apricots
celery

B—Alfalfa, apples

B—Potatoes, apples

B—Alfalfa

B—Sugar beets

B—Alfalfa

B—Alfalfa, apples

B—Alfalfa

B—Apples

B—Celery, beets,
vegetables

B—Pears, cherries, peaches, apricots

B—Peaches, pears, plums, olives

Mn—Peaches, apricots

B—Table beets, vegetables

Mn—Walnuts

B—Sugar beets, strawberries

Mn—Citrus

B—Broccoli, cabbage,
cauliflower

B—Alfalfa

Mn—Peas,
tomatoes

B—Sugar beets

B—Grapes

B—Olives

Legend

B —

Mn —

U.S. Plant, soil and nutrition
laboratory
Ithaca, N.Y. Jan.1945

Fig. 123. Generalized map of the occurrence of boron and manganese deficiencies in plants (4).

338

removal will eventually cause all well-drained soils of humid regions to need boron fertilizer. The trend is for many companies to add borax to fertilizer, even though they are not required to do so, in areas of known deficiencies. The fertilization of soils with boron should be done with caution. Soils with high exchange capacity can be fertilized with larger quantities of boron; also, soils neutral or alkaline in reaction may be fertilized with larger quantities. Soils which have low exchange capacity and low calcium saturation should receive less than 25 lb. of borax per acre as fertilizer. About 50 lb. of borax is adequate as fertilizer on soils with high exchange capacity and high calcium saturation.

Manganese. According to Wischhusen (36), the use of manganese as a fertilizer originated in Holland, where it was found that gray speck of oats was caused by manganese deficiency. McHargue and his associates in Kentucky have confirmed the observation that manganese deficiency causes gray speck of oats (13), and McHargue, who began his work in 1912, is given credit for establishing manganese as an essential element (22).

Occurrence of Manganese in Soils and Plants. Manganese-deficient soils have been found in southern California, along the Atlantic Coastal Plain —particularly in Florida—and on muck soils of the Great Lakes region (4). In the Florida area, manganese deficiency has been found in sandy soils, alkaline soils, and muck (36).

Manganese is most likely to be deficient in strongly leached sandy soils or in overlimed or calcareous soils. Manganese occurs in the soil as a cation and may be combined in primary or secondary minerals. The solubility of manganese is affected by pH in much the same way as iron. Lowering the pH by addition of sulfur increases the solubility of manganese, and manganese toxicity can be induced by such a practice (21). Raising the pH by liming decreases the solubility of manganese, and deficiency symptoms may be induced. The amount of exchangeable manganese in soils varies greatly, but most soils fall within the range of 20 to 200 lb. per acre.

The manganese content of plants may vary enormously in accordance with the availability of manganese. Morris (21) found that sweet clover grown in pots in the greenhouse contained from 29 to 858 p.p.m. of manganese, depending on the pH to which the soil was adjusted. The range in manganese concentration generally falls within a range of 20 to 400 p.p.m.

Robinson and Edgington (24) found the manganese content of 20 samples of oak leaves from several different Eastern states to vary from 425 to 4500 p.p.m. manganese, and pecan leaves from South Carolina contained 1075 p.p.m. manganese. These are exceedingly high values. The authors state that "exchangeable manganese in the organic layers of Podzol soils sometimes equals and occasionally exceeds the exchangeable calcium."

Relation of Manganese to Iron.   Where a soil is high in exchangeable manganese, it is possible for plants to take up too much manganese in relation to iron.   Somers and Shive (27) have suggested that a balance should exist between iron and manganese for normal plant growth; that is, a particular ratio of manganese to iron is desirable for a particular plant. Symptoms of iron toxicity correspond to symptoms of manganese deficiency, and symptoms of manganese toxicity correspond to those of iron deficiency.

Use of Manganese Fertilizers.   Manganese deficiency can be corrected by spraying manganese sulfate directly on plants, and this practice is preferable to soil application on alkaline soils.   Applications of manganese sulfate are successful when applied directly to organic soils or to nonalkaline mineral soils.   Soils which are fertilized with manure are not likely to develop manganese deficiency.

Copper.   The stimulating effect of copper was recognized around 1900 in areas where Bordeaux mixture was used as a spray on trees and truck crops, but the essentiality of copper was not investigated for several years. After several years of experimenting with dieback in citrus, Floyd (12) in 1917 recommended the use of Bordeaux mixture as a cure for dieback. In 1927 Felix (11) found that onions and lettuce could be grown on unproductive peat soils after the addition of copper sulfate.

Occurrence of Copper in Soils and Plants.   Sommer (29) writes that "soils high in organic matter, particularly newly cultivated peat soils, are those most frequently discussed in connection with copper deficiency." Copper deficiencies have been reported for mineral soils, particularly in sandy and gravelly soils.   Copper deficiencies have been mapped in Washington, California, Florida, South Carolina, and the Great Lakes region (4).

Copper exists in the soils in available form as a cation, which may occur in solution or held in exchangeable form.   It is most soluble in acid soils, and its solubility is decreased as the pH is raised.

Copper toxicity may result from adding too much copper to soils, and Sommer (29) believes that too much copper may interfere with the absorption of iron; that is, copper-toxicity symptoms resemble iron-deficiency symptoms.

Robinson and Edgington (24) cited unpublished data of R. S. Holmes (U.S. Department of Agriculture) showing that 25 samples of wheat grains from the Great Plains and Portugal contained no more than 7.5 p.p.m. of copper, and they cited the work of Lehman (16) who found that several nonagricultural plants which had grown on soils having 0.27 to 0.35 p.p.m. of copper contained from 223 p.p.m. to 560 p.p.m. of copper.   Davidson and LeClerc (9) reported that samples of spinach contained from 28 to 73 p.p.m. of copper.

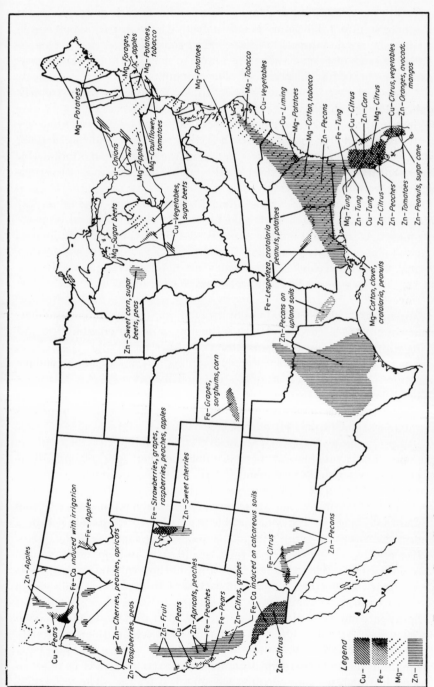

Fig. 124. Generalized map of the occurrence of copper, iron, magnesium, and zinc deficiencies in plants (4).

341

Use of Copper Fertilizers.   Copper is usually applied to soils and plants as copper sulfate.   The spray is most effective on plants on alkaline soils but may be applied directly to nonalkaline soils.

The amount of copper sulfate to apply to deficient soils depends primarily on the exchange capacity.   The amounts vary from 5 lb. on soils with extremely low exchange capacity to 300 lb. on soils with extremely high exchange capacity.

Zinc.   Although zinc had been recognized as a possible essential element since 1914, the use of zinc as a fertilizer did not begin until 1932, when several thousand acres of tung trees were treated in Florida (7). Since that time, zinc has been especially important in treating citrus trees suffering from zinc deficiency.

Occurrence of Zinc in Soils and Plants.   Robinson and Edgington (24) cite several studies which show that plants contain a few hundred parts per million of zinc, and only in cases of soils or solution cultures high in zinc did plants take up more than 1000 p.p.m. zinc.   They point out that pecans, which often show zinc deficiency, are not necessarily heavy feeders on zinc, because many healthy pecan leaves were found to be rather low in zinc.

Zinc may be related to chlorophyl production.   A characteristic deficiency symptom in citrus and corn is the appearance of green midrib and veins with white color in between the veins.

Zinc occurs in the soil as a cation or combined in primary and secondary minerals.   The solubility of zinc is affected by pH.   As the pH drops below 5.25 or rises above 6.0, the solubility is decreased.

Zinc deficiencies have been mapped along the Pacific Coast and throughout the Cotton Belt and in Wisconsin.

Camp (7) thinks the principal cause of zinc deficiency in the South is the removal of available zinc by continuous cropping with cotton without use of cover crops and green manure.   He cited data of Rogers, Gall, and Barnette (25) on a cover crop of weeds that contained 140 p.p.m. zinc, while a crop of crotelaria on the same soil averaged 8 p.p.m. zinc.   Camp argues that if a cover crop which is able to absorb zinc effectively is turned under, the succeeding crop will not be deficient in zinc.

Use of Zinc as a Fertilizer.   Zinc is added to soils in manures and organic wastes.   Where clean-tilled crops are grown continuously or a greater part of the time, it may be necessary to apply zinc sulfate as a fertilizer or to spray plants with zinc sulfate.

Sprays are more effective on alkaline soils or on very sandy soils.   Nonalkaline soils, except sands, may be fertilized directly with zinc sulfate.

Molybdenum.   Of the minor elements, molybdenum is apparently taken up in the smallest quantities, and some investigators have reported studies in which no molybdenum was found in plants.   The very small amounts were probably not measurable with techniques used.

Molybdenum is absorbed as the molybdate ion (an anion), and its solubility is increased by liming a soil. The solubility of molybdenum is low at low pH values because of precipitation by iron.

Anderson (2) has reported a very striking case of molybdenum deficiency in an ironstone soil in Australia, where a very small application of molybdenum gave a great response in pasture growth.

Rock phosphate and superphosphate contain small quantities of molybdenum. Florida phosphates usually contain more than 20 p.p.m. of molybdenum. The use of these fertilizers has helped to satisfy the needs of soils for molybdenum. Nevertheless, soils may be so low in molybdenum that the phosphate fertilizers will not satisfy completely the needs of crops for this element, and furthermore, molybdenum may not occur in the soil in available form.

Florida soils, used for production of citrus, are frequently deficient in molybdenum. Stewart and Leonard[1] have recently found that "yellow spot" in citrus is caused by molybdenum deficiency. The symptom appears as large interveinal chlorotic spots and has been known by the name of "yellow spot" for many years. The treatment consists of a foliar spray at the rate of 0.1 ounce of sodium molybdate per mature tree.

Soil applications of sodium molybdate have not been a satisfactory treatment for "yellow spot" in citrus, but this is not typical of all soil conditions. Some soils and crops respond favorably to soil treatment with molybdates, and some phosphate fertilizers are sold with the provision that they contain added molybdenum.

While molybdenum is rather new in soil and crop management there is a rapidly increasing volume of literature on the subject. The March, 1956, issue of *Soil Science* is devoted entirely to this subject, and is a good reference for a general overview of the subject.

Iron. While iron is frequently considered a minor element in plant nutrition, it is a macronutrient in so far as its occurrence in the soil is concerned. Iron is the third most abundant mineral element found in the earth's crust.

In terms of plant composition, there is less iron than boron, manganese, or zinc in most plants. Stiebeling (32) reported that apples, cucumbers, and watermelons contained less than 4 p.p.m. iron; bananas, celery, carrots, onions, and tomatoes contained from 4 to 8 p.p.m.; asparagus, beets, dock, and sorrel had from 8 to 16 p.p.m.; and cowpeas, dandelion leaves, parsley, and spinach contained over 16 p.p.m.

Iron is necessary to chlorophyl formation. A deficiency of iron causes chlorosis, which is readily apparent because of yellowing of leaves.

Causes of Iron Chlorosis. There are two main causes of iron chlorosis in soils, the most important of which is lime. The other cause is unbalanced ratios of iron to the other minor cations, particularly manganese.

[1] *Am. Soc. for Hort. Sci.*, **62**:111–115, 1953.

Lime-induced chlorosis may be found in any section of the world on calcareous or alkaline soils. The effect of pH on solubility of iron has been stressed in several sections of this book. The critical pH value for iron solubility varies with different plants. Soybeans become chlorotic in high-lime soils of Iowa where corn, oats, clover, and alfalfa show no chlorosis. Peach trees become chlorotic on Houston soils of Texas where cotton, corn, small grain, and clover show no chlorosis. Flower plants like rhododendrons and azaleas become chlorotic on soils with a pH above 6.0.

Manganese toxicity, which in all probability results from iron deficiency, occurs on acid soils where the soil is relatively high in exchangeable manganese. Excess copper has been observed to cause iron-starvation symptoms in greenhouse work (29). The effect of manganese, and perhaps copper, on iron is that iron is oxidized from the ferrous to the more insoluble ferric form.

Treatment of Iron Chlorosis with Ferrous Sulfate. Ferrous sulfate has been used for many years as a treatment for iron deficiency. The salt is soluble in water and can be applied as a foliar spray, or it may be applied directly to the soil in some cases. Florists will often include a small package of ferrous sulfate with potted plants like azaleas, which require appreciable quantities of soluble iron.

Ferrous sulfate is not recommended as a soil treatment for chlorosis on calcareous soils because of its ineffectiveness. The soluble ferrous sulfate quickly ionizes in the soil and recombines with other ions. The ferrous ion forms iron hydroxide, which has a very low solubility rate. The problem with calcareous soils is usually that of availability of iron rather than low content of iron before treatment; therefore, adding more iron to the soil in the form of ferrous sulfate is not effective.

Ferrous sulfate can be sprayed directly on the leaves of trees, shrubs, and field crops. Directions for preparing a spray solution may be found on page 196. One spraying has been enough to greatly increase yields of soybeans on high lime soils of Iowa. In some plants, however, several spray applications are required throughout the season. This is particularly true of citrus trees.

In Florida, where almost half the citrus trees have been affected by lack of iron, the use of ferrous sulfate has not proved satisfactory. Most of the soils growing citrus in that state are acid in reaction, but the low availability of iron is often caused by interference of other ions, particularly copper. It was at the Citrus Experiment Station in Florida that a greatly improved treatment of iron chlorosis was developed.[1] The treatment involves the use of chelates, the subject which follows.

---

[1] Significant work on this subject by Ivan Stewart and C. D. Leonard of the Florida Citrus Experiment Station at Lake Alfred has been published in the *Proc. Florida State Hort. Soc.*, **60**:49–54, 1953, and **68**:59–64, 1955, and in the *Proc. Soil Sci. Soc. Florida*, **14**:47–52, 1954.

The Use of Chelates with Minor Elements. The term chelate (pronounced kē'lāt) is derived from the Greek word meaning *claw*. Chelates are organic compounds which combine with metals in such a way that the metals are immobilized, yet the combination might remain water soluble. The metals are slowly exchangeable with other metals (or other cations). Iron sulfate is water soluble but it ionizes in the soil; then the iron is readily precipitated as ferric hydroxide. On the other hand, iron chelate is water soluble but it does not ionize in the soil. The iron is held in a form which is readily available for root absorption.

One of the best-known chelates for treatment of iron chlorosis is ethylene diamine tetra acetic acid (EDTA) known commercially as Versene or Sesquestrene. The structure is as follows:

The hydrogens of the carboxyl groups in EDTA may be replaced by such cations as Na, Fe, or other common cations of the soil. The term Fe-EDTA means that iron is held in place of the hydrogens of the carboxyl groups.

There is evidence from radioactive-tracer studies that the entire Fe-EDTA molecule is absorbed by the roots of plants. It is used primarily as a soil amendment rather than as a foliar spray, because it has been known to cause damage to leaves. Fe-EDTA is resistant to microbial attack, and is also resistant to hydrolysis. In terms of preventing chlorosis, it lasts as long as two years in the soil. Applications of 10 to 20 grams of actual iron per citrus tree have been effective in correcting chlorosis. The fate of the Fe-EDTA compound in the soil is not clearly known at the present time. The iron is gradually replaced by other cations, and in some cases the EDTA is adsorbed on clays. Inasmuch as the compound is water soluble, it is also subject to some loss by leaching.

The stability of Fe-EDTA in soils, and its effectiveness in controlling chlorosis, is much greater under acid conditions than under calcareous soil conditions. Rather than use Fe-EDTA under calcareous conditions, another material, hydroxyethyl ethylene diamine triacetic acid (Fe-EDTA-OH), is recommended. This latter material is much more stable in calcareous soils. It is quite expensive, but is economical to use on high-income crops like citrus.

On crops like soybeans, which respond favorably to foliar sprays of ferrous sulfate, soil applications of Fe-EDTA-OH are not being recommended.

The use of chelates for adding other minor elements like Cu, Mn, and Zn are being investigated and show considerable promise. However, Cu, Mn, and Zn sprays are much more effective than Fe sprays and there is less interest in chelated compounds of Cu, Mn, and Zn.

Chlorine. In 1954 Broyer and others,[1] at the University of California, recommended that chlorine be added to the list of essential minor elements. They found that chlorine was essential to the growth of tomato plants in solution cultures.

Since 1954 the studies on the essentiality of chlorine have been extended to other plants by the California workers. In a personal communication the following data were obtained:

Plants studied	Without chlorine Per cent of yield of normal plants grown with chlorine
Lettuce	30
Tomato	35
Cabbage	42
Sugar beet	49
Subterranean clover	50
Alfalfa	68

Other plants which have shown a less marked response are barley, buckwheat, corn, and beans. Data have not been worked out for cotton and tobacco but these crops have shown marked response to chlorine addition.

Although chlorine is one of the abundant elements contained in plants, it appears more logical to group this element with the minor elements. The principal reason for classification as a minor element is the amount needed in solution culture in relation to the amounts of other elements. The data on page 347 show the concentration of the different elements in a nutrient solution used in the California laboratory. There is a definite break in quantity when we come to chlorine in the list. It is more like the minor elements in this respect.

[1] T. C. Broyer, A. B. Carlton, C. M. Johnson, and P. R. Stout, Chlorine—A Micronutrient Element for Higher Plants, *Plant Physiol*, **29**:526–532, 1954.

The fact that such a very small amount of chlorine is needed (less than 2 p.p.m. in solution) raises a question as to the agricultural importance of chlorine. It has been indicated in previous chapters of this book that chlorine is one of the more abundant elements existing in soils. It is readily absorbed by plants and is stored in soils in organic form. Fur-

Elements in solution	γ—atoms per liter*	Elements in solution	γ—atoms per liter*
N (as NO₃)	14,000	Cl	50
N (as NH₄)	2000	B	25
K	6000	Mn	5
Ca	4000	Fe	4
P (as H₂PO₄)	2000	Zn	2
S (as SO₄)	1000	Cu	0.5
Mg	1000	Mo	0.1

* γ—atoms per liter may be converted to p.p.m. as follows:

$$(\gamma\text{—atoms per liter} \div 1000) \text{ atomic weight} = \text{p.p.m.}$$

thermore, the most widely used potassium fertilizer is KCl, which is over 45 per cent chlorine by weight. The chloride ion is readily removed by leaching, however, and in soils where very small amounts of chlorine are stored in organic matter one may find that crops will respond to addition of chlorides, along with additions of other elements a deficiency of which might be limiting plant growth.

REFERENCES

1. Alway, F. J., A. W. Marsh, and W. J. Methley, Sufficiency of Atmospheric Sulfur for Maximum Crop Yields, *Soil Sci. Soc. Amer. Proc.*, **2**:229–238, 1937.
2. Anderson, A. J., Molybdenum Deficiency on a South Australian Ironstone Soil, *J. Austr. Inst. Agr. Sci.*, **8** (2): 73–75, 1942.
3. Arnon, D. I., and P. R. Stout, Molybdenum as an Essential Element for Higher Plants, *Plant Physiol.*, **14**:599–602, 1939.
4. Beeson, Kenneth C., The Occurrence of Mineral Nutritional Diseases of Plants and Animals in the United States, *Soil Sci.*, **60**:9–14, 1945.
5. Bertramson, B. R., Maurice Fried, and Samuel L. Tisdale, Sulfur Studies of Indiana Soils and Crops, *Soil Sci.*, **70**:27–42, 1950.
6. Branchley, W. E., and K. Warrington, The Role of Boron in the Growth of Plants, *Ann. Bot.*, **41**:167–187, 1927.
7. Camp, A. F., Zinc as a Nutrient in Plant Growth, *Soil Sci.*, **60**:157–164, 1945.
8. Conrad, John P., Sulfur Fertilization in California and Some Related Factors, *Soil Sci.*, **70**:43–54, 1950.
9. Davidson, Jehiel, and J. A. LeClerc, The Variation in the Mineral Content of Vegetables, *J. Nutrition*, **11**:55–66, 1936.
10. Eaton, F. M., Deficiency, Toxicity, and Accumulation of Boron in Plants, *J. Agr. Research*, **69**:237–277, 1944.
11. Felix, E. L., Correction of Unproductive Muck by the Addition of Copper, *Phytopathology*, **17**:49–50, 1927.
12. Floyd, B. F., Dieback, or Exanthema of Citrus Trees, *Fla. Agr. Expt. Sta. Bull.* 140, 1917.
13. Hageman, R. H., J. S. McHargue, Donald G. Sherman, and E. S. Hodge, The

Production of Gray Speck of Oats in Purified Sand Cultures, *J. Am. Soc. Agron.*, **34**:731–735, 1942.

14. Hoagland, D. R., Molybdenum in Relation to Plant Growth, *Soil Sci.*, **60**:119–123, 1945.

15. Jones, H. E., and G. D. Scarseth, The Calcium-Boron Balance in Plants as Related to Boron Needs, *Soil Sci.*, **57**:15–24, 1944.

16. Lehman, K. B., Hygienische Studiern über Kupfer, *Arch. Hyg.*, **27**:1, 1896.

17. Lipman, Jacob G., and Adrienne B. Conybeare, Preliminary Note on the Inventory and Balance Sheet of Plant Nutrients in the United States, *N.J. Agr. Expt. Sta. Bull.* 607, 1936.

18. Lyon, T. Lyttleton, and James A. Bizzell, Lysimeter Experiments, *N.Y. Agr. Expt. Sta. (Ithaca) Mem.* 12, 1918.

19. Mazé, P., Determination des Éléments Mineraux Rares Nécessaires au Development du Maïs, *Compt. Rend. Acad. Sci.*, **160**:211–214, 1915.

20. Mehring, A. L., and G. E. Bennett, Sulfur in Fertilizers, Manures and Soil Amendments, *Soil Sci.*, **70**:73–82, 1950.

21. Morris, H. D., The Soluble Manganese Content of Acid Soils and Its Relation to the Growth and Manganese Content of Sweet Clover and Lespedeza, *Soil Sci. Soc. Amer. Proc.*, **13**:362–371, 1948.

22. McHargue, J. S., The Role of Manganese in Agriculture, *Soil Sci.*, **60**:115–118, 1945.

23. Nightingale, G. T., L. G. Schermerhorn, and W. R. Robbins, Effects of Sulfur Deficiency on Metabolism in Tomato, *Plant Physiol.*, **7**:565–595, 1932.

24. Robinson, W. O., and Glen Edgington, Minor Elements in Plants, and Some Accumulator Plants, *Soil Sci.*, **60**:15–28, 1945.

25. Rogers, L. H., O. E. Gall, and R. M. Barnette, The Zinc Content of Weeds and Volunteer Grasses and Planted Land Covers, *Soil Sci.*, **47**:237–243, 1939.

26. Shive, John W., Boron in Plant Life—A Brief Historical Survey, *Soil Sci.*, **60**:41–52, 1945.

27. Somers, I. I., and J. W. Shive, The Iron-Manganese Relation in Plant Metabolism, *Plant Physiol.*, **17**:582–602, 1942.

28. Sommer, A. L., Copper as an Essential Element to Plant Growth, *Plant Physiol.* **6**:339–345, 1931.

29. Sommer, A. L., Copper and Plant Growth, *Soil Sci.*, **60**:71–80, 1945.

30. Sommer, A. L., and C. B. Lipman, Evidence of the Indispensable Nature of Zinc and Boron for Higher Green Plants, *Plant Physiol.*, **1**:231–249, 1926.

31. Starkey, Robert L., Relations of Microorganisms to Transformations of Sulfur in Soils, *Soil Sci.*, **70**:55–66, 1950.

32. Stiebeling, Hazel K., The Iron Content of Vegetables and Fruits, *U.S. Dept. Agr. Cir.* 205, 1932.

33. Thomas, Moyer D., Russel H. Hendricks, and G. R. Hill, Sulfur Content of Vegetation, *Soil Sci.*, **70**:9–18, 1950.

34. Warrington, Katherine, The Effect of Boric Acid and Borax on the Broad Bean and Certain Other Plants, *Ann. Bot.*, **37**:629–672, 1923.

35. Whetstone, R. R., W. O. Robinson, and H. G. Byers, Boron Distribution in Soils and Related Data, *U.S. Dept. Agr. Tech. Bull.* 797, 1942.

36. Wischhusen, J. F., The Story of Fertilizer Manganese, *Fertilizer Rev.*, July–August, 1948.

CHAPTER 15

VARIATIONS IN PLANT COMPOSITION

There must be a balance between cations and anions in the soil solution at all times. Likewise there must be a balance between cations and anions within the plant at all times.

When a cation is absorbed by a plant, an equivalence in anions must be absorbed or be formed, otherwise an equivalence in cations must leave the plant.

When calcium, or any other basic cation, is taken up by the plant, an equivalent amount of ionized hydrogen takes the place of the base in the soil. The hydrogen may be excreted by the plant root, or CO_2 may be evolved by the root which will react with water to form carbonic acid, which, in turn, ionizes to release hydrogen. In other words, a soil has a certain capacity to hold cations, and as calcium, magnesium, and other bases are taken up by a plant, their place is taken by hydrogen.

When anions are absorbed by the plant, they are, for the most part, synthesized along with carbohydrates into complex organic compounds. After the anions are combined in organic matter, they are no longer considered as anions within the plant. When an anion is removed from the plant as a result of organic synthesis, a cation is left behind. The cation may be balanced by an incoming anion, or by the formation of an organic acid, or by the formation of a bicarbonate ion; otherwise the cation will diffuse back into the soil. At any rate, the total cations in the plant are balanced by anions (including the bicarbonate ions) plus organic acids.

For the most part, cations remain in water-soluble form in the plant. A small amount of magnesium is combined in chlorophyl, and perhaps some magnesium is combined in an organic compound in seeds. Practically all the potassium, calcium, and sodium and some magnesium are held in the inorganic form in plant tissue. The four cations calcium, potassium, magnesium, and sodium make up over 90 per cent of the cation content of plants. The elements sulfur, nitrogen, phosphorus, and chlorine form anions, and these four are usually considered in cation-anion studies. The data in Table 88 show the average percentage values for the principal cations and anion-forming elements.

349

It is evident from Table 88 that the total milliequivalents of sulfur, phosphorus, chlorine, and nitrogen exceed the total milliequivalents of potassium, sodium, calcium, and magnesium. This is due in part to the fact that some of the nitrogen, phosphorus, sulfur, and chlorine are combined in organic compounds and also that some of the nitrogen may have been absorbed as a cation in the form of ammonium.

TABLE 88. AVERAGE CHEMICAL COMPOSITION OF A LARGE NUMBER OF PLANTS GROWN UNDER COMPARABLE CONDITIONS (6)

Analyses	K	Na	Ca	Mg	S	P	Cl	N
Average %.....	1.47	0.37	0.77	0.30	0.26	0.22	0.73	1.52
% of K........	100	25	52	20				
% of N........	.....	.....	.....	.....	17	14	48	100
Meq./100 g.....	37.6	16.09	38.43	24.67	16.22	7.1	20.59	108.7
% of K, Meq...	100	43	102	66				
% of N, Meq...	.....	.....	.....	.....	15	7	19	100

Nitrogen is by far the predominating anion-forming element taken up by plants. The data in Table 88 show that more potassium is taken up by plants than any other cation. This is generally true of analyses of a large number of plants averaged together. On the other hand, if legumes are analyzed separately from grasses, it is found that more calcium than potassium is taken up. Table 89 shows the chemical composition of a large number of grasses and legumes.

TABLE 89. AVERAGE CHEMICAL COMPOSITION OF LEGUMES AND GRASSES (6)
Data* based on 274 samples of legumes and 320 samples of grasses. Percentage basis.

Plants	K	Na	Ca	Mg	S	P	Cl	N
Grasses..........	1.54	....	0.33	0.21	....	0.14	....	0.99
Legumes.........	1.13	....	1.47	0.38	....	0.18	....	2.38

* Data of Snider quoted by Cooper *et al.*

One important point which has not been shown by these tables is that plants which contain a high content of total anions will also contain a high content of total cations, although total anion-forming elements exceed total cations, as a general rule.

Effect of One Anion on Another. There is some evidence that an increase in phosphorus uptake by a plant will decrease the uptake of arsenic (13). There is also some evidence that increasing the uptake of sulfur by plants will reduce the uptake of selenium (14). Neither arsenic nor selenium is essential to the plant. The information is valuable, however, since some soils contain excessive amounts of arsenic or selenium, and these elements are poisonous to animals which eat the plants grown on the soils.

There is considerable evidence (22,23) that nitrogenous fertilizers may decrease the mineral content (including phosphorus) of crops, owing to the effect of nitrogen on rapid vegetative growth. The uptake of a large amount of phosphorus, however, is usually associated with a high nitrogen content of the plant. The high correlation between nitrogen and phosphorus percentage in plants is illustrated in Fig. 125.

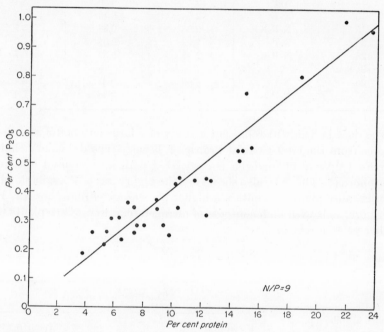

FIG. 125. The correlation of protein and phosphorus in samples of Kentucky bluegrass, Canada bluegrass, poverty grass, bent grass, timothy, and redtop grown in New York pastures (15).

There may be considerable variation in the ratio of nitrogen to phosphorus, even in the same variety, because of variation in availability of nitrogen and phosphorus. Hoagland and Arnon (11) have called attention to the fact that plants grown in moist soils may have a higher phosphorus content in relation to nitrogen than plants grown in a relatively dry soil. Data in Table 90 were taken from a table prepared by Lawton (16). While Lawton's data show that a deficiency of phosphorus in the soil may cause a wide nitrogen-to-phosphorus ratio in the plant, they also show that a high correlation exists between nitrogen and phosphorus percentages in the plant when the soil is fertilized with both nitrogen and phosphorus.

TABLE 90. VARIATION IN N AND P IN PLANTS GROWN IN THE GREENHOUSE
WITH DIFFERENT FERTILIZER TREATMENTS (16)

Soil moisture, per cent	Fertilizer treatment	Composition of corn plants		N to P ratio
		N, per cent	P, per cent	
Clarion loam:				
15	N-P	2.69	0.50	5.4
15	N-K	2.94	0.13	22.5
15	N-P-K	2.58	0.38	6.7
25	N-P	2.73	0.38	7.2
25	N-P-K	2.47	0.37	6.7
Clyde silt loam:				
25	N-P	3.63	0.57	6.4
25	N-P-K	2.77	0.38	7.3

The data in Table 91 represent a study of a large number of samples of grasses from the Gulf Coastal Prairie of Texas. The data show that an increased uptake of nitrogen is associated with an increased uptake of phosphorus. The data also show that the higher levels of available phosphorus cause plants to contain a higher percentage of phosphorus. Furthermore, soils with high contents of nitrogen tend to produce plants with higher protein percentage.

TABLE 91. VARIATIONS IN NITROGEN AND PHOSPHORUS IN PLANTS AS AFFECTED
BY THEIR SOIL LEVELS (8)

Active phosphoric acid in soils, p.p.m.	Total nitrogen in soils		
	0 to 0.12%	0.12 to 0.18%	Above 0.18%
Protein in forage			
0 to 16	7.34	8.93	9.73
16 to 30	8.15	9.14	10.88
30 to 100	9.87	9.59	11.37
101 or more	11.11	11.79	12.75
Phosphoric acid in forage			
0 to 16	0.26	0.31	0.32
16 to 30	0.26	0.32	0.32
30 to 100	0.36	0.43	0.48
101 or more	0.65	0.56	0.53

The data in Table 92 indicate the effect of increasing the phosphorus level of the soil on the phosphorus content of pasture plants. It is interesting to note that an increase in phosphorus uptake did not decrease nitrogen uptake. On the contrary, the increased uptake of phosphorus caused a slight increase in uptake of nitrogen.

TABLE 92. EFFECT OF SUPERPHOSPHATE ON CHEMICAL COMPOSITION OF PASTURE PLANTS (25)

Treatment	Kentucky bluegrass		White clover	
	Protein, per cent	P_2O_5, per cent	Protein, per cent	P_2O_5, per cent
Untreated.......	16.69	0.89	29.21	1.03
Superphosphate..	17.37	1.12	29.28	1.26

Effect of One Cation on Another. While there appears to be correlation in anion uptake, it has been well established that the increased uptake of one cation causes a decreased uptake of another.

This is one of the reasons that corn suffers for the lack of potassium on high-lime soils. Pierre and his associates (2,5,24) have shown that the increased uptake of calcium and magnesium is accompanied by a corresponding decrease in uptake of potassium.

It appears that a certain amount of phosphorus, nitrogen, and sulfur is necessary in synthesizing organic compounds in building the plant structures. On the other hand, the cations are not used in building organic compounds (except in the small amount already mentioned). It is desirable to have a certain balance, or ratio, of anions taken up by the plant, since they make up certain specific compounds. But with cations it is a different story. There is a minimum amount of each cation necessary to carry on plant growth. Once this minimum has been met, the additional amount of each cation taken up is largely for the purpose of cation balance. In other words, there is a certain cation balance in relation to anions in a plant that has to be maintained. Plants can show a great deal of variation between the ratios of different cations and still have normal growth. Hunter, Toth, and Bear (12) found that alfalfa could have a ratio of calcium to potassium anywhere between 1 to 1 and 5 to 1 and still have normal growth. They found that if the ratio was between 5 to 1 and 8 to 1, depression in yield occurred; and if the ratio was greater than 8 to 1, potassium-hunger signs appeared.

Stanford, Kelly, and Pierre (24) found that corn may have a $(Ca + Mg)/K$ ratio as wide as $3\frac{1}{2}$ to 1 and still have normal growth. The average ratio of $(Ca + Mg)/K$ is about 1 to 1 in corn.

Bartholomew and Jannsen (3) found that as they increased the available potassium in the soil, there was a corresponding increase in potassium percentage in the plant. They used the term *luxury consumption* to describe the uptake of excess potassium.

Lipman, Blair, and Prince (17) observed that liming of soil increased the percentage of calcium in corn and decreased the percentage of potassium in the plant. The importance of this relationship was pointed out in Chap. 11.

The greatest variations that occur in cation ratios are in potassium and calcium. These two cations appear to be antagonistic to a certain degree. Almost invariably, the increased uptake of one causes a depressed uptake of the other. This is also true of magnesium and calcium, and magnesium and potassium, but to a lesser extent. The data in Table 93, from solu-

TABLE 93. CHEMICAL COMPOSITION OF PLANTS AS AFFECTED BY HIGH AND LOW CONCENTRATIONS OF CALCIUM (19)

Crop	Solution	Relative ion equivalents				
		Ca	K	Mg	N	P
Barley plants.........	Control	8	20	5	50	17
Pea plants...........	Control	9	21	6	47	17
Barley plants.........	Low Ca	5	26	5	50	14
Pea plants...........	Low Ca	5	27	4	51	13

tion-culture work, show the marked tendency for calcium and potassium to replace each other.

Data in Table 94 show the variation in percentage of calcium and potassium in soybean hay as affected by potash fertilization. As the percentage of potassium increases in the plant as a result of potash fertilization, there is a corresponding decrease in percentage of calcium.

TABLE 94. PERCENTAGES OF K_2O AND CaO IN SOYBEAN HAY AS AFFECTED BY DIFFERENT LEVELS OF POTASH FERTILIZATION (1)

K_2O in fertilizer, lb.	Percentage in hay (air-dry basis)	
	K_2O	CaO
0	0.79	1.69
12	1.10	1.51
24	1.48	1.36
36	1.97	1.19
48	2.26	1.07
60	2.23	0.98

Critical Percentage of an Element in a Plant. A very interesting investigation was published by Macy (18) in 1936. He observed that when an element is deficient and a small addition is made, the increased uptake of the deficient element causes increased growth without an increase in percentage composition of that element. With increasing additions of the deficient element, however, the increase in growth levels off with the law-of-diminishing-returns curve, and the percentage compo-

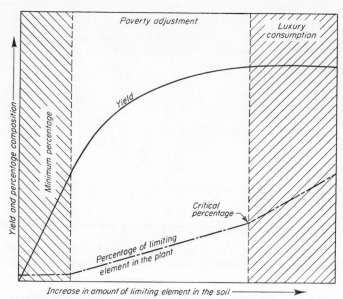

FIG. 126. A schematic diagram illustrating Macy's theory (18).

sition of the element increases. Finally, with still larger additions of the limiting element, yields are no longer increased, but the element is absorbed in greater quantities (more than is needed). He defined the point at which yields were no longer increased as the *critical percentage*. Figure 126 is a schematic diagram (drawn by W. H. Pierre) which shows Macy's ideas. Macy defines the term *critical percentage* as being the point (percentage of the limiting element in the plant) above which there is luxury consumption and below which there is poverty adjustment. In other words, the poverty adjustment means that plants are not getting 100 per cent sufficiency of the particular element.

Tables 95, 96, and 97 were selected by Pierre[1] to illustrate Macy's theory.

In the case of Bermuda grass, the first addition of phosphorus to the soil increased yield but did not increase the percentage composition.

[1] In "Lectures in Agronomy 655," Iowa State College, 1949.

This corresponds to the minimum percentage value that might occur in the plant. The second addition of phosphate caused further increase in yield and also an increase in percentage of phosphorus in the plant. The higher additions of phosphate caused the percentage of phosphorus in the plant to continue to increase, but the yield began to level off.

TABLE 95. EFFECTS OF DIFFERENT AMOUNTS OF SUPERPHOSPHATE ON BERMUDA AND RHODES GRASS (9)

Superphosphate, mg.	Total yield of dry matter, g.	Phosphoric acid in dry matter, per cent
Bermuda grass:		
0	19.5	0.18
200	52.5	0.18
400	59.5	0.24
800	72.8	0.32
1600	76.4	0.47
Rhodes grass:		
0	26.1	0.17
200	59.4	0.22
400	81.3	0.24
800	91.9	0.31
1600	95.0	0.59

One would judge from the data in Table 96 that 0.35 per cent is the critical percentage of phosphorus in oat grain. Adding more phosphorus to a soil producing grain with 0.35 per cent phosphorus would not be expected to increase yields.

TABLE 96. EFFECTS OF DIFFERENT AMOUNTS OF SUPERPHOSPHATE ON OAT GRAIN (Unpublished data, Iowa Agricultural Experiment Station)

Superphosphate, lb.	Gose farm		Smith farm		Purdie farm	
	Yield, bu./acre	P, per cent	Yield, bu./acre	P, per cent	Yield, bu./acre	P, per cent
0	39	0.29	52	0.33	46	0.35
150	57	0.31	62	0.37	45	0.37
300	64	0.35	65	0.39	48	0.41
450	66	0.36	64	0.43	51	0.44
600	55	0.42	65	0.43	49	0.44

If one could determine the critical percentage values for all the principal crops, it might be possible to predict fertilizer needs from knowledge of crop composition.

Apparently all the fields shown in Table 97 were deficient in phosphorus, and all had a high capacity to fix phosphorus.   There was no indication of 100 per cent sufficiency of phosphorus on any field.   Beeson (4) reported the data for a large number of alfalfa samples grown on various soils with various fertility levels.   He showed that alfalfa may have as much as 0.51 per cent phosphorus and as little as 0.15 per cent phosphorus.

TABLE 97. EFFECTS OF DIFFERENT AMOUNTS OF SUPERPHOSPHATE ON ALFALFA
(Unpublished data, Iowa Agricultural Experiment Station)

P_2O_5, lb.	Gose farm		Smith farm		Purdie farm	
	Yield, tons/acre	P, per cent	Yield, tons/acre	P, per cent	Yield, tons/acre	P, per cent
0	0.75	0.20	0.69	0.18	1.24	0.22
30	1.10	0.21	0.97	0.20	1.39	0.22
60	1.22	0.23	1.01	0.22	1.84	0.24
120	1.38	0.27	1.37	0.26	2.03	0.29
240	1.65	0.33	1.57	0.32	2.14	0.33

Macy pointed out in his article (18) that the theory of critical percentage in plants is application to anions but not to cations.   He bases his statement on the fact that one cation can replace another to a certain extent, while anions do not appear to be mutually replaceable in plants.

Relation of Age of a Plant to Its Chemical Composition.   By the time field crops have made 50 per cent of their growth, they may have taken up as much as 75 per cent or more of their total nutrients.   There is a definite lag in dry-matter accumulation as compared to nutrient accumulation, particularly in early growth.

It has long been recognized that pasture plants are more nutritious when young.   The percentages of protein and minerals are higher in young plants than in older plants.   The data in Table 98 show the chemical composition of orchard grass at different stages of maturity.

TABLE 98. CHEMICAL COMPOSITION OF ORCHARD GRASS CUT AT DIFFERENT
STAGES OF MATURITY (7)
Percentage basis

Age when cut, months	Protein	Fiber	P_2O_5	CaO
1	12.3	21.3	0.92	0.91
2	11.8	23.0	0.86	0.94
3	9.1	32.4	0.82	0.99

Figure 127 shows that when small-grain crops had made 20 per cent of
their growth (as measured by dry matter), they had taken up 45 per cent
of the total nitrogen and potassium.   The uptake of phosphorus is more
closely related to accumulation of dry matter.   This relationship is also

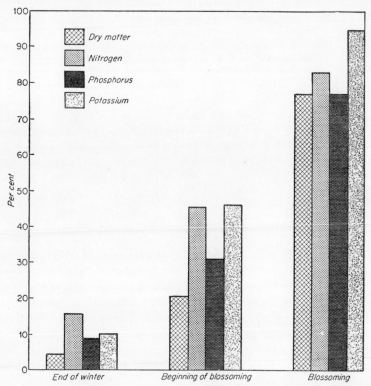

FIG. 127. The percentage of the total dry matter, nitrogen, phosphorus, and potassium
accumulated at different stages of growth.   Average of winter wheat, winter rye, and
barley grown in Germany (20).

brought out by Fig. 128, which represents data for corn.   In other words,
when 50 per cent of the dry matter is produced, a little over 50 per cent
of the phosphorus is taken up.

The rate of potassium uptake may be very high in early stages of growth
without injurious effect.   The data for corn in Fig. 128 show that more
potassium was taken up in midseason than at the end of the season.   This
was apparently due to potassium being excreted from the plant.   The loss
may be due to excretion to leaf surface where it may be washed off by rain,
or the potassium may diffuse back to the soil through the root system.

The fact that an excess of potassium may be taken up early in growth
without injurious effect is very important to the agronomist.   Enough

potassium to supply the entire crop needs may be placed in the hill at
planting time.   This would not be true of nitrogen.   The application of
nitrogen in the hill at planting time should be just sufficient to give the
crop a start.   If a large amount of nitrogen is applied at planting time,

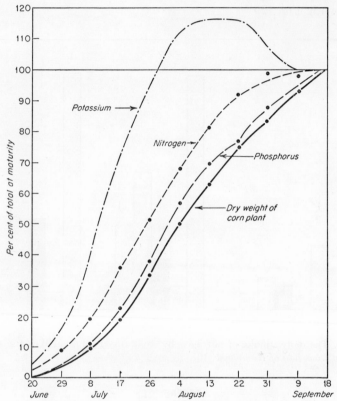

Fig. 128. The rate of uptake of nutrients compared to the growth rate of corn.   [*Calculated from data of Sayre* (21).]

there may be injury to the seedling; also, the uptake of excess nitrogen
early in growth may cause a depression in final yield.   *If the soil cannot
supply sufficient nitrogen from organic-matter decomposition after the first
month's growth, a side-dressing of nitrogen should then be made.*

By the use of the curve in Fig. 128, the number of pounds of nitrogen
needed per day for any size crop of corn grown on 1 acre may be calculated.   Assuming the yield to be 50 bu., and assuming 100 lb. of nitrogen
taken up by the crop, it would be found that about 20 lb. of nitrogen is
used during the first 20 days.   During the next 25 days, about 50 lb. of
nitrogen is taken up.   In other words, 1 lb. of nitrogen would be taken

up per day during the first 20 days, and 2 lb. of nitrogen per day from the twentieth to the forty-fifth day.

Hammond (10) found that soybeans took up less than a pound of nitrogen each day during the first 50 days of growth, but after the first 50 days they took up over 2½ lb. of nitrogen per acre per day. His data are shown in Fig. 129.

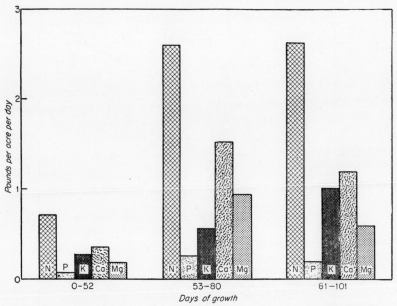

FIG. 129. The daily uptake of nutrients by soybeans growing on Webster silt loam. [*Prepared from data of Hammond (10).*]

REFERENCES

1. Adams, J. E., H. M. Bogg, and E. M. Roller, Effect of Fertilizers on Composition of Soybean Hay and Seed and of Crop Management on Carbon, Nitrogen, and Reaction of Norfolk Sand, *U.S. Dept. Agr. Tech. Bull.* 586, 1937.
2. Allaway, W. H., and W. H. Pierre, Availability, Fixation, and Liberation of Potassium in High-lime Soils, *J. Am. Soc. Agron.*, **31**:940–953, 1939.
3. Bartholomew, R. P., and G. Jannsen, Luxury Consumption of Potassium by Plants and Its Significance, *J. Am. Soc. Agron.*, **21**:751–767, 1929.
4. Beeson, Kenneth C., The Mineral Composition of Crops with Particular Reference to the Soils in Which They Were Grown, *U.S. Dept. Agr. Misc. Pub.* 369, 1941.
5. Bower, C. A., and W. H. Pierre, Potassium Response of Various Crops on High-lime Soils in Relation to Their Content of Potassium, Calcium, Magnesium and Sodium, *J. Am. Soc. Agron.*, **26**:608–614, 1944.
6. Cooper, H. P., J. H. Mitchell, and N. R. Page, The Relation of the Energy Properties of Soil Nutrients to the Chemical Composition of Plants, *Soil Sci. Soc. Amer. Proc.* **12**:359–363, 1947.

7. Fagan, T. W., The Influence of Management on the Nutritive Value of Herbage Plants, *Agr. Progress*, Vol. 8, 1931.

8. Fudge, J. F., and G. S. Fraps, The Chemical Composition of Forage Grasses from the Gulf Coast Prairie as Related to Soils and to Requirements for Range Cattle, *Tex. Agr. Expt. Sta. Bull.* 644, 1944.

9. Fudge, J. F., and G. S. Fraps, The Value of Different Phosphates for Various Texas Soils and Grasses, as Indicated by Pot Experiments, *Tex. Agr. Expt. Sta. Bull.* 672, 1945.

10. Hammond, Luther C., "Rate of Nutrient Uptake by Soybeans on Two Iowa Soils," Master's Thesis, Iowa State College, 1947.

11. Hoagland, D. R., and D. I. Arnon, Physiological Aspects of Availability of Nutrients for Plant Growth, *Soil Sci.*, 51:431–444, 1941.

12. Hunter, A. S., S. J. Toth, and F. E. Bear, Calcium-Potassium Ratio for Alfalfa, *Soil Sci.*, 55:61–72, 1943.

13. Hurd-Karrer, Annie M., Antagonism of Certain Elements Essential to Plants toward Chemically Related Toxic Substances, *Plant Physiol.*, 14:9–29, 1939.

14. Hurd-Karrer, Annie M., Selenium Injury to Wheat Plants and Its Inhibition by Sulfur, *J. Agr. Research*, 49:343–357, 1934.

15. Johnstone-Wallace, D. B., The Influence of Grazing Management and Plant Associations on the Chemical Composition of Pasture Plants, *J. Am. Soc. Agron.*, 29:441–455, 1937.

16. Lawton, Kirk, The Influence of Aeration on the Growth and Absorption of Nutrients by Corn Plants, *Soil Sci. Soc. Amer. Proc.*, 10:263–268, 1945.

17. Lipman, J. G., A. W. Blair, and A. L. Prince, The Effect of Lime and Fertilizers on the Potash Content of Soils and Crops, *Intern. Rev. Agr.*, 4:546–553, 1926.

18. Macy, Paul, The Quantitative Mineral Nutrient Requirement of Plants, *Plant Physiol.*, 11:749–764, 1936.

19. Newton, J. D., A Comparison of the Absorption of Inorganic Elements and of the Buffer Systems of Legumes and Nonlegumes, and Its Bearing on Existing Theories, *Soil Sci.*, 16:181–204, 1923.

20. Remy, T., Fertilization in Its Relationship to the Course of Nutrient Absorption by Plants, *Soil Sci.*, 46:187–209, 1938.

21. Sayre, J. D., Mineral Accumulation in Corn, *Plant Physiol.*, 23:267–281, 1948.

22. Sheets, O. A., Effect of Fertilizer, Soil Composition, and Certain Climatological Conditions on the Calcium and Phosphorus Content of Turnip Greens, *J. Agr. Research*, 68:145–190, 1944.

23. Smith, J. C., L. C. Capp, and R. C. Potts, The Effects of Fertilizer Treatment upon Yield and Composition of Wheat Forage, *Soil Sci. Soc. Amer. Proc.*, 14:241–245, 1949.

24. Stanford, George, Joe B. Kelly, and W. H. Pierre, Cation Balance in Corn Grown on High-lime Soils in Relation to Potassium Deficiency, *Soil Sci. Soc. Amer. Proc.*, 6:335–341, 1941.

25. Vinall, H. N., and H. L. Wilkins, The Effect of Fertilizer Applications on the Composition of Pasture Grasses, *J. Am. Soc. Agron.*, 28:562–569, 1936.

CHAPTER 16

CROP ROTATIONS AND SOIL FERTILITY

There are two reasonable criteria for estimating whether or not soil fertility is being maintained. The first measure, which is perhaps the most popular, is the maintenance of soil organic matter. The second is the maintenance of yields. Unfortunately, neither of the two alone serves as a satisfactory measure. Figure 130 illustrates this point. Iowa is used

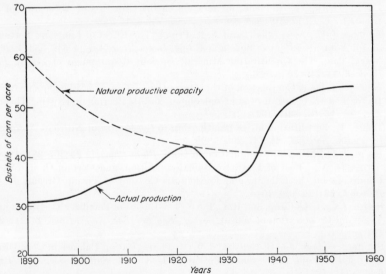

FIG. 130. The actual production of corn in Iowa compared to the natural productive capacity of the soil.

as the example here, since Iowa has long been recognized as a state with a high percentage of its land classified as grade A, or excellent. Corn is used as the crop example, since more than 40 per cent of the cultivated land of Iowa is planted to corn.

Numerous soil samples from cropland in Iowa which have been analyzed over the past several years have shown an average of about 4.0 per cent organic matter. Studies made by different individuals (1,17,18) have shown that the cropland has an average of about two-thirds as much organic matter as adjacent virgin soil. On the basis of such studies we may estimate that soils of Iowa originally contained an average of about 6.0 per cent organic matter. Furthermore, it is known from various studies (7,9) that soil organic matter decomposes rapidly when the soil is first cultivated, and then the rate slows down and gradually levels off; consequently, the line for decomposition is shown as a curve. Averaging a large number of Iowa soils together, it is believed that a soil will produce about 10 bu. of corn for each 1 per cent of organic matter. We estimate that Iowa soils were capable of producing about 60 bu. of corn per acre initially.

The present capability of Iowa soils may not be greater than 40 bu. The state has increased its annual fertilizer use from about 8000 tons for the years 1935 to 1939 to about 610,000 tons in 1954. Furthermore, Iowa ranks high among the states in use of lime. Hybrid corn came into prominence in 1939, and along with hybrid corn came many other improved cultural practices, including mechanization, contour tillage, and better control of insects and diseases. And not to be forgotten are the favorable climatic cycle and favorable prices, which induced farmers to do their best. It is quite possible that the difference between 40 bu. and present yields of 50 to 60 bu. may be due to increased fertility, which better cultural practices and hybrid corn have been able to utilize fully.

During the years 1890 to 1920, it is apparent that the natural fertility was not fully utilized. The open-pollinated varieties of corn were not making full utilization of the natural fertility. Yet during that period yields were gradually improving, while fertility was declining. To look at corn yields without cognizance of organic-matter changes, one would say that, for the state as a whole, fertility was gradually being improved from 1890 to 1920. We know this is not true when we recognize the losses of organic matter.

If we look at organic-matter maintenance as the criterion we can see its weakness, because if yields are climbing and organic matter is declining, we are more concerned with yields, and organic-matter level becomes secondary. After all, our primary aim in soil management is to seek the highest yields we can maintain consistent with greatest profit.

Organic-matter maintenance should not be forgotten, but neither should an attempt be made to set up a management system merely to maintain organic matter, assuming that maintenance of organic matter is soil conservation.

The organic-matter level that can be maintained in a given soil is determined by the income and outgo of nitrogen and carbon and the amount of tillage. Regardless of the management system, a soil will lose or gain organic matter and will finally reach an equilibrium level which can be maintained indefinitely under the same management system. The schematic diagram in Fig. 131 illustrates this principle.

It is assumed in Fig. 131 that intertilled crops in the rotation will not maintain the virgin level of organic matter of grassland soils. It is real-

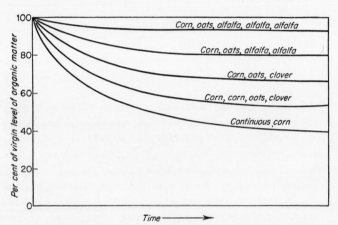

FIG. 131. A schematic diagram showing the effect of different cropping systems on soil organic matter, assuming use of enough mineral fertilizers for maintenance of mineral nutrients.

ized, however, that some well-managed forest soils have more organic matter after long periods of tillage than they had under virgin conditions (19). It is believed that a 3-year rotation of corn-oats-clover will maintain organic matter at about two-thirds of the virgin level in Middle Western soils. If a soil has been depleted of organic matter by continuous corn to half its virgin level, we would expect organic matter to be increased by a change to corn-oats-clover. On the other hand, if the level of organic matter is at, say, 90 per cent of virgin level because of "newness" of the soil or a rotation of, say, corn-oats-alfalfa-alfalfa, we would expect to realize a decrease in organic matter by changing to a corn-oats-clover rotation. Figure 132 is a schematic diagram illustrating the principle that *a gain or loss in organic matter of a soil under a given rotation is determined by the level of organic matter at the start of the rotation.* By the same reasoning we should expect a soil which is maintaining organic matter under corn-oats-clover to increase in percentage of organic matter if changed to corn-oats-alfalfa-alfalfa.

Rotation Studies in Maintenance of Organic Matter. *Missouri.* A study was made at Columbia, Missouri, on Putnam silt loam to determine the effects of the cropping system on the maintenance of organic matter. A summary of the data for the top 7 in. of soil is shown in Table 99.

The soil in the plots had been in cultivation about 60 years when the study was started and had been farmed under typical Missouri farming methods. The corn-wheat-clover rotation maintained organic matter. The contents of organic matter were increased slightly under corn, wheat, and clover with manure. The organic matter was increased considerably by the other cropping practices except with rye green manure. The

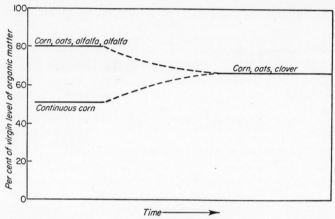

FIG. 132. A schematic diagram showing the effect of rotation on the change in organic-matter level of a soil.

organic matter declined steadily with rye because of no provision for income of nitrogen.

The study continued over a 24-year period, and in the corn-wheat-clover series there were eight clover crops. During that period 850 lb. of nitrogen was removed in crops and the soil gained 20 lb. of nitrogen. This means that eight red clover crops contributed 870 lb. of nitrogen, or an average of 109 lb. of nitrogen each year. This is based on the assump-

TABLE 99. PERCENTAGE NITROGEN CONTENT OF SURFACE SOIL AT DIFFERENT
SAMPLING DATES (12)
Each value is the average of two plots

Crops	1917	1921	1929	1934	1941
Corn-wheat-clover................	0.136	0.132	0.143	0.137	0.137
Corn-wheat-clover and manure....	0.139	0.132	0.149	0.148	0.146
Rye and cowpeas turned under...	0.137	0.144	0.141	0.147	0.151
Rye turned under................	0.137	0.128	0.116	0.109	0.105
Red clover, taken off............	0.143	0.140	0.155	0.158	0.160
Red clover, turned under.........	0.137	0.146	0.161	0.164	0.170
Alfalfa, taken off................	0.132	0.133	0.149	0.157	0.154
Bluegrass sod clipped............	0.105	....	0.125	....	0.132

tion that nitrogen lost by leaching is equivalent to the gain from rainfall and nonsymbiotic fixation.

The Sanborn field at Columbia, Missouri, was in virgin state of fertility when the experimental plots were laid out in 1888. Samples from the different plots were collected after 25 and 50 years. Table 100 shows the changes in nitrogen status of the variously treated plots. The continuous-

TABLE 100. NITROGEN CONTENT OF SURFACE 7 IN. OF SOIL ON UNTREATED
SANBORN FIELD PLOTS (9)
Columbia, Missouri

Cropping system	Total nitrogen, lb./acre			Percentage of total nitrogen depleted		Percentage of nitrogen depleted annually	
	Calculated for beginning of experiment*	After 25 years of cropping	After 50 years of cropping	First 25 years	50-year period	First 25 years	50-year period
Corn continuously..	3250*	1575	1420	51.5	56.3	2.06	1.13
Wheat continuously..	3250	2040	1750	37.2	46.1	1.48	0.92
Timothy continuously..	3250	2485	2363	23.5	27.3	0.94	0.54
Corn-oats-wheat-clover..	3250	2573	1917	20.8	41.0	0.83	0.83
Corn-oats-wheat-clover-timothy, 2 yr.	3250	2037	1943	37.3	40.2	1.49	0.82

* Average nitrogen content for beginning of experiment was determined from average nitrogen analyses of samples taken from adjacent virgin areas.

corn yields averaged 28.4 bushels from 1889 to 1898 and 12.7 bushels for the period 1928 to 1937, which represents a decrease of 55.2 per cent (9). The average decrease in nitrogen under continuous corn was 2.06 per cent during the first 25 years and only 0.2 per cent per year during the last 25 years. The organic-matter level had just about come to equilibrium by the end of 50 years at about 44 per cent of the virgin level.

The decrease in organic matter was beginning to level off under continuous wheat, continuous timothy, and the 6-year rotation of corn, oats, wheat, clover, and 2 years of timothy. But the decline of organic matter under corn-oats-wheat-clover did not appear to be leveling off after 50 years, and 41 per cent of the virgin level of nitrogen had been lost.

South Dakota. A study has been under way at the South Dakota Experiment Station to see the effects of different fertilizer treatments on the soil under a 5-year rotation of corn, wheat, barley, oats, and red clover. The experiment was started in 1908 on Barnes loam. The residues, including straw and cornstalks, are removed, and the clover is harvested for hay and seed. The plots are laid out as an N-P-K factorial (each nutrient alone and in all combinations). The plots receive 350 lb. of nitrate of soda, 200 lb. of superphosphate, and 200 lb. of muriate of potash each year except the year the plots are in clover. The nitrogen in the surface soil was steadily declining up to 1939 when the last report was published (14). The loss was nearly the same for treated and untreated plots. The reduction in organic matter ranged from 14.1 per cent on check plots to 16.8 per cent on N-P-K plots.

The soil contained 6.3 per cent organic matter at the beginning of the experiment (in 1908) and was rapidly losing organic matter in 1939. It is expected that the losses will decrease somewhat in the future until eventually an equilibrium level is established. The organic-matter content of the subsurface (below 7 in.) did not change significantly between 1908 and 1939.

Illinois. Lee and Bray (11) made a study of several experimental fields in Illinois to determine rates of organic-matter loss. A summary of their study is presented in Table 101. Every one of the rotation plots shown in Table 101 was losing nitrogen and organic matter in 1945. Lee and

TABLE 101. LOSS OF NITROGEN FROM DIFFERENT FIELDS IN ILLINOIS UNDER
DIFFERENT CROPPING SYSTEMS
Untreated plots

Field	Rotation	Decrease in N up to 1945	
		Number of years	Decrease, per cent
Light-colored soils:			
Ewing.............	Corn-oats-mixed hay-wheat	27	19.0
Raleigh...........	Corn-oats-mixed hay-wheat	27	12.9
Oblong...........	Corn-soybeans-wheat-timothy	14	16.7
Dark-colored soils:			
Joliet.............	Corn-soybeans-corn-oats-wheat-clover-alfalfa hay	18	15.8
Hartsburg.........	Corn-corn-oats-wheat	19	15.3
Kewanee..........	Corn-corn-oats-wheat	18	9.6

Bray found that fertilized plots as well as unfertilized plots were still losing nitrogen.

Table 102 shows the losses of nitrogen from variously treated plots. The greatest loss of nitrogen was from untreated plots, even though yields were lower. The smallest losses in nitrogen resulted from the fertilizers which gave the highest yields. The fertilizers stimulated nitrogen fixation. The nitrogen obtained from sources other than surface soil humus was directly proportional to added fertility.

TABLE 102. ESTIMATED LOSSES OF NITROGEN FROM FIELDS, 1935 TO 1945, AND ESTIMATED LOSS IN 34 YEARS (11)

Treatment	Soil nitrogen decrease, lb./acre	Nitrogen removed in crops, lb./acre	Nitrogen from sources other than surface-soil organic matter, lb./acre	Estimated loss of nitrogen in 34 years, lb./acre
Light-colored soils:				
0..................	240	126*	(−114)	860
R-L..............	130	275	145	442
R-L-P............	180	331	151	612
R-L-P-K..........	110	554	444	374
Dark-colored soils:				
0..................	315	597	282	1070
R-L..............	252	507	255	860
R-L-P............	205	521	316	697
R-L-P-K..........	95	549	454	323

0 = no treatment, no catch crop, and straw and stover removed; R = all stover and straw turned under, sweet clover catch crop turned under after small grain; L = lime added to correct acidity; P = 4 tons rock phosphate per acre prior to 1924; K = 400 lb. KCl per acre every 4 years.

* Includes nitrogen in straw and stover, which were removed only in check plots.

Iowa. Peevy, Smith, and Brown (13) investigated the changes in organic-matter content of soils under various rotations at Ames, Iowa. The soils are of the Clarion and Webster series and rather high in organic matter. In 1937, samples were collected and compared to samples which had been collected in 1917. Table 103 shows the changes in organic matter.

These plots were farmed prior to 1914, at which time the rotation experiments were started. The virgin level of organic matter is unknown for the plots. The important point to remember is that the organic-matter level was well below the virgin level when the soils were sampled in 1917.

The stover and straw were removed from the untreated plots, which caused a much greater loss of organic matter than occurred in the treated plots. Two tons of manure per year with lime but without residues did not maintain organic matter, while the return of residues with lime more than maintained the organic matter.

At Clarinda, Iowa, on Marshall silt loam, plots in corn-oats-red clover did not change in organic-matter content from 1931 to 1942. Neither did continuous-bluegrass plots change significantly in organic-matter content. The continuous-corn plot decreased from 3.39 per cent organic matter in

TABLE 103. CHANGES IN ORGANIC-MATTER CONTENT OF CLARION AND WEBSTER SOILS UNDER CORN-OATS-CLOVER ROTATION (13)

Treatment	Organic matter, per cent		
	1917	1937	Difference
None...........................	4.06	3.60	−0.46
	3.69	3.20	−0.49
	6.18	5.51	−0.67
Manure* and limestone..............	3.58	3.42	−0.16
	4.28	3.44	−0.84
	6.91	6.56	−0.35
Manure,* limestone, and rock phosphate†	3.68‡	3.69	+0.01
Crop residues and limestone...........	3.89‡	4.13	+0.24
Crop residues, limestone, and rock phosphate........................	4.54	4.47	−0.07
	2.78	2.70	−0.08

* 6 tons of manure every 3 years.
† 750 lb. of rock phosphate added every 3 years.
‡ No replicate data available.

1931 to 2.86 per cent organic matter in 1942 (8). These plots were located on a slope which had been farmed rather hard prior to the beginning of the experiment station in 1931. The soil organic matter was perhaps two-thirds of the virgin level in the rotation plots.

During the period 1931 to 1942, the average corn yield was 42.9 bu. per acre, the yield of oats averaged 29.8 bu. per acre, and the red clover yielded 1.3 tons per acre (5). Every 3 years a total of 125 lb. of nitrogen was removed in crops, therefore 125 lb. of nitrogen was added to the soil every 3 years by rainfall or nitrogen fixation, inasmuch as the nitrogen content of the surface soil remained the same. Even though hay was removed, the red clover contributed about 60 lb. of nitrogen during each rotation.

Pennsylvania. The land now occupied by the Jordan plots in Pennsylvania (second oldest plots in America) was farmed from 1838 to 1868. In 1869 the first plots were laid out and used for miscellaneous studies until 1880. In 1881 the plots were changed to a 4-year rotation of corn-oats-wheat-mixed hay, in which manurial treatment had been applied to corn and wheat.

The yields gradually declined in the unfertilized plots, while yields were maintained at about the original level with commercial fertilizers (where no organic matter was returned except in residues). Of course, the fertilized plots produced more roots and stubble, which caused them to have actually a greater turnover of organic matter than was available to the untreated plots. It is especially significant that yields were as great with commercial fertilizer as with 10 tons of manure (containing about the same amount of nitrogen as applied in the commercial fertilizer).

TABLE 104. YIELDS OF CROPS ON THE JORDAN PLOTS OF PENNSYLVANIA,
1882 TO 1930 (20)
By 8-year periods

Plot treatment	Total yield of all crops in rotation, lb./4 acres						
	Average of each two rotations						Average 1882–1930
	1882–1889	1890–1897	1898–1905	1906–1913	1914–1921	1922–1930	
Untreated............	14,562	11,907	8,855	8,432	8,215	8,266	10,037
P-K.................	17,448	17,697	15,653	17,248	16,434	17,549	16,781
N-P-K..............	18,577	19,901	17,964	19,456	18,868	17,885	18,783
10 tons manure........	17,014	18,585	18,590	19,615	19,467	18,346	18,602
6 tons manure and lime	17,306	18,974	17,787	19,417	19,342	18,274	18,516

P-K = 48 lb. P_2O_5 and 100 lb. K_2O per rotation; N-P-K = 48 lb. P_2O_{5}, 100 lb. K_2O, and 48 to 72 lb. N per rotation.

The organic-matter content of the plots compared with the grassland borders is shown in Table 105. The data represent averages of four tiers of plots, or four replicates.

The organic-matter content of soils receiving only phosphorus and potassium was considerably greater than that of untreated plots after 72 years. The difference in organic-matter content between N-P-K and

TABLE 105. ORGANIC-MATTER CONTENT OF THE JORDAN PLOTS COMPARED
WITH THEIR GRASSLAND BORDER AFTER 72 YEARS, 1869 TO 1940 (20)

Soil treatment since 1881	Organic matter		Percentage of grass borders on plot
	Cultivated plots, lb./acre	Grass borders, lb./acre	
Untreated.................	50,075	80,550	62.0
P-K......................	58,700	80,625	72.8
N-P-K....................	58,600	82,900	70.8
6 tons manure and lime......	69,050	85,150	81.2
10 tons manure..............	73,000	81,150	90.0

P-K = 48 lb. P_2O_5 and 100 lb. K_2O per rotation; N-P-K = 48 lb. P_2O_5, 100 lb. K_2O, and 72 to 100 lb. N.

P-K was not significant, but the average yields on N-P-K plots were 12 per cent greater than yields on the P-K plots. The addition of manure made considerable difference in organic-matter content of the soils compared to N-P-K treatments, but the crop yields were about the same.

The plots in tier 1 were sampled in 1922 and again in 1940. During the 18-year period the untreated plots lost 2100 lb. of organic matter, while the treated plots gained 1800, 2200, and 6700 lb. of organic matter, respectively, for P-K, N-P-K, and 6 tons of manure and lime; and the grass borders gained 15,800 lb. of organic matter.

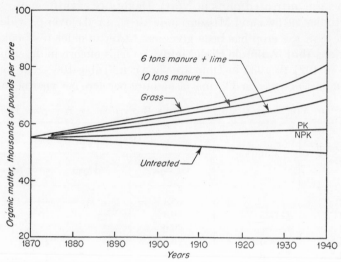

Fig. 133. The changes in organic-matter content of the Jordan plots as affected by fertility practices.

The amounts of organic matter were similar for the different plots in 1869, and furthermore, the grass borders were in cultivation in 1869. We do not know what the original amounts of organic matter were, but apparently the amount was about 55,000 lb. This amount may be off one or two thousand pounds but appears fairly close on inspection of Fig. 133. Figure 133 is the author's interpretation of changes that occurred in the organic-matter content of the Jordan plots from 1869 to 1940.

Summary of Studies in Maintenance of Organic Matter. The experimental plots in North Dakota and Illinois were still losing organic matter at the time of the reports, but these plots were at the virgin level of organic matter when the experiments were started. The plots in Iowa and Pennsylvania and the plots in Missouri (other than the Sanborn plots) were below the virgin level of organic matter to begin with, and in certain rotations (or treatments) the organic matter has been increased. Organic matter was maintained in Missouri and in Iowa with corn-oats-red clover where the soil contained approximately two-thirds of the virgin level of organic matter.

The addition of manure to rotation plots in Missouri and Pennsylvania caused an increase in organic matter, but of course these soils were well below the virgin level of organic matter when the experiments were started.

The studies in Pennsylvania and Illinois indicate that fertilizers help to maintain organic matter at a higher level than in untreated soils. On the other hand, the fertilized plots lost about the same amount of organic matter as the untreated plots in North Dakota or slightly more.

The studies in Iowa and Missouri indicate that red clover provides more nitrogen than the crop has been given credit for in older textbooks.

Rotations That Maintain High Yields. Yields of corn in different rotations from 1921 to 1935 in Ohio are shown in Table 106. All rotations in the Ohio study received 2 tons of manure per acre per year of rotation,

TABLE 106. YIELDS OF CORN IN VARIOUS ROTATIONS AT WOOSTER, OHIO (6)

Number of years	Rotation	Yields of corn, bu./acre		
		1st year	2d year	3d year
2	C-S	55.1		
2	C-O$_{Scl}$	66.4		
2	C-W$_{Scl}$	64.0		
3	C-W-RC	66.3		
3	C-O-RC	72.1		
4	C-O-W-RC	62.0		
4	C-C-W-RC	66.2	55.9	
4	C-S-W-RC	66.9		
4	C-O-RC-W$_{Scl}$	74.5		
4	C-A-A-A	78.4		
4	C-O-W-T	70.6		
5	C-C-S-W-RC	70.7	67.4	
5	C-C-C-W-RC	67.7	60.3	61.1
5	C-O-A-A-A	82.1		

C = corn; S = soybeans; RC = red clover; A = alfalfa; O = oats; Scl = sweet clover green manure; W = wheat; T = timothy.

all of which was applied to the first year of corn in the rotation. The soils were limed to pH 6.5 and received 32 lb. of P_2O_5 each year. The differences in corn yields between rotations might have been much greater had there been no manure applied. While longer experiments are desirable for comparing rotations, one may see that with the use of manure and fertilizers, moderately high yields can be maintained with as much as one-half to three-fifths of the cropland in corn. The rotation that yielded the least corn was a continuously clean-tilled rotation. The highest yields of corn were obtained where corn followed alfalfa and where corn followed sweet clover green manure in a 4-year rotation of corn, oats, red clover, and wheat (with sweet clover green manure).

The Morrow plots at Urbana, Illinois, were laid out in 1876 and represent the oldest experiments in this country.[1] Three systems of cropping have been investigated, along with the effect of manure, lime, and phosphorus on the yields of crops. Farm manure, including litter, is applied in proportion to the weight of the crops grown during the previous rotation and is plowed under before the corn crop.

The data for the Morrow plots from 1888 to 1942 are shown in Table 107.

The yields of corn were slowly declining in the corn-oats rotation up to 1942, while yields of corn remained high and at about the same level during the period from 1904 to 1942 where fertilizers were used and sweet clover was turned under.

The yields of corn were slightly higher, and yields of oats were considerably higher in the 3-year rotation of corn-oats-clover compared to the 2-year rotation of corn-oats (sweet clover).[2]

The yields of continuous corn have reached equilibrium levels of about 26 bu. on untreated plots and nearly 50 bu. on plots receiving manure and fertilizer.

The return of manure to the corn-oats (sweet clover) rotation is not representative of present farming practices, because farmers who follow such a system are usually cash grain farmers. It is probable that the equilibrium level with corn-oats (sweet clover) with only lime and phosphate would be a few bushels below the level where manure is also applied.

Most of the older rotation studies have been conducted with open-pollinated corn. The yields are lower than in studies made more recently with hybrid corn. One of the more recent rotation studies with hybrid corn is shown in Table 108. The study was started in 1942 at Clarinda, Iowa, on Marshall silt loam, and Table 108 is a summary of corn yields for the 5-year period from 1950 to 1954.

The Clarinda experiment has been run long enough to show trends in maintenance of yield, and the meadow rotations show up better than sweet clover–green manure rotations. At the present time, therefore, there is considerable margin in favor of the meadow rotations in so far as corn yields are concerned. The oat yields were practically the same in meadow rotations as in sweet clover–green manure rotations. There was no nitrogen fertilizer added to any of the plots, therefore the success of

---

[1] The data for the first 12 years were lost.

[2] Sweet clover shown in parentheses means that the crop is used as a catch crop for green manure.

the corn crop depended on the amount of green manure or meadow residues turned under. Where grasshopper damage was severe on the legume plots, the succeeding crop of corn was affected. A dry summer on sweet clover also had a serious effect on the yield of the succeeding crop of corn.

TABLE 107. COMPARISON OF THREE CROPPING SYSTEMS MODIFIED FOR STUDY OF EFFECTS OF SOIL TREATMENT (3)

Period	Years	Treatment system*	Crops			All crops		
			Corn, bu.	Oats, bu.	Red clover, tons	Value	Index	
							Gross	Net
Continuous corn, System I								
1888–1942	55	0	29.2	....	....	$14.60	100	100
1904–1942	39	0	24.9	....	....	12.45	85	85
		M-L-P	42.7	....	....	21.32	146	110
1931–1942	12	0	26.0	....	....	13.02	89	89
		M-L-P	50.3	....	....	25.13	172	137
Corn-oats, System II								
1888–1942	55	0	36.2	36.9	....	$14.66	100	100
1904–1942	39	0	34.0	34.7	....	13.62	93	93
		M-L-P$_{Scl}$	61.2	60.0	....	24.15	165	130
1931–1942	12	0	33.5	36.4	....	13.83	95	95
		M-L-P$_{Scl}$	61.8	61.3	....	24.65	169	134
Corn-oats-clover, System III								
1888–1942	55	0	48.0	49.6	1.44	$17.81	122	122
1904–1942	39	0	47.4	50.2	1.22	17.70	121	121
		M-L-P	66.5	68.2	2.66	27.12	186	150
1931–1942	12	0	43.2	59.1	1.26	17.31	119	119
		M-L-P	63.6	77.4	2.55	26.82	184	148

* Annual acre rates at which materials were applied through 1942 and the last years of application were as follows: L = lime, 300 lb. (1919); P = rock phosphate on west half, 338 lb., bone phosphate on east half, 84 lb. (1925). Scl = sweet clover green manure; M = manure.

There is no best rotation for any area, but there are several features about a rotation which should be emphasized. Rotations alone will not maintain high yields; high yields require a favorable soil reaction and an adequate supply of nitrogen and mineral elements supplied through a combination of legumes and commercial fertilizer. For permanently high productivity, the rotation should receive as much P_2O_5 as is removed in the highest yields expected. As much nitrogen should be added to the rotation by legumes or commercial fertilizer, or both, as is removed in the highest yields expected. Potassium should be applied with each crop in adequate amounts as indicated by soil test. As much SO_3 as P_2O_5 should be used either as a constituent of the regular fertilizer or as a supplement

TABLE 108. EFFECT OF CROP ROTATIONS ON YIELD OF CORN (2)
Marshall silt loam, Clarinda, Iowa*

Rotation	Percentage of cropland in corn	Average yields[†] 1950-1954 bu./acre	
		1st-year corn	2d-year corn
C-O-M-M	25	99.5	
C-O-M	33	103.7	
C-C-O-M-M	40	97.9	88.4
C-C-O-M	50	99.3	82.9
C-Os_{cl}	50	82.4	
C-C-Os_{cl}	67	81.1	
C-O	50	51.6	

C = corn, O = oats, M = meadow, Scl = sweet clover green manure.
* Plots receive 100 lb. 0-20-0 per acre per year.
† Data represent the average of triplicate plots.

to the regular fertilizer applications during the rotation. Minor elements should be regarded as a potential need, and small amounts should be tried in small plots every 5 to 10 years wherever yields are not so high as expected.

On soils which have low aeration porosity and are subject to erosion, rotations with a high proportion of legume hay crops should be used. On well-aerated soils not subject to erosion, the situation lends itself with greatest advantage to the growth of clean-tilled crops. On soils subject to erosion, where the erosion cannot be controlled by terracing and contour tillage, the longer rotations such as corn-oats-alfalfa (2 or 3 years) become a basic plan.

Cash Grain Farming versus Livestock Farming. The difference between cash grain farming and livestock farming is primarily the manner in which the crops are harvested. The same rotation may be followed for cash grain farming as for livestock farming. Both systems must provide for return of organic matter and nitrogen if high yields are to be maintained. Cash grain farming requires green manure as a source of organic nitrogen, while the livestock system requires the return of farm manure as a source of organic nitrogen.

Unfortunately, a philosophy has developed in this country that cash grain farming will deplete the soil, while livestock farming will maintain soil fertility.   It is true that many cash grain farmers are exploiting their soil with corn and small grain without a legume in their rotation, hoping that the soil will last as long as they do.   But at the same time, there are many livestock farmers who will admit that they have never been able to apply manure to their entire 160-acre farm during their regular crop rotation.   Furthermore, it is the unusual livestock farmer who applies manure to all his cropland at least once in the rotation from hay and grain produced only on his own farm.

To compare the effects of the two systems of farming, let us assume a situation in which a farmer is following a 3-year rotation of corn-oats-red clover on 150 acres of cultivated land, with average yields of 65 bu. of corn, 50 bu. of oats, and 2 tons of red clover hay.   While he can harvest 2 tons of hay, he leaves about $\frac{1}{2}$ ton of clover residues, which he turns under after the second cutting of hay.   Based on average plant composition and the most conservative estimate of nitrogen fixation, the following figures show nitrogen removed in grain and nitrogen contained in the clover hay and residues:

Nitrogen removed from soil	*Nitrogen fixed from air**
In corn (1 lb./bu.) = 65 lb.	In clover hay (50 lb./ton) = 100 lb.
In oats (0.6 lb./bu.) = 30	In clover residues (50 lb./ton) = 25
Total = 95 lb.	Total = 125 lb.

* Based on the assumption that the nitrogen in the tops equals the nitrogen fixed by symbiotic bacteria.

If the farmer feeds the grain and hay, he can expect to feed the equivalent of 195 lb. of nitrogen and may return about 65 lb. of nitrogen to the soil in farm manure if he is careful.   He turns back to his soil 65 + 25, or 90 lb. of nitrogen per acre, in 3 years and removes 95 lb.   This system is practically balanced in nitrogen gains and losses.

If the farmer sells the grain and turns under the clover hay he will be adding about 30 lb. more nitrogen per acre per rotation than he removes.

In the livestock system the farmer would sell off 30 lb. of P_2O_5 and 30 lb. of K_2O.   In the grain system the farmer would sell off 40 lb. of P_2O_5 and 30 lb. of K_2O.

The author is making no attempt to discourage livestock farming, realizing that the livestock system offers other advantages.   The production of livestock provides the farmer with a means of more efficient use of his labor, particularly by providing him with winter employment.   Every farmer cannot be a livestock farmer, however, because the need for grain for human food requires that some farmers sell their grain directly from the farm.   Furthermore, as the population pressure on the land increases, there must be a greater proportion of cropland devoted to cash grain farming.

A large part of the food which is consumed by livestock is destroyed and must be exhaled or thrown off as carbon dioxide, water, urea, etc. Of the small percentage of the food that is actually retained in the animal tissues, only about one-half to two-thirds is recovered as human food. Swine are more efficient than cattle in producing human food from dry substance consumed. About 20 per cent of the feedstuff consumed by swine is eventually edible, while only 10 per cent of the feedstuff consumed by beef cattle is eventually recovered for human food. In other words, 80 to 90 per cent of the energy value of feed consumed by livestock is lost in so far as human food is concerned.

A friend of the author told of a friendly argument that recently developed between two farmers who went to a cafe together. One of the farmers, who was a livestock farmer, placed an order for a steak and told the waitress to bring his friend only a bowl of cereal, because that was all he produced on his farm. It turned out that both farmers were actually following a program that balanced the income and outgo of nitrogen and organic matter.

Use of Catch Crops for Green Manure. A livestock farmer has the opportunity of operating a larger volume of business on his farm and can usually expect more income than the cash grain farmer if both follow identical rotations. For example, a cash grain farmer who follows a 3-year rotation of corn-oats-red clover must use one-third of his land for green manure each year without realizing any direct income. He might make one cutting of hay and sell it from the farm, but the profit from producing the hay would not be much greater than the cost of fertilizer elements removed in the hay which he would have to purchase to maintain fertility. Therefore cash grain farmers make every effort to realize some cash grain income from every acre every year.

Several systems of green manure–catch crop rotations are popular over the country. In the Southeast, farmers grow vetch in the winter after corn, to be turned under green ahead of cotton. Thus a 2-year rotation of corn and cotton is followed, in which a leguminous green manure crop is grown.

In the blacklands of Texas, farmers follow a 3-year rotation of corn-cotton-oats (hubam clover). The oats are seeded in the fall after the cotton is harvested, and the hubam clover is overseeded in the oats in midwinter. By the time the oats are harvested in June, the hubam clover is well established, and a good cover of hubam clover is produced during the remainder of the season. About 90 per cent of the oats grown in Ellis County (just south of Dallas), Texas, are overseeded with hubam clover.

Two-year rotations of corn-oats (sweet clover) and 3-year rotations of corn-soybeans-oats (sweet clover) are popular in the Middle West.

Soil conservationists have discouraged the cash grain rotations with sweet clover catch crops, particularly with soybeans in the rotation, because of "breakdown" in soil structure and because of erosion. A soybean crop leaves the soil very loose and is as much of an erosion hazard as corn. A 3-year rotation of corn-soybeans-oats (sweet clover) will lose about twice as much soil by erosion as will a 3-year rotation of corn-oats-red clover.[1]

We must not overlook the erosion hazard in rotations with catch crops of green manure; but on land not subject to serious erosion because of gentleness of slope, or on land protected by terraces, the cash grain rotations with catch crops can be planned to maintain fertility.

Using average values for plant composition, a 2-year rotation of corn-oats (sweet clover) will maintain nitrogen for yields of 70 bu. of corn and 50 bu. of oats if as much as 100 lb. of nitrogen is contributed by the sweet clover crop. A 3-year rotation of corn-soybeans-oats (sweet clover) will maintain nitrogen for yields of 70 bu. of corn, 30 bu. of soybeans, and 50 bu. of oats if 2 tons of sweet clover green manure is turned under (it is assumed that the amount of nitrogen fixed by soybeans is equal to the amount harvested in the beans).

On soils not subject to erosion, and where soil aeration is good, a 3-year rotation of corn-corn-oats (sweet clover) receiving 5 lb. of nitrogen starter on each corn crop, 40 lb. of side-dressed nitrogen on second-year corn, and 20 lb. of nitrogen on oats should maintain yields of corn at 60 to 70 bu. and oats at 50 to 60 bu. if 2 tons of sweet clover green manure is turned under, in so far as nitrogen is concerned. Phosphorus, potash, and calcium would also have to be added.

The 3-year rotation of corn-corn-oats (sweet clover) would be an erosion hazard and might also be hard on soil structure, but there are some soils that should respond quite satisfactorily to such a system. Heavy and poorly aerated soils would soon deteriorate under such treatment because of loss of granular structure.

Use of Nitrogen in Lieu of Legumes. It has long been believed that legume crops are necessary in the rotation if yields are to be maintained. But with the development of our synthetic-nitrogen-fertilizer industry, we are no longer dependent on legume crops to maintain organic matter or to maintain high yields.

The economy of using synthetic nitrogenous fertilizers in lieu of legumes is largely a question of adaptability of legumes at the present time. Where sweet clover is adapted and can be used as a catch crop in the rotation, it is more economical to grow sweet clover than to buy nitrogen. A good crop of sweet clover will add from 100 to 125 lb. of nitrogen (or more in nitrogen-deficient soils well supplied with minerals). It costs only about $1.50 to $3 to seed sweet clover, and one may expect the crop to add from

[1] Based on data contained in *Mo. Agr. Expt. Sta. Bull.* 518.

$7 to $15 worth of nitrogen (anhydrous ammonia nitrogen sells for $7 per 100 lb., while ammonium nitrate sells for about $12 per 100 lb. of nitrogen).

In the blacklands around Austin, Texas, the use of small grain is not successful because of plant diseases. Therefore hubam clover (which is the most successful legume crop in this area) must be grown in the rotation, not as a catch crop but as a regular crop. Farmers in this section

Fig. 134. The tall corn is growing where lespedeza grew the previous year. The short corn is growing where cotton grew the previous year. (*Soil Conservation Service.*)

harvest a crop of seed and turn under the residues and find that hubam clover is a profitable cash crop, and the cotton or corn crop following the hubam clover is very favorably affected by the legume residues. The demand for sweet clover seed is not great enough for this practice to be expanded much farther. The question we must raise, then, is how we can meet our nitrogen needs and maintain organic matter in areas where legumes cannot be used as a catch crop. The question of meeting nitrogen needs can easily be answered with cheap nitrogenous fertilizers, *but what about organic matter?* Agronomists generally hold the belief that nitrogen mineralized from organic matter is still our best source of nitrogen. However, research conducted during the next decade may prove that we have overemphasized organic-matter maintenance. In the meantime, we must stay with practices backed up by research. We know that practices which maintain high content of soil organic matter will also maintain high yields of clean-tilled crops. We should therefore make the best use of crop residues and apply commercial nitrogen where legumes are not adapted or where the legume seed is too expensive for seeding.

Frank App of New Jersey, formerly head of agronomy at Rutgers University, was cited as growing better than 100 bu. of corn per acre in *continuous corn* by growing rye grass as a *winter cover crop* to be turned under green in the spring (4). He split his nitrogen applications by fertilizing the rye grass in the fall and side-dressing the corn at the last cultivation in the summer. App was quoted as emphasizing maintenance of organic matter even though he made heavy applications of commercial nitrogen.

There are several states which are investigating the effects on soil of continuous corn without green manure. The studies generally indicate that high yields of corn can be grown without rotating corn with other crops. Soil structure does deteriorate to some extent in fine-textured soils, but the damage is not permanent. Erosion is an important problem with such a program and must be controlled by mechanical means. Steps must also be taken to control such insects as corn rootworms, which cause greater damage with continuous cropping. Furthermore, weeds and diseases are more difficult to control with continuous cropping. Nevertheless, these associated problems of disease, insects, weeds, and erosion can be solved satisfactorily with techniques now well known to farmers. There is no reason to fear any permanent damage to soils by continuous cropping of clean-tilled crops as long as erosion is under control. The fertility level can be maintained by use of commercial fertilizers and lime where needed.

The Indiana Experiment Station[1] conducted a test with nitrogen fertilization of continuous corn from 1944 to 1949. The plots had been in continuous corn since 1919. The continuous corn receiving 80 lb. of nitrogen each year yielded 82.3 bu. per acre. Plots of continuous corn without nitrogen yielded 47 bu. per acre during the 6-year period 1944 to 1949. All of the plots received 200 lb. of 0-12-12 fertilizer annually. The test was discontinued after 1949.

The Missouri Experiment Station has conducted a test with continuous corn since 1948. The years 1953 and 1955 were rather droughty, and the year 1954 was so dry that no corn was harvested. Nevertheless the 8-year average, 1948 to 1955, resulted in a yield of 77.4 bu. per acre. The plots

[1] Unpublished data of the Agronomy Department, Purdue University, distributed as Mimeo. AY 11c, 1952.

received adequate phosphorus and potassium and 150 lb. of nitrogen each year. In the favorable 4-year period 1948 to 1951 the plots produced over 100 bu. of corn each year.[1]

It is only in recent years that continuous corn appeared to be a feasible practice. During the early years of our experiment stations in the Corn Belt, continuous corn was generally grown without nitrogen fertilizer and the yields were very low. The soil became very low in decomposable nitrogenous material. A good illustration of the tremendous value of nitrogen under such conditions is provided by the experience at the Soil Conservation Station at Clarinda, Iowa. During the 20-year period from 1932 to 1951 the continuous-corn yield averaged about 18 bu. per acre per year. In 1952 the plots received 180 lb. of nitrogen, plus adequate phosphorus and potassium, and the yield of corn was 103 bu. per acre. Very obviously the soil on these plots of Marshall silt loam had not been permanently damaged, although they had decreased greatly in their content of organic matter. The organic-matter content declined during the period from 1932 to 1951 because of the very small amount of residues reaching the soil each year. As fertility is increased and yield levels are raised, it is logical to expect more crop residues to be returned. With greater amounts of residues, one would expect greater amounts of organic matter to be maintained.

One often hears the argument that the residues from 100 bu. of corn will provide as much organic carbon as one would get in the residues from a crop of alfalfa. And further, that if nitrogen is plowed down with the cornstalks, just as much organic nitrogen might be left in the soil. There are two points that should not be overlooked in such an argument. One is that only a limited amount of nitrogen plowed down with cornstalks will be immobilized or converted to organic nitrogen (see page 220). The other point is that more organic matter (and organic nitrogen) will accumulate from the alfalfa residues because of lack of disturbance of the soil. The tillage of the soil for corn hastens decomposition of organic matter, while leaving the soil undisturbed in alfalfa provides an opportunity to increase the organic-matter content. Furthermore, the structure of the soil improves under alfalfa whereas it deteriorates in some soils under corn.

On heavier soils, there is little doubt that maintenance of organic matter is desirable because of the favorable effect of organic matter on soil structure. On the other hand, the structure of sandy soils is not altered to any appreciable extent by addition of organic matter. It is on sandy soils, like those in the Southeastern states, that we may expect the greatest use of commercial nitrogen with continuous cropping with nonlegumes. Krantz (10) reported the following remarkable observation: Continuous corn had been grown for 4 years with and without

[1] Personal communication from George E. Smith.

nitrogen in 1947 on experimental plots in North Carolina. In 1947, the continuous corn without nitrogen yielded 19.1 bu., while a plot receiving 180 lb. of nitrogen yielded 120.9 bu. Krantz (10) also reported that "the average yields from plots receiving 0, 40, 80, and 120 pounds of nitrogen were 28, 53, 71, and 81 bushels (of corn) per acre in the 49 nitrogen experiments conducted during 1944–48" in North Carolina.

Fertility Indexes. One of the most original schemes in determining the effect of a rotation on soil fertility was worked out by Salter and Green of Ohio (15). Their basic data are shown in Table 109A. It was assumed that the original level of nitrogen was similar for all plots. They assumed that the annual rate of nitrogen loss under corn and small grain in rotation would be the same as in continuous cropping. They calculated that the timothy in the 5-year rotation represented an annual gain of 0.64 per cent and the clover hay in the 3-year rotation an annual gain of 2.87 per cent nitrogen.

TABLE 109A. BASIC DATA FOR CALCULATING PRODUCTIVITY INDEXES (15)

Experiment	Year	Nitrogen	
		Average content, lb./acre	Annual loss until 1925, per cent
5-year rotation, C-O-W-Cl-T.............	1894	2176	
	1907–1908	1885	
	1911	1727	
	1921	1566	
	1925	1546	1.06
3-year rotation, C, W, Cl, begun in 1897...	1907	1918	
	1925	1780	0.69
Continuous corn since 1894..............	1913	1053	
	1925	840	2.97
Continuous oats since 1894..............	1913	1553	
	1925	1365	1.45
Continuous wheat since 1894............	1913	1675	
	1925	1315	1.06

C = corn, O = oats, W = wheat, Cl = clover, T = timothy.

From these basic data, Salter, Lewis, and Slipher (16) prepared the productivity indexes for individual crops in Ohio and published them in 1936. Since that time revised editions have been published, and the erosion factor has been included. The most recent edition was published in 1941.

Klemme and Coleman of Missouri published similar productivity ratings in 1939 and again in 1949 (9).

The productivity indexes are used in the following manner: A 3-year rotation of corn-oats-red clover would have—2 for corn, —1 for oats, and +2 for clover. If straw and stover are turned back, the rotation should be credited with +0.25 for cornstalks and +0.25 for oat straw, leaving

TABLE 109B. SOIL-PRODUCTIVITY INDEXES FOR INDIVIDUAL CROPS AND CROP TREATMENT IN OHIO (16)

Crop on rotated land and crop treatment	Soil-productivity index (changes effected by 1 year of growth)
Corn, as grain or silage	−2.0
Potatoes, tobacco, and sugar beet	−2.0
Oats, wheat, barley, rye, and buckwheat	−1.0
Credit for crop residues, such as wheat straw or cornstalks	+0.25
Alfalfa for change effected by end of first hay year	+2.5
Alfalfa for change effected during second hay year	+0.5
Timothy and other grass sod	+0.25
Clover-timothy mixed, hay or pasture	+1.25
Common clovers, hay or pasture	+2.0
Sweet clover, crop plowed in April or May	+2.5
For each ton of manure applied	+0.15
For each 200 lb. of average commercial fertilizer applied	+0.15

−0.5. In other words, additional soil-improvement practices would have to be used to maintain productivity at a high (or near-virgin) level.

REFERENCES

1. Anderson, Marvin A., "Some Physical and Chemical Properties of Six Virgin and Six Cultivated Iowa Soils," Master's Thesis, Iowa State College, 1949.
2. "Annual Summary of Studies at the Soil Conservation Experimental Farm, Page Co., Iowa," 1955.
3. Bauer, F. C., and Associates, Effects of Soil Treatment on Soil Productivity, Ill. Agr. Expt. Sta. Bull. 516, 1945.
4. Bloomfield, Howard, Fertilize the Year Before, Country Gentleman, September, 1950, p. 22.
5. Browning, G. M., R. A. Norton, A. G. McCall, and F. G. Bell, Investigation in Erosion Control and the Reclamation of Eroded Land, U.S. Dept. Agr. Tech. Bull. 959, 1948.
6. Handbook of Experiments in Agronomy, Ohio Agr. Expt. Sta. Spec. Cir. 53, 1938.
7. Jenny, Hans, Soil Fertility Losses under Missouri Conditions, Mo. Agr. Expt. Sta. Bull. 324, 1933.
8. Johnston, J. R., G. M. Browning, and M. B. Russell, The Effect of Cropping Practices on Aggregation, Organic Matter Content, and Loss of Soil and Water in the Marshall Silt Loam, Soil Sci. Soc. Amer. Proc., 7:105–107, 1942.
9. Klemme, A. W., and O. T. Coleman, Evaluating Annual Changes in Soil Productivity, Mo. Agr. Expt. Sta. Bull. 405, 1939, and 522, 1949.
10. Krantz, B. A., Fertilize Corn for Higher Yields, N.C. Agr. Expt. Sta. Bull. 366, 1949.
11. Lee, Ching-Kwei, and Roger H. Bray, Organic Matter and Nitrogen Contents of Soils as Influenced by Management, Soil Sci., 68:203–212, 1949.

12. Miller, M. F., Studies in Soil Nitrogen and Organic Matter Maintenance, *Mo. Agr. Expt. Sta. Res. Bull.* 409, 1947.

13. Peevy, W. J., F. B. Smith, and P. E. Brown, Effects of Rotational and Manurial Treatments for 20 Years on the Organic Matter, Nitrogen, and Phosphorus Contents of Clarion and Webster Soils, *J. Am. Soc. Agron.*, **32**:739–753, 1940.

14. Puhr, Leo F., Soil Changes as Influenced by Cropping and Fertilizer Treatment, *S. Dak. Agr. Expt. Sta. Tech. Bull.* 4, 1945.

15. Salter, R. M., and T. C. Green, Factors Affecting the Accumulation and Loss of Nitrogen and Organic Carbon in Cropped Soils, *J. Am. Soc. Agron.*, **25**:622–630, 1933.

16. Salter, R. M., R. D. Lewis, and J. A. Slipher, Our Heritage—The Soil, *Ohio State Univ. Agr. Ext. Serv. Bull.* 175, 1936 (3d ed., 1941).

17. Thompson, L. M., "The Mineralization of Organic Phosphorus, Nitrogen and Carbon in Virgin and Cultivated Soils," Ph.D. Thesis, Iowa State College, 1950.

18. Ulrich, Rudolph, "Some Physical and Chemical Properties of Planosol and Wiesenboden Soil Series as Related to Loess Thickness and Distribution," Ph.D. Thesis, Iowa State College, 1949.

19. Wheeting, Lawrence C., Changes in Organic Matter in Western Washington Soils as a Result of Cropping, *Soil Sci.*, **44**:139–150, 1937.

20. White, J. W., F. J. Holden, and A. C. Richer, Maintenance Level of Nitrogen and Organic Matter in Grassland and Cultivated Soils over Periods of 54 and 72 Years, *J. Am. Soc. Agron.*, **37**:21–31, 1945.

CHAPTER 17

SOIL EROSION AND ITS CONTROL[1]

The maintenance of soil fertility requires that erosion be kept at a rate low enough to permit soil formation to keep pace with erosion. Bennett (1) states that it takes from 300 to 1000 years for nature to build a single inch of topsoil. While Bennett's estimates are probably correct for the rate of soil building by natural processes, man can build a productive soil at a much faster rate, and we do not have to restrict erosion on all soils to the rate of 1 in. of soil loss in 300 years. If it took 300 years to build an acre-inch of soil, we would have to limit soil losses to about ½ ton per acre per year, since an acre-inch of soil weighs about 150 tons. Browning (8) estimates that fertility can be maintained in soils developed from deep loess if the rate of erosion is reduced to 5 tons per year (or 1 in. every 30 years).

Soils which have developed from deep unconsolidated materials may lose soil as rapidly as 1 in. in 30 years and still be kept in fertile condition. Soils which have developed from consolidated materials (such as granite, sandstone, or limestone) should not be permitted to lose more than ½ ton of soil per acre per year. This means that soils developed from rock should be kept under continuous cover of grass or protected by terraces so that erosion is completely under control.

Soil-fertility and crop-rotation studies have generally been conducted on soils not subject to erosion, particularly prior to 1931 (13). Data are seriously lacking to show how much erosion can be permitted in different regions for different soils. Smith *et al.* (31) found from research studies that Shelby soils (developed from glacial till) may be allowed to lose 4 tons of soil per acre per year. They pointed out that on some soils of Missouri the tolerable loss is only 2 tons per acre per year.

Problem of Soil Erosion in the United States. According to the Division of Physical Land Survey, U.S. Department of Agriculture, approxi-

---

[1] Parts of this chapter pertaining to factors affecting erosion, mechanical practices that control erosion, and gully control were published by L. G. Jones, of Texas A. and M. College, and the author in 1941 in a book entitled "Soil Erosion and Its Control," which is now out of print.

mately 70 per cent of the land area of the United States is subject to erosion.   Much of the remaining 30 per cent is unsuited to agriculture. A survey completed in 1934 showed that 4 million acres (0.2 per cent) was completely destroyed by erosion; 109 million acres (5.7 per cent) was essentially destroyed for further tillage; and approximately 192 million more acres (10.1 per cent of all land) had lost three-fourths or more of its topsoil.[1]

FIG. 135. Low fertility can contribute to erosion, since the crop cover is so poor that the soil is afforded very little protective cover.   (*Soil Conservation Service.*)

There are approximately 1903 million acres confined within the limits of the United States, and in 1934, 16 per cent of the land had been severely damaged by erosion.   This area of land is larger than the states of Texas and Oklahoma combined.   Figure 136 shows the distribution of erosion in the United States in 1934.

The most seriously damaged areas are in the western part of the Corn Belt (Iowa, Nebraska, and Missouri), the humid part of the Southwest (Texas and Oklahoma), and the Southeastern states, where cotton has been the chief cash crop.

The soils of southern Iowa, southeastern Nebraska, and northern Missouri are particularly well adapted to corn.   Even though much of the

---

[1] This report is summarized in an article by W. C. Lowdermilk, Soil Erosion and Its Control in the United States, *Proc. Intern. Congr. Soil Sci.*, **2**:180–194, 1935.

topography is rolling, corn has been planted in rows running up and down hill to permit check-row cultivation, and erosion has taken a heavy toll. The soils of Oklahoma and Texas have been severely eroded because clean-tilled crops have been grown on soils where erosion is a year-round threat. A relatively high proportion of the rainfall of this area comes in torrential showers.

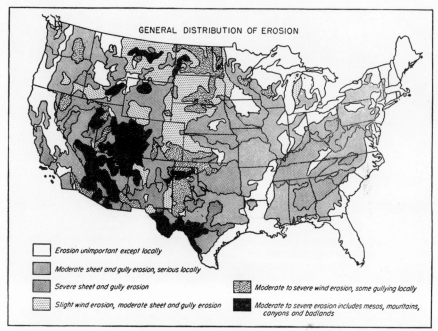

FIG. 136. Distribution of erosion in the United States.   (*Soil Conservation Service*.)

The rainfall of the Southeastern states comes better distributed than that of the humid Southwest, though in greater amount.   In the Southeast the soils are also less erosive than the soils of the Southwest.   The main reasons the Southeastern soils are so severely damaged are that they are subject to erosion the year round and that they have been in cultivation for a long period.   Many of the farms have been cultivated for over 200 years.   Most of the cultivated soils of Texas, Oklahoma, Iowa, Missouri, and Nebraska have been broken out of grass during the past hundred years.

While the areas just discussed are the most severely eroded parts of the country, there has been some damage in all parts of the country wherever sloping land has been cultivated.

The recognition of the seriousness of erosion by the people of this country caused the creation of the Soil Conservation Service by Congress in 1935. Unfortunately, much damage was done before people began to recognize the problem. Agronomists, particularly soil surveyors, had long recognized the seriousness of erosion, but research in erosion control on cropland was not started in this country until 1917, and the first research bulletin was published by the Missouri Experiment Station in 1923 (11).

Fig. 137. This wheat crop is almost a total loss because it is being covered by soil which was blown from an unprotected field nearby. (*Soil Conservation Service.*)

Lipman and Conybeare estimated that losses of nutrients by erosion exceeded the losses by cropping in the United States in 1930. Table 110 shows their estimates for the six macroelements obtained from the soil.

TABLE 110. Loss of Plant Nutrients by Cropping and Erosion, 1930 (23)
In pounds per acre

Losses	N	P	K	Ca	Mg	S
Removed in crops...	25.1	3.8	17.3	6.0	2.8	2.8
Lost by erosion......	24.2	10.6	141.1	152.0	73.0	6.1

The table shows that the loss of nitrogen by erosion was just about equal to the amount removed by crops, while the loss of the other nutrients was much greater by erosion than by crop removal.

Damage to Soils by Erosion. When one looks at the losses of minerals by erosion one immediately thinks of the high cost of fertilizers to replace

these elements.   But one often forgets that the subsoil may contain more
of these same elements than the topsoil.

Bradfield (5) raised the question in 1946, "Do we want to prevent
erosion or do we want to control erosion?"   In reference to soils of New
York he wrote,

These soils are frequently underlain with great depths of unconsolidated
material which is often higher in potash, phosphorus, and lime than surface soil.
I think we need to explore ways and means of exploiting these subsurface reserves
as those in the surface become exhausted instead of trying to balance the books
completely by the purchase of commercial plant food.

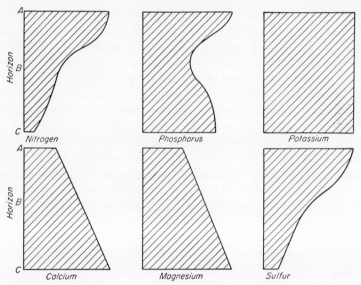

Fig. 138. Schematic diagram showing the relative proportion of the macronutrients
in the A, B, and C horizons of a representative soil profile.

While the profile distribution of the macronutrients has been discussed
earlier in this book, we should again observe their distribution as shown
in Fig. 138.

The most serious losses in nutrients from erosion are nitrogen, sulfur,
and phosphorus.   The phosphorus in the subsoil is lower in quantity and
availability than that in the topsoil.   The replacement of organic matter
with its nitrogen, sulfur, and phosphorus, therefore, constitutes the major
problem in reclaiming eroded soils.   The eroded soil will usually contain
a greater total supply of calcium, magnesium, and potassium than the
original topsoil.

Another problem in erosion is the loss of a silty or sandy surface soil and
the leaving of a heavy clay layer exposed at the surface.   Under such

conditions, erosion severely damages the soil, because the heavy clay layer may not contain enough aeration porosity to support a good crop. The loss of topsoil from strongly differentiated profiles presents a problem for which research has not shown a suitable means of management. We may find that if the C horizon is composed of deep unconsolidated material, the clay layer can be removed or mixed with underlying material by plowing to a depth of 2 or 3 ft. with special equipment.

The undifferentiated profile is relatively simple to manage if the topsoil is removed. The management is largely that of replacing the organic matter or fertilizing with nitrogen, phosphorus, and sulfur after the topsoil is removed.

Factors Affecting Erosion. The major factors affecting erosion are (*a*) amount and distribution of precipitation, (*b*) seasonal temperatures, (*c*) topography, (*d*) land cover, and (*e*) soil characteristics. The first four factors are predominant in determining the rate of erosion for a given soil. These same factors are also important in soil-forming processes. The factors responsible for the development of a soil may also destroy the soil when their balance is lost because of interference by outside agencies.

Amount and Distribution of Precipitation. The amount of annual precipitation is highly important in influencing the type of land cover and the type of soil developed. However, the annual precipitation is not a true measure of the influence of precipitation on erosion. If a large proportion of the year's precipitation falls as slow gentle showers, the water will be entirely absorbed by many soils. Under these conditions there is no runoff and no erosion. If much of the annual precipitation falls as snow on unfrozen soil, and if the blanket of snow becomes deep enough, little freezing of the soil occurs. Under these favorable conditions the water resulting from the thawing of the snow soaks directly into the soil without runoff, and consequently, little or no erosion takes place.

If the soil is frozen deeply under a thick cover of snow, and more particularly, if thawing of the snow is accelerated by heavy warm rains, most of the resulting water must run off over the surface. Essentially these conditions prevailed in some areas in the Northeastern states in March, 1936. And the unprecedentedly high floodwaters at Pittsburgh and Johnstown, Pennsylvania, at Hartford, Connecticut, and at all other cities and villages and farms along the larger rivers in that part of the country were the result of that combination of circumstances.

Precipitation does not come uniformly in many sections of the United States. Two different unfavorable conditions result from irregular distribution of rainfall: one is the moderately heavy rain which continues over a number of consecutive days; the other, the extremely heavy rain of short duration.

Rainfall Intensities. A close relationship exists between erosion and the excess of rainfall over the absorptive capacity of the soil. If the intensity of the rainfall is high, that is, if rain falls five or ten times as rapidly as the soil can take it up, heavy runoff and severe erosion are the result on unprotected slopes, regardless of the capacity of the soil to hold water.

Under average farming conditions most soils escape erosion from average rainfall. And total annual precipitation is not so important as the intensity of the rainfall. During the period from 1933 to 1942 at Clarinda, Iowa, 128 rains occurred which caused soil losses. Two of these rains,

Fig. 139. The running of rows up and down hill has been one of the most important causes of serious erosion. (*Soil Conservation Service.*)

representing only 1.6 per cent of the total precipitation, caused slightly more than 25 per cent of the total soil loss during the period. Eight rains, accounting for 6.3 per cent of the total precipitation, caused 50 per cent of the total soil loss. One 4-in. rain falling in 2 hours removed 80 tons of soil per acre, while another 4-in. rain falling in 27 hours removed only 9 tons of soil per acre (34).

Loss by erosion cannot be entirely avoided in the case of the heaviest downpours such as occur but once in 50 or 100 years. Surely it is wise management to be prepared at all times for heavy rains such as are likely to come on the average of once in 25 years. Flood control, as well as erosion-control problems on the farm, should be attacked on the basis of rainfall intensities.

According to Yarnell (37), we may expect a 3-in. rain in 24 hours once in 25 years in northwestern New Mexico; a 5-in. rain during the same period on the high plains of Texas; a 10-in. rain on the Gulf Coast of Texas; and as much as 11 in. in southern Louisiana during the same period of time.

Terraces, drainage ditches, and culverts should be designed to carry the maximum amount of water expected during a 24-hr. period once in 25 years.

Seasonal Temperature. In the northern part of the United States the soil is normally frozen from 3 to 4 months or more out of the year, and during this period the precipitation occurs as snowfall. In extreme cases, and especially in higher altitudes, the period during which precipitation occurs as snow is considerably longer than 4 months. To the south the period during which the soil is frozen becomes shorter and shorter until along the Gulf Coast freezing of the soil is insignificant, and little or no snow falls along the Gulf Coast.

While the soil is solidly frozen no washing occurs. However, if rapid thawing is accomplished by warm rains, the thawed part of the soil, especially if the land is bare, washes very readily.

Practically all the precipitation occurs as rainfall in the Southern states, and erosion is a year-round threat. Land that has a cover of grass or forest is essentially safe from erosion. Land that is used for the production of clean-tilled crops, such as cotton or corn, is usually left bare and exposed to erosion throughout the winter.

The rate of decomposition of organic matter is greatly influenced by temperature. As progress is made from a cooler to a warmer climate, organic-matter content of the soil decreases. This factor further complicates the erosion-control problem in the Southern states. On the other hand, the winter temperatures are favorable for the growth of winter cover crops, which not only provide for erosion control in the South but also furnish a direct or indirect source of farm income.

Topography. Slope is usually expressed in percentages by soil conservationists. A drop of 10 ft. perpendicularly in 100 ft. of horizontal distance is called a slope of 10 per cent. A 100 per cent slope would be equivalent to a 45-degree slope.

The slope of the land is usually considered the most important factor in determining the erosion-control methods in a given area, inasmuch as slope is most important in causing erosion. In planning for erosion control for any area it is necessary to determine effect of slope on erosion in order to recommend which areas should be retired from cultivation, which areas should be left in cultivation, which areas should be terraced, and which slopes can be successfully handled with strip crops, cover crops, and contour tillage alone. Each of these practices has certain limitations, and all are nearly always first affected by slope. Water flows slowly along slopes of around 1 per cent, and silting occurs as the slope is reduced below 0.5 per cent, but as the slope becomes steeper the speed of runoff is increased and the power of water to move soil is also increased. The effect of slope on loss of soil and water is shown by Fig. 140.

Figure 140 shows that as the per cent of slope is doubled, the rate of soil loss is more than doubled. This relationship has been verified by labora-

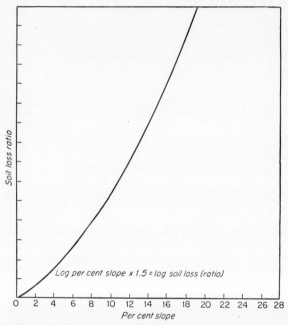

Fig. 140. The relation of soil lost by erosion to the percentage of slope.

tory studies (36), by use of artificial rain equipment on different slopes in the field (3), and by plots receiving rainfall under natural conditions over a period of years (17). The steepness of the curve varies with soil conditions, and the curve in Fig. 140 was suggested by Browning (8) as being an average of published data.

While the rate of soil loss is more than doubled by doubling the steepness of slope, the amount of runoff follows a curve with an exponential value of less than 1 and finally levels off, as illustrated in Fig. 141.

The curve must flatten out eventually for runoff, because the amount of runoff is limited by the amount of rainfall.

The length of slope is another important factor in erosion of soil, and the data on this point are frequently misinterpreted. Doubling the length of slope more than doubles the soil loss, but the loss per acre is not doubled. Figure 142 illustrates this.

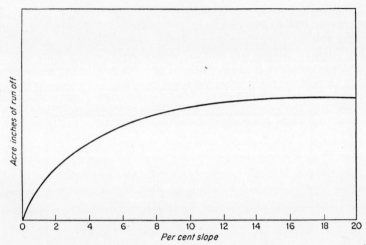

FIG. 141. A schematic diagram showing the relation of runoff to the percentage of slope. [*Based on studies of Duley and Hays* (12).]

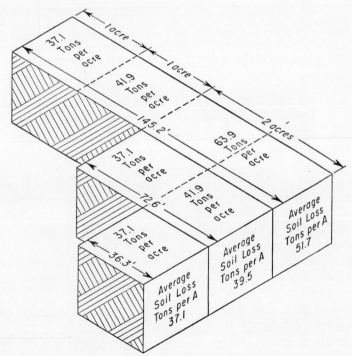

FIG. 142. The effect of length of slope on soil losses from continuous corn planted up and down hill, Marshall silt loam. [*Soil Conservation Experimental Farm, Clarinda, Iowa,* 1933 *to* 1941 (34).]

Continuous-corn plots 36.3 ft. long lost 37.1 tons per acre, while continuous-corn plots of the same width but 72.6 ft. long lost over twice as much soil but only 39.5 tons per acre. By increasing the length of slope to 145.2 ft., the soil loss was increased to 51.7 tons per acre.

A curve for soil loss plotted against slope length is shown in Fig. 143. This is an average curve suggested by Browning (8). The steepness of the curve varies with intensity of rainfall, per cent of slope, and nature of the soil.

The lower part of a long slope suffers more erosion than the upper part. The lower part of the slope not only receives water which falls directly on the slope but also receives runoff water from the upper part of the slope. The management of a short slope is comparatively simple because the quantity of water is relatively small, but the management of long slopes is more difficult. Gullies begin at the lower end of a slope and work back

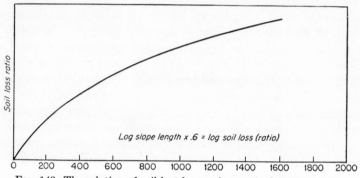

FIG. 143. The relation of soil lost by erosion to the length of slope.

up the slope. Furthermore, gullies are the result of concentrated runoff. Long slopes are more likely to develop gullies, because of the accumulation of large volumes of water, which become concentrated in low areas at the lower part of slope. Terraces furnish the most practical means of shortening slopes. A discussion of terraces will be presented later.

Land Cover. Of the five major factors affecting soil erosion, probably the vegetative cover should be given the greatest emphasis in planning an erosion-control program. As we seek methods with which to protect our soils, we find that natural vegetation is our greatest aid. We cannot return all our land to pasture, meadow, or forest, however, and supply the needs of our population.

Cultivated crops vary in the way in which they affect erosion. It is necessary, therefore, to consider the differences in soil losses from areas planted to different crops as well as soil losses from areas protected by natural vegetation.

Natural Land Cover. We find that nature protects the soil with an almost complete cover of vegetation in humid regions. As progress is made toward arid regions, less vegetative cover is afforded because of the limited rainfall. Because of the relationship between rainfall and natural land cover, it is of interest to observe the erosion map, Fig. 136. Here we find that erosion is rather severe in regions of very low rainfall. It is the author's opinion, after traveling through these areas for the purpose of studying erosion, that a large part of this is geological erosion. Since much of the area supports only a small amount of vegetation, it is reasonable to assume that erosion is very severe during torrential rains. Forests cover only 13 per cent of the land area west of the 100th meridian. The remaining 87 per cent is protected by herbaceous vegetation and shrubbery. However, we cannot overlook the tremendous amount of soil wastage in the Western range lands due to fires, carelessness in mining, overgrazing, and the misuse of the land in farming and the cutting of roads.

Studies in the effect of land cover on erosion in the humid region of the United States furnish some interesting relationships. The entire land area of the humid region was formerly clothed with a dense cover of vegetation, but man removed the natural cover in preparing land for cultivated crops, and erosion has progressed to enormous rates in this region.

Forest cover furnishes an ideal protection against erosion. The rainfall cannot strike the soil directly, because the drops of water first strike the trees or the forest litter. This is a very significant factor in erosion. As raindrops fall directly on unprotected soil, the soil is beaten into suspension and is easily moved by runoff water. A complete cover of grass acts similarly in protecting the soil from the direct impact of rainfall.

Table 111 gives the result of a plot experiment to show the effect of forest cover and grass on erosion and runoff, as measured on the Kirvin fine sandy loam at Tyler, Texas, and on Stephenville fine sandy loam at Guthrie, Oklahoma. In both instances the ground cover of litter was decidedly light as compared with the average forest-floor litter of the country.

The data in Table 111 show that forest as well as good stands of grass give practically complete protection from erosion on these very extensive and important soil types. The water losses also have been exceedingly small, especially where the ground cover of forest litter has not been burned. The difference in effectiveness between grass and forest is very slight.

Because of the effectiveness of natural vegetation in controlling erosion, trees, grass, and shrubs may be considered man's last line of defense when other expedients have failed.

Effect of Crops on Erosion Losses. Crops vary tremendously in their effect on erosion. The denseness of the cover, the nature of the root system, the spacing of the plants, the canopy effect of the leaves, and the time the crop grows in relation to distribution of rainfall are some of the many factors to consider in choosing crops to reduce erosion.

Fall-planted small-grain crops are especially well suited for protecting the blackland soils of Texas, since much of the annual rainfall comes during the winter months of the year. The conservation of soil and water

TABLE 111. EFFECT OF FOREST ON EROSION AND RUNOFF COMPARED WITH GRASS (10,29)

Soil	Percentage slope	Annual rainfall	Vegetative cover	Water loss, per cent	Soil loss, tons/acre
Stephenville..	7.7	30.22	Bermuda grass, clipped	0.91	0.02
	5.17	29.52	Bermuda grass and native grass	0.02	0
	5.17	30.57	Undisturbed virgin woods	0.12	0.01
	5.17	30.57	Woods burned over once a year	3.74	0.11
Kirvin.......	8.75	40.66	Bermuda grass	1.01	0.08
	16.5	41.48	Bermuda grass	0.27	0.01
	12.5	40.95	Woods not burned	0.34	0.05
	12.5	40.95	Woods burned	2.61	0.36

is due to the cover afforded by the small grain and its stubble when it actually occupies the land, rather than to the aftereffects of the small grain on any of the other crops in the rotation. This is shown by comparing the erosion losses from continuous corn with the losses under corn in a rotation with oats and cotton at Temple, Texas.

TABLE 112. LOSS OF SOIL UNDER CONTINUOUS CORN AND UNDER CORN-OATS-COTTON ROTATION AT TEMPLE, TEXAS, 1931 TO 1942 (19)
Austin clay, 4 per cent slope, 32.74 in. of annual rainfall

Crop	Runoff, per cent	Soil loss, tons/acre
Continuous corn.....................	13.6	20.6
Corn in rotation.....................	14.5	19.6
Oats in rotation.....................	3.3	2.1
Cotton in rotation..................	13.4	17.2

The losses of soil on corn plots were high because there was no protection of the soil during the winter ahead of corn, and rainfall was high during the winter and early spring. Small grain is relatively much more effective in Texas than in Iowa in reducing soil losses.

By far the greater part of the rainfall comes during the warm months in Iowa, and there is little or no erosion during the winter months, because the ground is frozen and precipitation normally comes as snowfall. Oats are planted in the spring, and occasionally hard rains cause erosion before the oats cover the ground.

Table 113 shows that soil losses under rotation corn were about twice as great as under rotation oats at Clarinda, Iowa. Soil losses under continuous corn were about four times greater than under rotation oats.

TABLE 113. LOSSES OF SOIL UNDER DIFFERENT CROPPING SYSTEMS AT CLARINDA, IOWA, 1933 TO 1942 (7)

Marshall silt loam, 9 per cent slope, 28.8 in. of annual rainfall. Plots 72.6 ft. long

Crop	Runoff, per cent	Soil loss, tons/acre
Continuous corn on topsoil...........	18.7	38.3
Continuous corn on subsoil............	20.2	51.6
Corn in rotation.....................	12.6	18.4
Oats in rotation.....................	9.9	10.1
Clover in rotation...................	3.8	5.4*
Continuous alfalfa...................	2.2	0.1
Continuous bluegrass................	1.2	0.03

* This loss resulted from failure of clover because of drought and grasshopper damage in 1937 and 1938. The annual report, published March, 1950, shows no soil loss under rotation clover from 1943 to 1949.

Figure 144 shows the effect of preceding crops on the soil losses from corn and soybeans at McCredie, Missouri.

The Missouri studies (31) show that soybeans grown in rows and cultivated allow as much erosion as corn, but drilled soybeans allow less erosion than corn. These studies also show that erosion under corn is about two-thirds greater following sweet clover green manure than under corn following grass-clover hay. Furthermore, they show that soil loss under corn following corn one year after sweet clover is about two-thirds greater than soil loss from corn following sweet clover. And corn following sweet clover green manure allows less than one-half as much soil loss as corn following oats.

Data from the Soil Conservation Experiment Station at Statesville, North Carolina, are presented in Table 114. The soil is Cecil sandy clay loam on 10 per cent slope. The length of slope is 72.6 ft. The average annual rainfall was 47.8 in. during the period of observation, 1931 to 1938.

The results from the rotation study in North Carolina show that a 4-year rotation of corn, wheat, lespedeza, and cotton cut erosion to less than one-half compared with continuous cotton. The losses under corn were higher than under cotton, since corn followed cotton without a winter cover crop. The rotation cotton lost about two-thirds as much soil as continuous cotton because of the residual effects of the lespedeza.

The residual effect of legume residues reduced erosion under the succeeding crop in the Missouri and Iowa studies as well as in North Carolina. Corn following clover in Iowa lost only one-half as much soil as was lost under continuous corn.

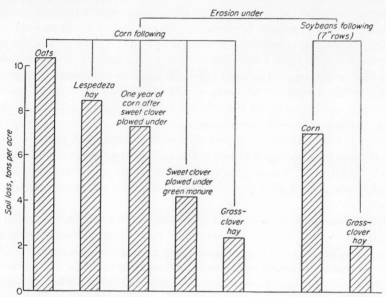

FIG. 144. Effect of preceding crop on erosion under corn and soybeans during the period from April 27 to October 7. [*Missouri Soil Conservation Experiment Farm, McCredie* (31).]

Soil Characteristics. Soil characteristics must be taken into account as different erosion-control practices are studied. All soils do not respond to the same treatments for erosion control. If they did, it would be a relatively simple matter to outline an erosion-control program for any community.

TABLE 114. AVERAGE RUNOFF AND SOIL LOSS FROM A 4-YEAR ROTATION (9)
Control plots at Statesville, North Carolina

Crop	Runoff, per cent	Erosion, tons/acre
Corn in rotation.....................	10.7	28.69
Wheat in rotation...................	13.5	5.61
Lespedeza in rotation................	5.3	1.52
Cotton in rotation...................	10.4	21.82
Continuous cotton...................	12.4	31.22
Rotation average....................	10.0	14.41

There are three main factors to consider in studying the soil from an erosion-control viewpoint. First, the amount of water the soil will hold; second, the rate at which the soil will absorb water; third, the resistance the soil has to erosion when it has absorbed all the water it can hold. If a soil could absorb all the rain as fast as it falls, there would be no erosion. All through the United States we may expect occasional torrential showers; therefore unprotected soils on slopes are always subject to erosion.

Inasmuch as soils vary in respect to the amount of water and the rate at which they will absorb it, it is natural to expect a difference in the rate of erosion. The term *erodibility* is used to designate the susceptibility of a soil to erosion. The erodibility of a soil is influenced by the following characteristics: (*a*) texture, (*b*) structure, (*c*) organic matter, (*d*) depth, (*e*) character of the subsoil, and (*f*) fertility status. Each of these characteristics will be considered in detail.

Soil Texture. Coarse-textured soils such as sands and gravelly sands absorb water rather rapidly, and if the soil is deep, erosion will be negligible. Infiltration is somewhat rapid in fine sandy soils, but as fine sandy soils become filled with water, the fine particles are swept away by runoff water.

Soils with a high percentage of clay may be beaten into suspension by falling raindrops, and the surface pores may become clogged with fine material. The result is that erosion may be quite severe because of the high percentage of runoff compared to adjacent sandy soils. If, however, the aggregates of the soil are water-stable, erosion may be relatively slight, because the pore spaces are larger in a well-aggregated soil, and the aggregates are more resistant to movement by water than are the finer particles.

Bouyoucos (4) found that the clay ratio obtained by dividing the percentage of sand plus silt by the percentage of clay, that is

$$\frac{\text{Per cent sand} + \text{per cent silt}}{\text{Per cent clay}}$$

was a criterion of some value in estimating the erodibility of soils. He found that soils with low ratios (high percentage of clay) were generally less erodible than soils with high ratios (low percentage of clay). The clay soils which he studied, however, were lateritic in nature (high percentage of kaolinite or high in hydrated oxides of iron and aluminum) and it is now recognized that lateritic or kaolinitic materials are resistant to erosion.

The fact must not be overlooked that finer particles are moved more easily by running water than coarser particles. The density of the particle is also a determining factor. If two particles have the same diameter with a difference in specific gravity, it would require a different force to move each one.   An aggregate of clay particles is porous and when filled with water will be lighter in weight than a grain of sand with the same diameter.   This, of course, is because mineral-soil particles are more than twice as heavy as the water which they displace.   It is obvious, then, that when clay aggregates are reduced in size and half their volume is water, they will be easily moved by running water.

Stones on the surface of a soil help to reduce erosion.   They catch the impact of the raindrops and slow the movement of runoff water, thus greatly reducing soil loss.   The comparison in Table 115 was made at

TABLE 115. EFFECT OF REMOVAL OF STONES ON LOSSES OF SOIL AND WATER (22)

Crop	Conditions	Loss of water, per cent	Loss of soil, lb./acre
Corn.............	No stones removed	11.09	8,580
Corn.............	Stones removed	18.92	16,192

the Soil Erosion Experiment Station near Ithaca, New York.   The soil under comparison was Lordstown stony silt loam, the slope 20 per cent, the length of plots 72.6 ft., and the rainfall from May 1 to Nov. 13, 1935, was 23.96 in.   All stones larger than from 1½ to 2 in. in diameter were removed from one plot but were left undisturbed on the other.   Cropping, fertilization, cultivation, and management were identical on the two plots. The removal of stones from the first plot was the only difference.

Soil Structure.   The term structure has reference to the arrangement of soil particles.   Soils with a crumb or granular structure are more open and more porous and will absorb water much more rapidly than those which are dense or tightly packed.   When left undisturbed for several months, cultivated soils tend to run together through the influence of rainfall and their own weight.   Plowing, therefore, aids in preparing a soil to absorb water.   One of the primary objectives in improving a soil, from an erosion-control viewpoint, is increasing the rate of infiltration. Maintenance of good tilth is probably the most important part of the soil-management phase in an erosion-control program.   Very little can be done by the farmer toward changing the texture, nature of the clay, or depth or character of the subsoil.   He can, however, greatly influence the structure of the soil.

Lutz (24), in comparing a much eroded, sandy clay loam with a clay soil not especially subject to erosion, found that the latter permitted greater percolation of water because of a higher state of aggregation, larger aggregates, and more of them.   He concluded further that the non-erosive nature of Davidson clay was due to the nonhydrated condition and the high degree of flocculation of the colloidal fraction into large, porous, and stable aggregates, whereas the erosiveness of the Iredell soil was due to its ease of dispersion and its low state of aggregation and dispersion.

There are two aspects of soil structure to be considered in the study of erosion. The first is the physicochemical property of the clay which causes it to become aggregated and remain in stable aggregates in the presence of water. The second is the biological property of having an abundance of organic matter in a state of active decomposition. Figure 145 illustrates the principle.

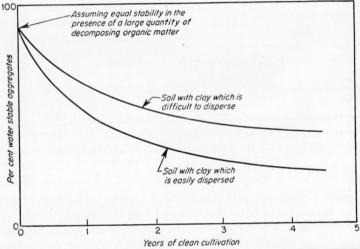

Fɪɢ. 145. A schematic diagram illustrating the effect of the physicochemical properties of clay on erodibility of soils.

Soils with a high percentage of clay can be artificially aggregated and developed into almost completely water-stable aggregates in several weeks by adding sugar and a complete nutrient solution. The population of microorganisms becomes phenomenally great under such treatment (32). After the two soils are allowed to incubate without further additions of sugar, the microbial population decreases and the stability of aggregates decreases correspondingly. The equilibrium level at which stability decreases no further is determined by the physicochemical properties of the clay.

The biological properties of aggregate stability became widely recognized following the publications of Martin and Waksman (26), Peele (28), McCalla (25), and others in about 1940. While the aggregate stability due to organic matter was explained only recently by microbiologists, the effect of organic matter on soil structure has long been recognized. Miller and Krusekopf (27) reported in 1932 that corn following corn caused almost twice as much erosion as corn following clover. There appears to be little doubt at the present time that a large part of the reduction in erosion following clover is due to stability of aggregates caused by the binding effect of products of decomposition. When the clover (or other legume residues) is turned under, the microbial population is large and the stability of aggregates is high. As the readily available energy material disappears, the microbial population decreases and the aggregate

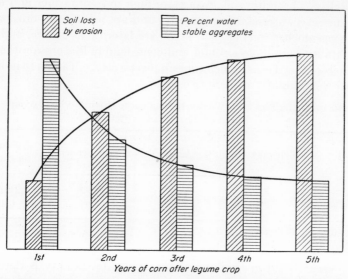

Soil loss by erosion

Per cent water stable aggregates

1st 2nd 3rd 4th 5th
Years of corn after legume crop

FIG. 146. The negative relationship between aggregate stability and soil erosion. [*Based on studies in Iowa* (7) *and Missouri* (31).]

stability decreases. The most significant decrease in microbial numbers is the fungi population, which has been shown by McCalla (25) to be the most effective group of microorganisms in causing aggregate stability. The big change in aggregate stability comes during the first year of cultivation after the legume is turned under. The change during the second year is small, and the change in aggregate stability is hardly measurable during the third year. The change in aggregate stability is negatively correlated with erosion losses and is shown schematically in Fig. 146.

The physicochemical properties of clay have been recognized as important in erodibility for many years. Early workers in the Soil Survey Division (U.S. Department of Agriculture) recognized that some clay soils were plastic when wet while others were friable. They recognized that the main chemical difference between the two groups was the silica to sesquioxide ratio.[1] The critical ratio was recognized as 2. Soils with higher ratios were generally plastic and erosive, and those of lower ratios were friable and nonerosive.

One seldom sees the term *silica to sesquioxide* ratio in recent literature. We now recognize that montmorillonitic clays have a high silica to sesquioxide ratio, and we know these soils swell when wet and are plastic, and the aggregates are only slightly stable in water. Kaolinitic clays do not swell appreciably on wetting and are slightly plastic, and they form rather stable aggregates. Illitic clays are between montmorillonite and kaolinite in erodibility. Lateritic soils which are high in sesquioxides and low in silica form very water-stable aggregates and are resistant to erosion.

The Nacogdoches soils of east Texas are lateritic in nature, and their water stability permits less runoff and considerably less erosion than the Kirvin soils of east Texas, which contain plastic clay. Table 116 indicates the relative erodibility of these two soils.

TABLE 116. AVERAGE SOIL AND WATER LOSSES FROM KIRVIN* AND NACOGDOCHES†
SOILS OF EAST TEXAS (29)

Soil	Slope, per cent	Crop	Runoff, per cent	Soil loss, tons/acre
Kirvin	8.75	Cotton	19.92	24.07
Nacogdoches	10.0	Cotton	13.89	6.46

* 1931 to 1940, 40.66 in. rainfall.
† 1932 to 1940, 41.68 in. rainfall.

The present trend in thinking about aggregate stability is that clays have a characteristic water stability due to their physicochemical properties, which can be modified and improved by addition of readily decomposable organic materials, but that the improvement is temporary. Under field conditions, about two-thirds of the improvement in aggregate stability caused by a legume is lost during the first year of clean cultivation.

[1] If the analysis of a clay shows the presence of 44.86 per cent silica, 7.40 per cent iron oxide, and 22.04 per cent alumina, the silica to sesquioxide ratio is found as follows:

$$44.86 \div 60.3 = 0.7440$$
$$7.40 \div 159.8 = 0.0463$$
$$22.04 \div 102.0 = 0.2161$$

The quotients represent the relative chemical unit quantities of these three substances in the clay. If 0.744 is divided by the sum of 0.0463 and 0.2161, the quotient is 2.84, the silica to sesquioxide ratio. This means that for each unit of the alumina and iron oxide, taken together, there are 2.84 units of silica. The two oxides, alumina (Al_2O_3) and iron oxide (Fe_2O_3), are the only two oxides in soils, in any considerable quantity, in which the elements are present in the ratio of 2 to 3, or 1 to $1\frac{1}{2}$; hence the term sesquioxide.

Organic Matter. Organic matter has already been discussed from the standpoint of its effect on soil structure, and the structure effect is probably the most important contribution of organic matter.

Undecomposed organic matter which accumulates on the surface of undisturbed soils acts somewhat as a cushion in protecting the soil from the direct impact of falling raindrops. As the soil becomes filled with water, runoff is impeded by the organic debris.

Organic matter has a high water-holding capacity. It will hold two or three times its weight in water, but the absorptive power of organic matter is only a minor factor. The decrease in runoff and erosion caused by organic matter is largely through slowing down runoff water, increasing the rate of infiltration, and causing the soil aggregates to remain stable in the presence of moving water.

The data of Copley et al. in Table 117 show the effect of addition of organic materials to control plots in North Carolina from 1933 to 1940. The average annual precipitation was 43.82 in., and the soil was Cecil sandy clay loam on 10 per cent slope. The application of 8 tons of stable

TABLE 117. AVERAGE ANNUAL RUNOFF, SOIL LOSS, AND CROP YIELDS FROM COTTON ORGANIC-MATTER PLOTS (9)

Treatment		Runoff, per cent	Soil loss, tons/acre	Yield of seed cotton, lb./acre
Material	Tons/acre annually			
None............................	..	14.86	36.18	591
Manure......................	8	5.86	6.63	1887
Compost......................	60	1.23	0.86	2631
Compost......................	18	5.11	4.67	1444
Compost......................	18	3.77	4.19	1901
Compost......................	12	8.83	13.91	1793
Compost......................	12	8.88	12.55	1889
Pine-needle mulch..............	24	0.62	0.01	
Pine needles spaded...........	24	3.49	3.36	1395

manure was more effective than 12 tons of compost in reducing runoff and erosion. Copley and his associates do not explain this difference. The author is of the opinion that the composted manure has lost much of the readily available energy material which causes a large population of fungi and actinomycetes. The reader is referred to Chap. 13 for a discussion of the effect of composting manure on the disappearance of readily decomposable organic materials.

Depth of Soil. Deep permeable soils are less erodible than shallow permeable soils, other factors being equal. The depth of the soil is one of the major factors determining the amount of water the soil will hold. The Norfolk sands of the Southeastern states are well known for their unusual depth. These soils are capable of absorbing large amounts of water. As a consequence, the Norfolk soils of Texas are seldom eroded to an appreciable degree. In contrast to the Norfolk soil, the Houston clay shallow phase can be cited as an example. The western part of the blackland region of Texas is dominated by this type. Erosion has removed so much of the shallow soil that the entire area is characterized by white spots in fields, which are nothing but exposed parent material.

Character of the Subsoil. The permeability of the subsoil is influenced by the texture and structure. Since the soil and subsoil usually differ in texture and structure, it is necessary to consider the subsoil as an individual characteristic of prime importance. Soil loss from Kirvin fine sandy loam in cotton on an 8.75 per cent slope was four times greater than from Nacogdoches fine sandy loam in the same crop on a 10 per cent slope (29). Having had experience in mapping these soils, the author has observed a marked difference in the permeability of the subsoils in the two soil types. The Nacogdoches series is characterized by a granular and permeable subsoil, whereas the Kirvin series is characterized by a dense and slowly permeable subsoil.

The Lufkin soils of east Texas have shallow surface soils overlying dense and impervious subsoils. The soils, in addition to being low in productivity, are highly erodible because of the limited amount of water they will absorb during heavy rains. A similar situation is found in the West Cross Timer region of Texas. The Windthorst soils have an almost impervious subsoil. As a consequence, when these soils are terraced it is necessary to give the terrace enough grade to allow removal of the excess water. In this area of subhumid climate, level terraces would help hold water on the soil in order to tide crops over droughty periods. Because of the impervious nature of the subsoil, however, the much-needed water must be carried away or there will be risk of damage to level terraces during heavy rains.

All along the edge of the humid part of the United States the character of the subsoil is the most important factor in determining whether the graded terrace or the level terrace is used on slopes. The Marshall and Monona soils of western Iowa are well adapted to level terraces, because these soils are only slightly differentiated and the subsoils are fairly permeable. The Sharpsburg and Winterset soils which occur in south central Iowa have subsoils heavy enough so that graded terraces are generally recommended (35).

Soil Fertility. By improving the fertility of a soil one causes an improvement in crop growth. The improvement in crop growth furnishes a better protective cover for the soil, and greater quantities of residues are returned after the harvest. As a general rule, the quantity of organic matter in the root system is proportional to the top growth.

Experiments conducted at the McCredie farm in Missouri showed that 200 lb. of 10-20-20 fertilizer cut soil losses in half under oats following corn, and 200 lb. of 0-20-10 cut soil losses by 40 per cent under wheat following soybeans.

The effect of use of manure as a fertility practice and as an erosion practice has been shown already in Table 117. There are numerous examples that could be cited to show the beneficial effect of fertility on the control of erosion.

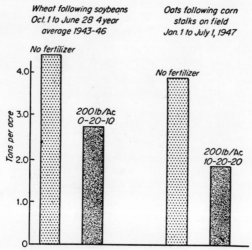

FIG. 147. Effect of fertilizer on erosion under small grain (31).

In planning a system of farming to control erosion, we should credit fertility practices as well as rotation and mechanical practices as means of reducing erosion.

Mechanical Practices That Control Erosion. The most important mechanical practices that control erosion are contour tillage, strip cropping, and terracing. In many areas erosion has developed gullies, which require special treatment and which will be discussed under a separate heading.

Contour Tillage. Contour tillage is the most fundamental step toward erosion control on cultivated land. The value of contour tillage was realized by Thomas Jefferson, who, in 1817, wrote as follows:[1]

[1] For more discussion of early conservation practices see A. R. Hall, Early Erosion-control Practices in Virginia, *U.S. Dept. Agr. Misc. Pub.* 256, 1937.

A method of plowing our hillsides horizontally, introduced into this most hilly part of our country by Col. T. M. Randolph, my son-in-law, may be worth mentioning to you. He has practiced it a dozen or 15 years, and its advantages were so immediately observed that it has already become very general, and has entirely changed and renovated the face of our country.

Contour cultivation reduces runoff by temporarily holding back the water, thus allowing more time for penetration. The runoff water must travel some distance down the furrow before it breaks across at a low point

Fig. 148. A modern farmer following an old practice. Thomas Jefferson practiced contour tillage on his farm in Virginia in 1813. (*Soil Conservation Service.*)

to be finally carried off the field, and it therefore moves off the field slowly. In direct contrast, the furrows that are formed by plowing up and down hill quickly carry the water to the bottom of the slope with much greater velocity, and consequently, more soil is carried away.

The simple practice of contour tillage, however, is inadequate for most cultivated slopes. Contour tillage may actually encourage concentration of water by virtue of the fact that not every row is exactly on the contour. Most of the rows will have a few inches fall per 100 ft. The water will slowly run down the graded rows until a low point is reached and will then break over into the next furrow. And of course, the next furrow will break and the water begin to concentrate and run down the slope across the furrows carrying its silt load.

If the slope is gentle and the runoff and soil loss are significantly high, the concentrated water must be spread out to cause deposition of the silt load and prevent the cutting of a channel. This is usually accomplished by growing strips of close-growing crops on the contour between strips of clean-tilled crops.

Where the per cent of slope or length of slope is so great that the volume of water can no longer be controlled by contour tillage and strip cropping, terraces are necessary to break the slope into a number of short slopes. The terrace must be high enough to impound all the water falling on the slope above it or must be constructed with a grade so that the excess water will be carried off the field.

FIG. 149. Contour farming on a community basis. An aerial view of a part of the Elm Creek Watershed near Temple, Texas. (*Soil Conservation Service.*)

The significance of contour cultivation has been overlooked in a number of recommendations made to farmers in the Southwest. Large machinery, commonly used in that section, is somewhat limited where contour tillage is practiced because of point rows. There have been advocates of the practice of running rows the length of the field without regard to direction of the terrace, but this damaged the terrace system to the extent that the labor saved with large machinery was not enough to offset the labor required to rebuild the terraces.

One important feature of contour tillage is that crops are more uniform when grown on the contour, because soil-type boundaries roughly parallel contour lines.

Table 118 illustrates the difference in soil losses on contour-tilled land and land cultivated with the slope.

The results obtained at Auburn are fairly representative of results obtained at other stations. The U.S. Soil Conservation Experiment Station at Guthrie, Oklahoma, in 3 years of studies, found that 24.25 tons was lost from contour-tilled plots as compared to 56.64 tons on plots with rows up and down hill. Experiments conducted at the various experiment stations show that contour tillage reduces erosion by about 50 per cent.

TABLE 118. LOSS OF SOIL FROM NATURAL RAINS DURING PERIOD OF CULTIVATING COTTON*

(Alabama Polytechnic Institute, Auburn, Alabama)

Slope, per cent	Soil lost (lb./acre) when rows run	
	With slope	On contour
5	11,412	4,178
10	58,580	29,696
15	88,160	47,212
20	121,046	67,338

* 1931 to 1937, 36 in. rainfall.

The Plum-Beaver Soil Conservation District in Nebraska made a study of the labor necessary in tillage operations on both contour-tilled and non-contour-tilled farms in 1939. The data were compiled and presented by Flynn (14). The survey was made on 139 fields of corn, barley, and oats. Of these fields, 79 were on contour and 60 followed the "up-and-down-hill" method. Special forms were prepared on which the farmers kept their records. On the whole, the same kind of equipment was used by both groups of farmers. The data, however, are presented so that comparisons are made on farms using similar methods and equipment. Table 119 shows the average time and fuel used in producing an acre of listed corn on 24 contoured farms and 11 noncontoured farms.

TABLE 119. AVERAGE TIME AND FUEL USED PER ACRE ON 24 CONTOUR- AND 11 NONCONTOUR-LISTED CORNFIELDS (14)

Operation	Min./acre		Fuel, gal./acre	
	Contoured fields	Noncontoured fields	Contoured fields	Noncontoured fields
Disking...................	20.3	19.8	0.47	0.52
Listing.....................	27.5	30.7	0.74	0.85
Harrowing.................	9.2	10.1	0.22	0.24
Go-deviling................	19.7	23.1	0.39	0.59
Cultivating (second).........	26.1	29.4	0.57	0.69
Cultivating (third)...........	23.6	26.0	0.54	0.56
Total.................	126.4	139.1	2.93	3.45

Table 120 shows average time used per acre on 23 contour-listed and 14 noncontour-listed cornfields where horses were used for power.

TABLE 120. AVERAGE TIME USED PER ACRE ON 23 CONTOUR- AND 14 NONCONTOUR-LISTED CORNFIELDS (14)

Operation	Man-minutes/acre		Horse-minutes/acre	
	Contoured fields	Noncontoured fields	Contoured fields	Noncontoured fields
Disking........................	37.2	43.9	168.1	198.2
Listing........................	80.3	79.1	321.2	316.4
Harrowing.....................	20.0	17.4	80.0	69.6
Go-deviling....................	40.7	38.8	162.8	155.2
Cultivating (second)...........	64.7	63.3	165.6	162.0
Cultivating (third)............	51.4	71.8	159.0	192.0
Total....................	294.3	314.3	1056.7	1093.4

The studies represented in Tables 119, 120, 121, and 122 are rather typical of studies comparing up-and-down-hill farming with contour farming. There is some difference in saving of time by contour tillage, but there is a decided difference in saving of fuel in favor of contour tillage. Browning (6) estimates that contour tillage saves about 10 per cent in fuel.

The reason contour tillage saves on fuel is that driving a tractor on the contour permits a uniform speed and fuel output, while the up-and-down-

TABLE 121. AVERAGE TIME AND FUEL USED PER ACRE IN SEEDBED PREPARATION AND SEEDING OF SMALL GRAIN (14)
11 contour- and 7 noncontour-drilled fields

Operation	Man-minutes/acre		Tractor fuel per acre, gal.	
	Contoured fields	Noncontoured fields	Contoured fields	Noncontoured fields
Disking........................	20.3	19.8	0.47	0.52
Disking........................	20.3	19.8	0.47	0.52
Drilling........................	23.9	29.5	0.55	0.61
Total....................	64.5	69.1	1.49	1.65

hill method requires more frequent change of gears and speed, which causes greater fuel consumption.

TABLE 122. AVERAGE TIME USED PER ACRE IN SEEDBED PREPARATION AND
SEEDING OF SMALL GRAIN, USING HORSES (14)
3 contour- and 2 noncontour-drilled fields

Operation	Man-minutes/acre		Horse-minutes/acre	
	Contoured fields	Noncontoured fields	Contoured fields	Noncontoured fields
Disking......................	37.2	43.9	168.1	198.2
Disking......................	37.2	43.9	168.1	198.2
Drilling......................	55.0	56.5	219.8	226.6
Total..................	129.4	144.3	556.0	623.0

Browning (6) is quoted as follows:

Planting corn [surface-planted] on the contour cut losses about 50 per cent.
Listing on the contour, a common practice in Western Iowa, lowered them by
80 per cent. . . .
We also cooperated with 260 farmers to measure the effect of contouring on
yields. Over a 5-year period and under the different weather conditions included
in this sample, farming on the contour raised yields an average of 7.3 bushels per
acre for corn, 2.7 bushels for soybeans, and 5.4 bushels for oats.

The beneficial effects of contour cultivation on yield are primarily the
improvement in stand and better utilization of rainfall. A severe rain-
storm on up-and-down-hill farming frequently makes it necessary for
farmers to replant their crops on lower slopes because of washing and
silting.

Strip Cropping. There are several different methods of growing crops
in strips to reduce the hazards of erosion. The most commonly recognized are contour strip cropping (ordinarily called strip cropping), wind
strip cropping, field strip cropping, border strip cropping, and planting
of buffer strips (21).

Strip cropping is the planting of strips of clean-tilled crops alternated
with strips of close-growing crops on the contour.

Wind strip cropping is the planting of ordinary field crops in parallel
without regard to the contour, but at right angles to prevailing winds.

Field strip cropping is the growing of ordinary farm crops in strips
across the slope but not on the contour. This method is inferior to contour strip cropping from the erosion-control point of view, but the strips
are uniform in width and are easier to cultivate and harvest. This
method should be used only on soils highly resistant to erosion.

Border stripping is used against both water and wind erosion. The method involves the growing of a protective strip around the border of a field or farm.

A buffer strip is a more or less permanent protective strip used in connection with contour strip cropping.

Contour Strip Cropping.   Strip cropping is a relatively new practice in the Southwest and Middle West, while it has been known for quite a while in the Northeast and Southeast.   Inasmuch as the practice was

Fig. 150. A good example of contour strip cropping.   Strips of corn are alternated with strips of red clover on this farm.   (*Soil Conservation Service.*)

a new one in the Southwest and Middle West, strip cropping was perhaps the most important method of soil conservation in these areas during 1935 and 1936.   There was little known about the limitations of strip cropping, consequently the method was overused because of its simplicity and economy.   In the blacklands of Texas, mainly the Houston soils, strip cropping was recommended instead of terracing on nongullied slopes up to 3 per cent.   Recently the trend is to strip-crop only short slopes of less than 1 per cent in the same region.   On the more permeable soils such as the Clareville series of south Texas and the Nacogdoches series of east Texas, strip cropping is recommended on slopes up to 2 per cent where the length of slope is not in excess of 1000 ft., and of course where there are no gullies.

Strip cropping has all but disappeared in western Iowa because of grasshopper damage and damage done by hot winds.   The grasshoppers are harbored in the meadow strips, and they damage the adjacent strips of corn. The hot winds burn the few outside rows of corn, and strip cropping presents more outside rows for burning. Consequently, the practice has not been popular. However, strip cropping is still popular in eastern Iowa and on to the Atlantic Coast.

It has been stated that runoff water must be spread to prevent concentration, which leads to gully formation. Strip cropping is an effective means of spreading water. As the water flows across the clean-tilled strip, there is a tendency toward concentration of water, which picks up a load of suspended soil. Then, as the silt-laden water passes into the protective strip, the velocity is reduced, resulting in deposition of the silt

Fig. 151. Contour strip cropping reduces soil losses by slowing the runoff water, thereby causing soil deposition. (*Soil Conservation Service.*)

load. Furthermore, the water is spread out because of the close-growing plants in the protective strip. As the water leaves the protective strip, it is no longer concentrated and is moving much more slowly than when it entered the strip. The water leaving the protective strip is added to the water falling on the next clean-tilled strip. The second protective strip again slows the runoff water, causing more deposition of soil and further spreading of the water. As the water moves on down the slope, the amount of water is increased with each successive strip, so that the last strip on the lower part of the slope may receive so much water and with such great velocity that its comparative effectiveness is reduced. Its beneficial effect is great, but not so large a percentage of the silt load is deposited as in the upper strips. This would indicate, then, that length of slope is quite a factor in strip cropping without terracing.

Even though strip cropping is supposed to spread water and prevent concentration, the presence of a gully is one of the most important limiting factors. The stand of the protective strip crop is usually inferior in the gully, and therefore the concentrated runoff water runs on through the strip following the gully with little or no water spreading or silt deposition.

There are two recommended practices where strip cropping alone is to be tried on gullied land. One is to fertilize the gully very liberally and plant extra seed in the affected area. The other is to make a fill at the upper edge of the protective strip by pulling soil up high enough so that the water will be diverted away from the gully. This last practice is probably the most successful but requires a good deal of patience and interest.[1]

Experimental Results. Experimental results at Guthrie, Oklahoma (10), and at Bethany, Missouri (30), have shown that strip cropping cuts erosion to about 25 per cent of the losses sustained by planting the crops up and down hill.

Tests at Temple, Texas (19), showed that soil losses were 3.81 tons on terraced land, 6.54 tons on strip-cropped land, and 53.34 tons per acre with rows up and down hill.

Width of Strips. The width of the protective strip depends largely on the erodibility of the soil, the per cent of slope, and the intensity of the average rainfall. According to studies made at Waxahachie, Texas, in 1936, with Houston black clay ranging from 1 to 2 per cent slope, the

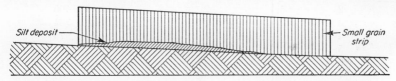

Fig. 152. Cross section of the protective strip showing silt deposition.

minimum width should be about 24 ft. It was noted that silting occurred over a distance of 18 ft. It is assumed that the crop in the strip 18 to 24 ft. from the upper edge had some influence on the spreading of the water, thereby causing deposition to continue for 18 ft. Had the strip been only 18 ft. wide, the silting at the lower edge of the strip would probably have been less due to the acceleration of runoff as the water leaves the protective strip.

With a recommended minimum width of protective strip it is not necessary to mention a maximum width. The wider the protective strip in

[1] Another alternative is to develop a grass waterway and never cultivate it. While this system is very popular in the Middle West, fields with gullies should be terraced. A great deal of soil is carried off the fields down the grass waterways.

relation to the clean-tilled strip, the more effective the strip-crop plan will be.

As the slope increases, the water moves more rapidly as it enters the protective strip, and therefore it takes a wider strip to cause the runoff water to slow down and spread out. The following minimum widths are recommended for different slopes:

Slope, per cent	Minimum width of protective strip, ft.
0–3	24
3–6	36
Over 6	48 to 60

The maximum width of the clean-tilled strip should be no greater than the horizontal interval between terraces for a given slope. Furthermore, any general recommendation for maximum width should be based on results obtained on soils with the highest rates of erosion. Any deviation from the recommended widths will probably be toward widening the ratio between the clean-tilled strip and the protective strip. The following formula, which is known as Bentley's formula for terrace spacing, is recommended for spacing of clean-tilled strips:

$$\text{Slope} + 2 \div 2 = \text{vertical interval}$$

Slope, per cent	Vertical interval	Horizontal distance
1	1.5	150
2	2	100
3	2.5	84
4	3	75
5	3.5	70
6	4	66
7	4.5	64
8	5	62
9	5.5	61
10	6	60
11	6.5	59
12	7	58

The above figures give an indication of maximum width desired, but they do not fit into a plan for a recommended rotation. The figures may be grouped to give widths useful in planning a strip-crop rotation.

Slope, per cent	Maximum width of Clean-tilled strip, ft.
0–1	144
1–3	96–108
3–6	72
Over 6	48–60

In planning the widths of strips, the first decision is the ratio of close-growing crops to clean-tilled crops in the rotation. Suppose a farmer wishes to plant from one-fourth to one-third of his field to oats and the remainder to corn. Assuming that his field averages 2 per cent slope, he would plant 24-ft. strips of oats and 72-ft. strips of corn. Or, if the farmer preferred a wider strip, he could maintain the same ratio and plant strips 36 and 108 ft. wide.

On slopes ranging from 3 to 6 per cent, the minimum width of the protective strip should be 36 ft. and the maximum width of the clean-tilled strip should be 72 ft. So with this range in slope, a farmer could possibly plant one-third of his field in close-growing crops and two-thirds in clean-tilled crops.

On slopes ranging from 6 to 12 per cent, half the field should be planted to close-growing crops. Therefore either the 48 and 48 ft. combination or the 60 and 60 ft. combination should be used.

Slope Limitations in Strip Cropping. The recommendations above are conservative and based on results observed on erodible soils. However, they have wide application. The problem of the steepness of slope which can be strip-cropped should be regarded as regional. For example, Region 4 of the Soil Conservation Service, which includes the Southwest Gulf states, confines strip cropping alone to slopes of less than 3 per cent; and on certain soils, strip cropping is confined to slopes of 1 per cent or less. Toward the eastern part of the Cotton Belt, slopes up to 6 per cent are handled by strip cropping. To the north of Region 4 in Iowa and Illinois, slopes up to 16 per cent are strip-cropped; while in the vicinity of New York, slopes up to 25 per cent are strip-cropped if the soil is fairly absorptive and rather naturally resistant to erosion. On these soils of New York that are erosion-resistant, wider strips of clean-tilled crops could be grown. However, it seems to be universally stated that 200 ft. should be the maximum width of a clean-tilled strip, and from the standpoint of practical tillage operations, 48 ft. would be the minimum.

Length of Slope That Can Be Strip-cropped Alone. The longer the slope the greater the volume of water that will pass through the strips on the lower part of the slope. It is necessary, therefore, to break the length of long slopes by either terracing the upper part of the slope or putting in one or more diversion terraces at intervals to take care of the excess water.

On well-drained soils, slopes up to 1000 ft. may be handled successfully, while on poorly drained soils, 500 ft. should be the maximum length of slope strip-cropped without terracing.

Temporary Strips versus Permanent Strips. There is a serious disadvantage to temporary strips, namely, that the field may be free of crops at the time washing rains occur. A gully may form during the interval prior to the growth period of the temporary protective crop, and it may become necessary to terrace the field.   Even though no gullies are formed, there may be considerable sheet erosion between the growth periods of the protective crops.   Another problem is the failure to get a good stand of the protective crop.

The Elm Creek Soil Conservation Project at Temple, Texas, which is located in the blackland prairies, has had considerable success with permanent meadow strips.   The principal grass is little bluestem (*Andropogon scoparius*), harvested for hay.   Any adapted permanent bunch grass that can be harvested for hay would seem useful in such a system.

Alfalfa has been used with a lesser degree of success in the same region. Of course, alfalfa is only semipermanent.   Its use is restricted to soils well supplied with lime and free of cotton root rot in the South.

Care must be exercised in choosing the grass for permanent strips.   The agressive sod-forming grasses must not be recommended unless the farmer is thoroughly familiar with their control.   Unless the grass has utility other than erosion control and pasture, its use will not be profitable.   The hay crops or seed crops, therefore, are more useful in permanent strips.

The permanent strip is usually referred to as a meadow strip, since its utility is for hay production.

Protective Strip Crops.   The small grains are probably the most widely used crops for the protective strip.   They are especially important in the Cotton Belt because they protect the land in the winter and early spring while the clean-tilled strips are bare.   In the Southwest, the grain sorghums are extensively used, and in south Texas, where small grains are killed by rust, the grain sorhums are the leading crops for the protective strip.   The grain sorghums are most effective if sown broadcast but are quite effective even in rows.   The disadvantage of the sorghums is that they are planted late in the spring.   Timothy and brome grass are used a great deal in the North, since either makes a good hay crop.

The following legumes are recommended, since they are planted broadcast or drilled: for the South, bur clover, hairy vetch, lespedeza, alfalfa, all the sweet clovers, and kudzu; in the North, red clover, alsike clover, crimson clover, sweet clover, and alfalfa.

Laying Out Strip-crop Lines.   The first step is to determine the widths of strips.   Assume 36 ft. for the protective strip and 72 ft. for the clean-tilled strip, which will make 24 rows 3 ft. wide.   These figures added together total 108 ft.   The contour lines should therefore be 108 ft. apart in the closest place.   The laying off of the contour lines is best accomplished by using a farm level or some other similar surveying equipment. The first line should be started 72 ft. from the upper side of the field at about the steepest part of the slope.   The line should be staked out by driving stakes every 50 ft., and it is preferable to mark the line with a plow immediately.   Then a new contour line is begun 108 ft. down the slope (at the steepest part of the slope). Each successive contour line should be 108 ft. from the next one at the narrowest place.

The next step after all lines are marked with a plow is to mark the edge of the row-crop strip. If the row-crop strip is to be planted first, 24 rows are laid off above each contour line, using the contour line as the first row. The intervening area will probably be irregular in width but is marked for the protective crop. If the protective crop is to be planted first, the following procedure is suggested: Use a rope, wire, or heavy string 72 ft. long. Have one man walk on the contour line holding one end of the rope and have another man walk holding the rope perpendicular to the contour line.

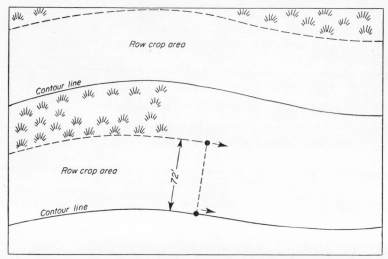

Fig. 153. Procedure followed in marking boundary of row-crop areas where the protective crop is to be planted before the rows are laid off for the row crop.

Then follow the second man with a plow and mark the new line which will separate the row-crop area from the protective-crop area.

Rotating Strip Crops. Figure 154 illustrates the rotation of the clean-tilled strip with the protective strip. With this system the contour line is permanently marked. The first year the contour line is between the strips on the lower edge of the clean-tilled strip; the second year it is exactly in the middle of the row-crop strip; and the third year it is again between the strips but on the upper side of the clean-tilled strip. The fourth year should appear the same as the first year.

Strip Cropping with Terraces. The practice of strip cropping with terraces is recommended as the most effective erosion-control plan for cultivated land. There are two conditions in which the combination is especially recommended. One is on the steeper slopes ranging from 5 per

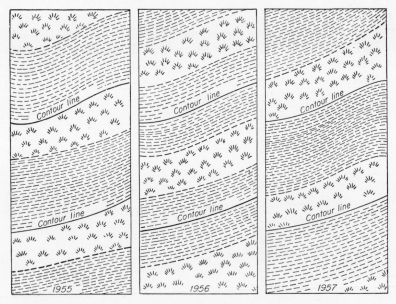

FIG. 154. Contour strip cropping. Shows method of rotation.

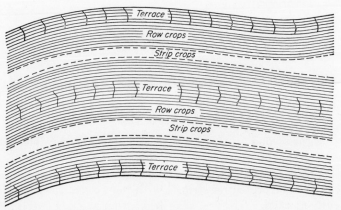

FIG. 155. Strips placed between terraces to take up point rows. (*Soil Conservation Service.*)

cent on up, and the other is on new terraces which may be planted to a broadcast or drilled crop the first year they are built.

The protective strip is especially helpful in taking up point rows. It also helps to prevent cross gullying between terraces and thereby prevents silting and filling in of the terrace channel.

The strips do not have to be so wide as where strip cropping is practiced without terracing. The minimum width of 12 ft. is often recommended by soil conservationists. The strip placed on top of a new terrace, however, should be as wide as the terrace.

Laying Out Strips on Land to Be Terraced. The construction of a complete terracing system, including outlets, requires some time and a

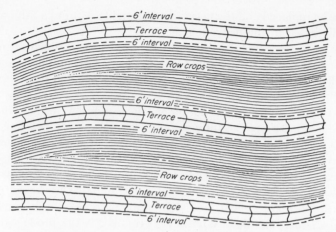

Fig. 156. Strips placed on top of the terraces. (*Soil Conservation Service.*)

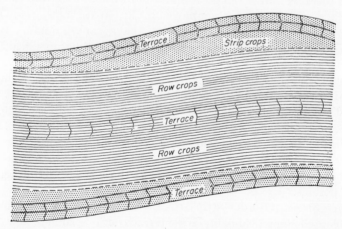

Fig. 157. Strips on every other terrace, planted to take up all point rows. (*Soil Conservation Service.*)

considerable cash outlay. It will have to be done when soil and weather conditions will permit work in the fields. This limitation of time may interfere with the production of the regular farm crops or cause damage to growing crops unless they are planned to facilitate terrace construction.

In laying out strips on land to be terraced, the operator can arrange his crops so that a strip of early-maturing vegetation will occupy the actual area to be disturbed by the construction of the terrace.   This will necessitate a complete survey of the land to be terraced and the establishment of all terrace lines before seeding.   As soon as the crops are harvested on the terrace contour, construction can be started without damage to the area between terraces.   After the terracing is completed, this temporary system can be replaced and the permanent one laid according to the suggested plans discussed in the preceding section.

Field Strip Cropping.   Field strip cropping is a modified form of contour strip cropping.   Areas laid out for field strip cropping are simply divided into parallel strips across the general slope and may or may not be on the contour.

This is not a good system and under some conditions may result in more harm than good if not carefully watched, because water may have a tendency to accumulate in low areas where no accumulation occurred when the rows were run up and down slopes.   Natural or seeded grassed waterways, carefully maintained wherever rows tend to collect water, will do much to carry away any surplus water accumulated by field strips, and under careful management field strip cropping may be quite successful.

Wind Strip Cropping.   Wind strip cropping is the production of the regular farm crops in long, relatively narrow, parallel strips, placed crosswise to the direction of the prevailing wind without regard to the contour of the land.   This system is employed in the Great Plains, where soils are subject to severe wind erosion and usually have scanty rainfall.   Its application, therefore, is somewhat limited.   It is sometimes modified by using vegetation or crops that are not a part of the rotation or that may not be harvested.   Sometimes Sudan grass or some of the grain sorghums are planted in very wide rows on land which will be seeded solid later to grass or small grain.   This gives protection from the wind until the regular crop becomes established.   In some areas of scanty rainfall, where summer fallow is practiced, strips of stubble, sweet clover, Sudan grass, or stooling varieties of sorghum can be used in alternate strips to break the force of the wind, hold snow, and otherwise protect the small grains during critical windy periods.

Border Strips.   Border strips consist of close-growing fibrous-rooted crops planted along field boundaries, terrace outlet channels, and roadside ditches and are useful from the standpoints both of erosion control and good farm management.

Buffer Strips.   The term *buffer strip*, in soil-conservation work, refers to a more or less permanent contour strip, usually of variable width, planted to a sod or other erosion-resisting form of vegetation which is not part of the regular farm rotation and therefore may or may not be harvested.   The width of these buffer strips is usually between 8 and 20 ft., sometimes as wide as 200 ft., depending on the type of vegetation used, relief, soil type, rainfall, and type of farming practiced.   A series of these buffer strips may be used on a long cultivated slope to break up the erosive force of the water by spreading it out and causing it to deposit its load of silt.   By cultivation and plowing, eventually a berm will be thrown up along the upper side of this permanent buffer strip which will act very much like a terrace.

Terraces.   The use of terraces in soil conservation is recognized as one of the indispensable methods.   It is impossible to conduct a satisfactory soil- and water-conservation program without this device.

Fig. 158. A grass waterway sodded to Bermuda grass.   The fields on either side will be terraced after the grass is well established.   (*Soil Conservation Service.*)

The earliest terraces were of the *bench type* and are still in use in Europe, Asia, South America, and parts of North America.   The other types of terraces have developed in recent years and are roughly divided into the *broad base* and the *channel type* of terrace.

In planning a terrace system for the control of soil erosion, it generally pays to put the cart before the horse.   In the past, farmers usually built terraces without much regard for the water that emptied out of the terrace channels.   When water from the channels started gullies in fields, pastures, or roadside ditches, there was little that could be done except to provide makeshift outlets.   Modern terrace planning reverses the old procedure.   Instead of building terraces and then worrying about safe outlets, the recommended practice now is to put the outlets in first—

anywhere from 1 to 4 years in advance of actual terrace construction. The procedure is to select the desirable natural waterways, sod them down or seed them to grass or other types of close-growing vegetation, and then build terraces from year to year as the outlets become established.   This makes possible a systematic terracing program over a period of years and, at the same time, cuts down the cost of terracing by doing away with the necessity for expensive concrete and masonry outlet structures.

Variation of Terraces According to Regions and Soils.   On the steeper slopes of the Piedmont region, the terraces are a great deal different from those found on the Great Plains.   Some of the terraces in the Pied-

FIG. 159. Terraces help to break the length of slopes and conduct excess water slowly off the field.   (*Soil Conservation Service.*)

mont have gradually been developed into benchlike formations, with the lower side of the terrace gradually developing an abrupt slope with a cover of permanent vegetation, while on the Great Plains a broad-base terrace 30 to 40 ft. wide on a 1 per cent slope is not at all uncommon.   A terrace designed for a steep slope must be different from one designed for almost level topography.   On steep fields of 10 to 12 per cent slope, the terraces are close together and a narrower terrace is desirable.   At the same time, the available farm machinery is usually adapted to a narrow high terrace; but in the Great Plains, where slopes are long and gentle and available machinery is very large, the farmer prefers a wide terrace without so much height.

Rainfall has a great deal of influence on the type of terrace used. In humid areas, the rainfall is so great during a single storm that it is almost impossible, and certainly impractical, to build a terrace to hold all the water that falls. As a matter of fact, if all the water were held, there would be drowning crops in the channel besides delaying tillage operations. But in semiarid regions rainfall must be conserved, and terraces are built so as to hold all the water that falls. In the subhumid regions we find transitional practices between level terracing and construction of graded terraces. In subhumid regions, soil characteristics have the predominating influence on terrace design. Well-drained soils may be managed satisfactorily with level terraces having one or both ends open, but graded terraces are necessary if internal drainage is slow. This is illustrated at Vernon, Texas, where Foard clay loam requires a terrace open at the end, while Vernon fine sandy loam responds well to management with level terraces with both ends closed.

Bench Terrace. The early bench terrace had a horizontal or nearly horizontal top. It was developed in Peru, Chile, Germany, Spain, China, Japan, and Korea. Because of the steep face of the bench terrace, much harm can be done by water unless rock retaining walls are used.

In Puerto Rico, where arable land per capita is limited and cultivated fields sometimes rise as sharply as 85 ft. in every 100, bench terraces that look like a huge flight of steps are sometimes built. By the usual construction methods, usually hand labor, these terraces may cost as much as $250 an acre. In recent years, however, the Soil Conservation Service has developed a method by which they have been built at from $10 to $15 an acre. Barriers of dense-growing vegetation are planted across the slope wherever a terrace is needed. A small amount of earth is thrown downhill against the barrier in a simple plowing operation. In 3 to 5 years, soil erosion and silting build up a series of well-formed terraces that check the downhill rush of water and divert it slowly across the slope to a protected outlet.

In cooperation with the Puerto Rican Reconstruction Administration, the Soil Conservation Service has helped cane sugar, coffee, tobacco, and fruit growers of the island to hold their soil under unusual conditions of topography and climate. In addition to the steep slopes, there is the problem of wide variations in rainfall, which ranges from an average of 20 in. a year in some parts of the island to more than 100 in. in others.

The bench type of terrace observed frequently in the Southeast is the result of continued plowing of the soil downhill toward old terraces. It is quite common to see small terraces with a cover of natural vegetation in this section, and through plowing of the soil downhill the bench formation is gradually developed and the natural vegetation protects the steep face of the bench.

A few farmers are trying out the bench type of terrace. A citizen of Tuskegee, Alabama, purchased a strongly rolling farm just east of Tuskegee recently and had bench-type terraces constructed. The author visited this farm and was very much impressed with the possibilities of the system.

Broad-base Terrace. The first broad-base terrace was designed and introduced by Priestley H. Mangum on his farm near Wake Forest, North Carolina, in 1885 (15). This type of terrace practically replaced the hillside ditch or channel type of terrace in the Southeast because it made it possible to cultivate the channel as well as the ridge.

At the present time, the majority of the terraces constructed in the Southeast are of the improved channel type, and most of the terraces in the Southwestern and Northern United States are broad-base terraces. However, the channel type is coming into prominence through the Cotton Belt from central Texas east and in the Middle West as far as western Iowa.

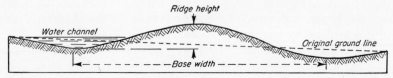

FIG. 160. Diagram of a broad-base or ridge-type terrace designed by Mangum.

The broad-base terrace is built by pulling the soil from both sides into a broad low-rounded ridge. This type of terrace is perhaps the only one to be seen in dry-farming sections. Since its height is mostly above the ground, it has a tendency to spread water much farther back of the terrace than does the channel type of terrace. Furthermore, large machinery can be used, since the terrace can be made wide enough so that no interference is recognized.

It appears at the present time that the broad-base terrace will gradually be replaced by the improved channel type of terrace wherever a graded terrace is needed. This is more or less a revolutionary change, and it will take quite a number of years for the change to be complete.

Recent experimental evidence acquired at Tyler and Temple, Texas, indicate that grades of more than 3 in. fall per 100 ft. caused scouring of the channel. Further recommendations from these and other experiment stations indicate that 2000 ft. is the maximum length that should be recommended and 1500 ft. is preferable. However, in some cases it becomes necessary to make the terrace more than 2000 ft. long, and in this case the grade should be increased to 4 in. fall each 100 ft. past 2000 ft.

The variable-graded terrace is without doubt superior to the uniform-graded terrace. The idea is that at the upper end of the terrace there is less volume of water so that it will move slowly toward the outlet without piling up at the terrace and breaking over, but toward the outlet there is an increasing volume of water that must be moved on a little faster as the outlet is approached in order to keep the water from overtopping the terrace.

TABLE 123. GRADIENTS FOR VARIABLE-GRADED TERRACES

Length of terrace, ft.	Fall along terrace, in./100 ft.	
	Permeable soils	Slowly drained soils
0– 500	Level	1
500–1000	1	2
1000–1500	2	3
1500–2000	3	4*
Over 2000	4*	

* Not recommended unless necessary in order to reach a desirable outlet.

Any time the terrace is built with a fall greater than 3 in., it is to sacrifice some scouring of the channel in preference to the risk of the terrace breaking.

It seems advisable to recommend that if a fall of 4 in. is exceeded, the channel of the terrace should be sodded to a perennial grass. A variable-graded terrace should be started with at least a 1-in. fall per 100 ft. on slowly permeable soils.

TABLE 124. TERRACE SPECIFICATIONS*

Slope of land, ft./100 ft.	Vertical fall between terraces, ft.	Horizontal distance between terraces, ft.	Base width of terrace, ft.	Height of terrace ridge, in.	Linear feet of terraces per acre	Acres terraced per mile of terrace
2	2	100	24	18	436	12.1
3	2½	83	24	18	525	10.1
4	3	75	22	18	581	9.3
5	3½	70	22	20	622	8.5
6	4	67	20	20	650	8.1
7	4½	64	20	20	681	7.8
8	5	62	20	22	703	7.5
9	5½	61	18	22	714	7.4
10	6	60	18	22	726	7.3

* Vertical interval may be varied as much as 6 in. either way where necessary to obtain a desirable outlet condition. Vertical interval should be reduced 6 in. on loose sandy soil.

Channel Type of Terrace. The improved channel type of terrace is known as the Nichols terrace (18). It is named for the man who brought it into prominence during the past few years, M. L. Nichols, an engineer and a member of the Soil Conservation Service.

During the period of 1820 to 1855 in the Piedmont region, the channel type of terrace, known as a hillside ditch or "guard ditch," was the only known method of diverting water from the fields. The bench terrace was too expensive. The Piedmont region, with its productive soils on steep slopes, led the United States in developing a terrace system. It was in this same section of the country that the broad-base terrace was originated. Gradually the broad-base terrace replaced the hillside ditch because the channel of the latter was below the ground level. The Nichols terrace has only part of the channel below the ground level, and both the channel and the ridge may be cultivated.

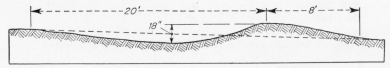

FIG. 161. Diagram of the improved channel type of terrace referred to as the Nichols terrace.

For slopes where water has to be diverted from the field, the Nichols terrace seems superior to the Mangum terrace. The following are the advantages:

1. Less cost for construction on steeper slopes, since the soil is moved downhill only.

2. Since there is less ridge height, a break due to overtopping does less damage.

3. There is no steep face on the lower side of the terrace as on the Mangum. This steep face causes rapid runoff and the beginning of small gullies between terraces.

4. Less cost of maintenance, since leaving the dead furrow in the channel is sufficient treatment.

The Nichols terrace has grown quite popular as far west as the blackland prairies of central Texas in the South and western Iowa in the North. However, it is not expected that this type of terrace will find favor in the subhumid and semiarid sections. The base width of the ridge is somewhat less than the Mangum ridge and therefore is less favorable for large machinery. Furthermore, the effective height of the Nichols terrace depends primarily on the depth of the channel. But in the drier regions it is best to have most of the effective height above the ground level so as to spread the water farther above the terrace.

Diversion Terraces. Diversion terraces are used to divert water from an area where damage might be done. The main danger of diversion terraces is that they usually have to carry more water than planned. It is not advisable to use a diversion terrace below an unterraced cultivated field unless a wide strip of cover crops or sod can be left or established above before the diversion terrace is constructed, because one hard rain might silt it completely in places and cause breaks. Such a strip should also be used in connection with a diversion terrace below a gullied pasture or woodland which is not protected from fire and grazing.

A diversion terrace located outside the cultivated field may be given a grade up to 1 per cent and built with a narrower ridge than one in a cultivated field, since it will not receive regular maintenance and will become covered with native vegetation.

Effectiveness of Terraces in Controlling Erosion. If the channel-type or broad-base terraces are not broken or overtopped by heavy torrential rains, erosion can be effectively controlled on cultivated land up to about 12 per cent slope under climatic and soil conditions of the United States. On slopes of more than 12 per cent the land should not be tilled if contour cultivation and strip cropping will not control the erosion. For the reader in a Southern state, this latter statement may sound rather strange. But in northeastern Iowa and in Wisconsin, strip cropping has been very effective on slopes of 12 to 16 per cent. Where terraces are used on slopes above 12 per cent they are too close together and the back slope of the terrace becomes too steep for tillage.

Studies at Clarinda, Iowa, from 1933 to 1940 (7) showed that level terraces gave complete protection, while graded terraces allowed erosion of ¼ to 1 ton per acre per year, depending on the grade and length of the terrace. A uniform grade of 6 in. fall per 100 ft. allowed about 1 ton of soil loss per acre, while the variable-graded terrace allowed less than ½ ton per acre where the grade never exceeded 4 in. fall per 100 ft.

Studies at Statesville, North Carolina, showed that level terraces were not satisfactory because of silting of the channel and overtopping of the terraces. Erosion losses on graded terraces ranged from about 2 to 6 tons of soil per acre on slopes of about 6 to 17 per cent slope with grades ranging up to 9 in. fall per 100 ft. The most satisfactory results were obtained with variable-graded terraces with maximum grade of 6 in. fall per 100 ft. The variable-graded terraces under the latter conditions lost less than 2 tons of soil per acre (9).

At Guthrie, Oklahoma, terraces with variable grades up to 4 in. lost about 5 tons of soil per acre, while level terraces completely controlled erosion (10).

Soil losses at Tyler, Texas, on fields with variable-graded terraces of commonly recommended specifications suffered losses of around 5 tons per acre per year (29).

Soil losses at Temple, Texas, on terraced fields ranged from about 2 to 5 tons per acre per year (19).

These studies are only a few of the many observations made by the Soil Conservation Service to determine the effectiveness of terraces on cultivated land. The losses from fields in humid regions terraced according to Soil Conservation Service specifications will range from less than 1 ton per acre to about 5 tons per acre per year. Losses from level terraces in subhumid regions are negligible if the terraces are built according to accepted standards and properly maintained.

Browning (8) estimates that under average conditions, terraces will reduce erosion to 15 per cent of the losses sustained by up-and-down-hill farming.

Gully Control. There are big and little gullies. They vary in size from rills on a gentle slope to the Grand Canyon, which is over a mile deep. Some big gullies in the Middle West and Southwest are over 100 ft. deep. They are formed by concentration of water from various causes, such as cattle trails, improperly managed cotton fields or cornfields, and old woods; also cutting back of water from roadways into fields, creeks cutting back into farms, and old terrace breaks. It is better to prevent gullies than to have to remedy them, but once they are formed, every effort should be made to control them.

The control of gully erosion involves three important procedures: (a) the control of the water above the gully, (b) the stabilization of erosion in the bottom of the gully and the removal of the overfall at the head of the gully, and (c) the establishment of vegetation in the gully itself.

There are two principal soil conditions to consider in planning gully control. One is the heavy subsoil and compact parent material that naturally slough and cave off along the gully banks, forming a slope on which vegetation can grow successfully. The other soil condition is that of friable subsoil and substratum which maintain a vertical bank; before vegetation can be established, the gully banks require sloping to about a 45-degree angle or 1 to 1 slope.

The Houston soils of Texas, Alabama, and Mississippi are good examples of the conditions first described. Gullies formed in these soils are easily controlled if the headwaters are diverted away. The Orangeburg, Ruston, and Norfolk soils of the South and the deep loess soils like those in Mississippi, Iowa, and Missouri develop deep gullies with vertical banks, and therefore considerable difficulty is encountered in getting vegetation established on the sides of the gullies. The gullies with vertical banks should be sloped before vegetation is established.

Gullies in Cultivated Fields. If gullies in cultivated fields are too large to be controlled by terracing and filling them, they should be fenced in with adjoining woodland or pasture if at all possible.

Gullies too large to be crossed by terraces may be used for receiving terrace runoff, provided that they have been formed in a former natural waterway and that the grade of the channel has been stabilized, that is, if the bottom of the channel has cut as deeply as existing topographic conditions will permit. If utilized in this manner, the gully banks should be sloped and a sod-forming grass well established before construction of the terraces. If the channel grade of the terrace is not completely stabilized, the terraces should carry the water away from the gully and not into the gully.

Vines, shrubs, and trees are excellent for gully control, but they do not furnish sufficient protection where the amount of water entering a gully is increased by diverting terrace water.

Gullies in Pasture or Woodland. Gully control in pastures is relatively simple. The first thing to do is to divert the water to a place where grass is well established; the gullies will usually then "heal over" without further treatment. Very often gullies are caused by runoff from fields above the pasture. Terracing these fields will in most cases greatly reduce or almost entirely eliminate the drainage into gullies. The cultivated area may be so nearly flat and uneroded that erosion classification would not call for terracing, but nevertheless the terracing of the field may be the only economical and effective method of stopping gully erosion on the farm. In some cases a diversion terrace may be used at the bottom of such a cultivated field, provided that the field is strip-cropped or a permanent buffer strip at least 50 ft. wide is maintained immediately above the terrace.

If it has been decided that a gully should be treated and diversion of runoff is impracticable, it may be necessary to use some form of temporary structure to assist in the establishment of sod. Trees may be planted on the banks of the gully, but sod is necessary in combination with temporary structures to ensure stabilization of the bottom of the gully at the end of the effective life of the dam. The height of temporary structures of any type should not exceed 12 to 15 in., since the overfall left by their eventual disintegration must be cared for by sod, and the higher the structure the less chance there is for successful control. Temporary structures should not be built on regular grade intervals but should be placed at strategic points to assist in the control of overfalls and to reduce the grade of the bottom of the gully. By careful planning it should be possible to avoid the use of an excessive number of temporary structures.

Gullies can be most effectively and economically controlled by sloping and sodding without the use of temporary dams. For a gully with a very small drainage area, no additional treatment may be necessary. Whenever the nature of the drainage area and the amount of vegetative cover make it practical, the drainage area of a gully should be contour-ridged or contour-furrowed to reduce the amount and rate of runoff. Under favorable conditions this method of treatment may suffice for drainage areas up to 2 acres. Methods of runoff control other than retention or diversion, in combination with sloping and sodding, should be used only after it has been definitely ascertained that either or both of those means are impracticable or inadequate for a particular situation.

Permanent Structures. Only in rare instances is it practicable and economical to stabilize a gully with permanent structures. This situation might occur in the case of an active gully with large drainage area, so located as to make diversion of headwaters impossible or impracticable, or where the value of the land protected is sufficient to justify the expense of the work, or where the gully is endangering a public road, farm building, or other valuable improvements. In such cases permanent structures are necessary to drop the water to a stable grade if recession of an overfall or activity of the gully is to be stopped; but these structures should be used only where vegetative treatment would be ineffective and the value of the land protected is sufficient to justify the expense of the work.

Predicting Soil Losses under Different Systems of Management. It is possible to predict the approximate rates of erosion under different management systems for different regions of the humid part of the United States.[1]

We know that the effect of slope on erosion varies somewhat with climate and soils, but Fig. 140 (page 393) is near enough to the average to be used as a basis for prediction. Browning (8) assigned values to the curve based on studies at Clarinda, Iowa, and his data are shown in Table 125. He observed that Marshall silt loam in corn-oats-meadow lost about 10 tons of soil per acre per year on a 9 per cent slope on plots 72.6 ft. long.

TABLE 125. RELATIVE SOIL LOSS FROM DIFFERENT DEGREES OF SLOPE

Slope, per cent	Factor
2	0.1
4	0.3
6	0.5
8	0.8
9	1.0
10	1.1
12	1.5
14	1.9
16	2.3
18	2.6
20	3.1

[1] For a discussion of this concept, see G. M. Browning, C. L. Parish, and John Glass, A Method for Determining the Use and Limitation of Rotation and Conservation Practices in the Control of Soil Erosion in Iowa, *J. Am. Soc. Agron.*, **39**:65–73, 1947.

If a 9 per cent slope loses 10 tons, we would expect a slope of 18 per cent to lose 2.6 times as much soil, or 26 tons, per acre if other factors are equal. Browning (8) also prepared other tables to show how losses might be predicted. The curve in Fig. 143 was used to prepare a table for the length of slope. The soil losses at Clarinda were again used, and since 10 tons of soil was lost on plots 72.6 ft. long, Browning used this length as a unit of measure in Table 126.

TABLE 126. RELATIVE SOIL LOSS FROM DIFFERENT SLOPE LENGTHS

Slope, ft.	Factor
72.6	1.0
100	1.2
200	1.8
300	2.4
400	2.8
500	3.2
600	3.6
700	3.8
800	4.2
900	4.5
1000	4.8

The rotation of corn-oats-meadow lost 10 tons of soil per acre, while continuous corn lost about 40 tons per acre. Oats lost about 10 tons per acre, while the losses under meadow were negligible. The studies in Missouri (31) provided Browning with a basis for estimating the effect of second-year corn on erosion and the effect of oats and sweet clover, or of oats alone, on erosion. While soybeans are not shown in Table 127, we can assume their losses to be equal to corn (31). The losses under cotton are also about equal to losses under corn.

TABLE 127. RELATIVE SOIL LOSS FROM DIFFERENT ROTATIONS

Rotation	Factor
C, continuous	4.0
C-C-O	3.0
C-C-O$_{Scl}$	2.0
C-O	2.0
C-O$_{Scl}$	1.5
C-C-O-RC	1.4
C-O-RC-C-O$_{Scl}$	1.2
C-O-RC	1.0
C-C-O-A-A	0.9
C-C-O-A-A-A	0.8
C-O-A-A	0.6
C-O-A-A-A	0.4
C-O-A-A-A-A	0.3
C-O-A-A-A-A-A	0.2

C = corn, O = oats, O$_{Scl}$ = oats with sweet clover green manure, A = alfalfa, RC = red clover.

The Soil Conservation experiment stations desurfaced plots in order to study the effect of erosion on subsequent erosion as well as the reclamation of eroded soils. Basing his work on these studies, Browning estimated that a slightly eroded soil will permit less erosion than a moderately eroded soil. He established moderate erosion as 1.0 in order to fit the Clarinda data. Since desurfaced plots lost about 30 per cent more soil than moderately eroded plots, the factor for severely eroded soils was established at 1.3.

TABLE 128. RELATIVE SOIL LOSS FROM DIFFERENT DEGREES OF EROSION

Degree of erosion	Erosion factor
Slight: 0–25% of surface soil removed	0.8
Moderate: 25–50% of surface soil removed	1.0
Severe: more than 50% of surface soil removed	1.3

Soils vary greatly in erodibility, and different soils need to be classified according to the rate at which they might erode under certain practices. The Marshall soils are about the most erosion-resistant soils in Iowa. Those soils, however, are not so resistant to erosion as the Cecil soils of the Piedmont or the Nacogdoches soils of east Texas. We shall consider the Marshall soils of Iowa as our standard in order to fit the Clarinda data used as standards in the previous tables.

TABLE 129. EROSION FACTORS FOR DIFFERENT SOILS

Soil description	Factor
Deep and permeable soils, friable when wet	0.5
Deep soils with permeable subsoils	0.8
Deep soils with moderately permeable subsoils	1.0*
Moderately deep soils with slowly permeable subsoils	1.2
Shallow surface soils with dense subsoils	1.5
Shallow soils overlying rock	2.0

* Soils with 1.0 or larger are assumed to be the kind with aggregates of low water stability under continuous clean culture.

It has been pointed out that fertility practices help to reduce erosion. The Marshall soils in the Clarinda studies might be considered as about the average, and Browning suggested that poor fertility practice might increase erosion by 30 per cent, while good practice might reduce erosion by 30 per cent. He is probably on the conservative side in the latter.

TABLE 130. RELATIVE SOIL LOSS FROM DIFFERENT SOIL-FERTILITY PRACTICES

Soil-fertility practices	Factor
Poor, no manure, most crop residues removed	1.3
Medium, manure occasionally, some crop residues returned	1.0
Good, manure regularly, lime and fertilizer if and when needed	0.7

The last factor we shall use in estimating soil losses is the supplemental or mechanical treatment employed. The studies at Clarinda on Marshall silt loam, 9 per cent slope, 72.6 ft. long, with corn-oats-clover rotation, moderate erosion, and medium fertility, were made with rows up and down hill; therefore the factor of 1.0 is used. It has been pointed out in the earlier part of the chapter that contour tillage or strip cropping will cut erosion about in half. Terracing reduces erosion on the average soil

TABLE 131. RELATIVE SOIL LOSS FROM DIFFERENT SUPPLEMENTAL PRACTICES

Supplemental practices	Factor
Rows up and down hill	1.0
Contour cultivation, surface planted	0.50
Contour listing	0.25
Strip cropping, surface planted	0.25
Terracing	0.15

to about 15 per cent of the erosion suffered in uphill farming, and contour listing without terraces will reduce erosion to about 25 per cent compared to uphill farming.

The erosion factors are used as follows:

1. The factor which best fits the soil condition or management system is selected from each of the seven tables.

2. The factors are multiplied together.

3. The final answer is multiplied by 10. This gives the estimated erosion loss in tons per acre for the particular situation.

Example:

Condition	Factor
9% slope	1
72.6-ft. length	1
Corn-oats-meadow	1
Moderate erosion	1
Deep soil with moderately permeable subsoil	1
Medium fertility	1
Rows up hill	1

The multiplication of the factors equals 1, and 1 × 10 = 10 tons of soil loss, which fits the Clarinda data.

As a general guide, Table 132 is suggested for deciding the permissible soil loss.

TABLE 132. PERMISSIBLE SOIL LOSS

Soil description	Permissible soil loss, tons/acre
Shallow soil on bedrock	0.5
Deep soil on bedrock	1.0
Soils with dense subsoils over unconsolidated materials	2.0
Soils with slowly permeable subsoils over unconsolidated materials	4.0
Soils with moderately permeable subsoils over unconsolidated materials	5.0
Soils with permeable subsoils (slightly differentiated) over unconsolidated materials	6.0

Example:

Condition	Factor
6% slope	0.5
300-ft. length	2.4
C-O$_{Scl}$	1.5
Moderate erosion	1.0
Moderately deep soil with slowly permeable subsoils	1.2
Good fertility	0.7
Contour tillage	0.5

$$0.5 \times 2.4 \times 1.5 \times 1.0 \times 1.2 \times 0.7 \times 0.5 = 0.75$$
$$0.75 \times 10 = 7.5 \text{ tons/acre}$$

This system does not bring the erosion loss within the tolerable loss of 4 tons per acre per year. We could keep the same rotation and use terraces to come within the permissible loss.

Application of the Erosion Factors. The erosion factors were prepared from data of the various soil conservation experiment stations. The factors are applicable to conditions in Iowa, Texas, and other states east to the Atlantic Coast. By assuming losses under cotton to be equal to those under corn, the factors fit, within reasonable limits, the data from Zanesville, Ohio; Statesville, North Carolina; La Crosse, Wisconsin; Bethany, Missouri; Guthrie, Oklahoma; Temple, Texas; and Tyler, Texas.

Even though rainfall varies in amount and distribution and the soils of the North are protected by frost in the winter, the factors fit the soil losses of the different stations surprisingly well.

It is the flash flood that does most of the damage to soils of the United States, and flash floods may appear anytime anywhere. The author realizes that he is contradicting established concepts regarding the difference in erosion in the North and South, but erosion is more severe in the North than is generally recognized, even by agronomists.

Restoring Fertility in Eroded Soils. It has been pointed out on page 386 that, in 1934, erosion had removed more than three-fourths of the topsoil on about 16 per cent of the land in the United States. The badly gullied land represents a total loss under our present economy, because the cost of leveling this land and preparing terraces would not pay off. Perhaps some time in the future the population pressure on the land may cause the reclamation of such land to become a profitable venture. We should not lose sight of the fact that any unconsolidated mixture of sand, silt, and clay can be built into a productive soil if enough labor and capital are put into the project.

Studies in reclamation of eroded soils are in their infancy. Progress on a few of the studies now under way has been reported recently.

The Ohio Experiment Station initiated a study in 1937 to determine the difference in production on topsoil and subsoil. Uhland (33) reported on the progress through the 1941 crop yields shown in Table 133.

TABLE 133. YIELDS OF VARIOUSLY TREATED PLOTS OF TOPSOIL AND SUBSOIL IN OHIO (33)

Soil-management system*	Hay yield in 1940, tons/acre		Corn yield in 1941, bu./acre	
	Topsoil	Subsoil	Topsoil	Subsoil
C-O-W-RC.................	2.8	1.4	67	32
C-O-W-RC+L.................	3.1	1.3	64	28
C-O-W-RC+L+F.............	3.1	2.2	83	44
C-O-W-RC+L+F+M...........	3.6	2.7	108	64
C-W-A-A+L+F.............	3.7	3.4	121	76
C-W-A-A+L+F+M...........	4.1	3.6	125	86

* C = corn; O = oats; W = wheat; RC = red clover; A = alfalfa; L = lime; F = fertilizer; M = manure.

The yields in the Ohio study were much higher on topsoil than on subsoil, but the data suggest that moderately high yields may be obtained on subsoils by good fertility management.

In the fall of 1941, seven control plots at Bethany, Missouri, were spaded and the following spring were planted to corn to determine the producing ability of the subsoil of the Shelby soil. The plots had received various treatments for 11 years. The 1942 corn yields for the seven plots were as follows (30):

Bushels

4-year rotation of C-W-M-M:
Surface soil without treatment...................................... 43.0
Subsoil without treatment... 20.5
Subsoil with lime and 4-12-4 fertilizer with oats...................... 34.6
3-year rotation of C-O-M:
Subsoil with lime and 4-12-4 fertilizer with oats...................... 32.2
3-year rotation of C-O-Scl:
Subsoil limed, 4-12-4 fertilizer with oats, 2d year of sweet clover plowed under... 44.0
Subsoil limed, 0-20-0 fertilizer with oats, 2d year of sweet clover plowed under plus 8 tons manure on all previous corn crops................. 64.6
Continuous grass and legume meadow for 11 years without crop removal but with an original treatment of lime and 4-12-4 fertilizer............ 44.2

The Missouri data show that corn yields on well-managed subsoil were about 50 per cent higher than on untreated surface soil, in spite of the fact that the surface soil was in a rotation of corn-oats-meadow-meadow.

Unfortunately, the experiment did not have a fertilized topsoil for comparison with fertilized subsoil.

In 1939 the Wisconsin Experiment Station placed five severely eroded and five moderately eroded plots under uniform treatment. At the beginning of the experiment the severely eroded plots had from 2 to 3 in. of surface soil, and the moderately eroded plots had 6 to 7 in. of surface soil remaining.

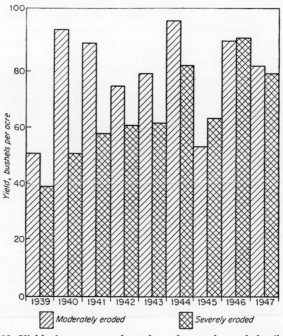

FIG. 162. Yield of corn on moderately and severely eroded soils (16).

A 5-year rotation of corn-small grain-meadow (3 years) was established in such a manner that corn and oats appeared in each set of five plots each year.

All plots were limed and fertilized to bring them to pH of 7, a level of 200 lb. of available potassium and 75 lb. of available phosphorus per acre.

Two crops of hay were removed from the meadow plots each year, and the residues were turned under along with 8 tons of manure ahead of the corn.

The organic-matter content of the severely eroded plots increased from 0.71 per cent in 1939 to 1.0 per cent in 1945. The organic-matter content of the moderately eroded soil did not change during the same period. Samples of the surface soil and subsoil from nearby slightly eroded soil contained 1.55 and 0.59 per cent organic matter, respectively.

The yields of corn on the severely eroded and moderately eroded plots were not significantly different after 1944. On the other hand, the yields of oats were considerably greater on the moderately eroded plots.

The data from the Wisconsin experiment provide a very good illustration of the concept that it is not the total organic matter of the soil that counts most for high yields but the readily decomposable organic matter added during the rotation.

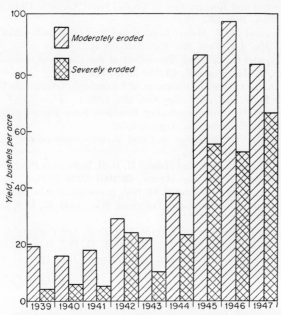

FIG. 163. Yield of grain on moderately and severely eroded soils. Barley 1939 to 1944; oats, 1945 to 1947 (16).

REFERENCES

1. Bennett, H. H., "Soil Conservation," McGraw-Hill, New York, 1939, p. 8.
2. Borst, H. L., A. G. McCall, and F. G. Bell, Investigations in Erosion Control and the Reclamation of Eroded Land, Zanesville, Ohio, 1934–42, *U.S. Dept. Agr. Tech. Bull.* 888, 1945.
3. Borst, H. L., and Russell Woodburn, Rain Simulator Studies of the Effect of Slope on Erosion and Run-off, 1938, Zanesville, Ohio, *Soil Conservation Serv. Tech. Paper* 36, August, 1940.
4. Bouyoucos, John George, The Clay Ratio as a Criterion of Susceptibility of Soils to Erosion, *J. Am. Soc. Agron.*, **27**:738–741, 1935.
5. Bradfield, Richard, Where Are the New Discoveries in Soil Science Leading? I. The Physical Chemistry of Soil-Plant Relationships, *Soil Sci. Soc. Amer. Proc.*, **11**:3–8, 1946.
6. Browning, G. M., Save That Soil, *Iowa Farm Sci.*, **2** (8): 3–5, 1948.

7. Browning, G. M., R. A. Norton, A. G. McCall, and F. G. Bell, Investigations in Erosion Control and the Reclamation of Eroded Land, Clarinda, Iowa, 1931–42, *U.S. Dept. Agr. Tech. Bull.* 959, 1948.

8. Browning, G. M., Unpublished paper presented to a meeting of the Soil Science Society of America, Cincinnati, Ohio, 1947.

9. Copley, T. L., Luke A. Forrest, A. G. McCall, and F. G. Bell, Investigations in Erosion Control and Reclamation of Eroded Land, Statesville, N.C., 1930–40, *U.S. Dept. Agr. Tech. Bull.* 873, 1944.

10. Daniel, Harley A., Harry M. Elwell, and Maurice B. Cox, Investigations in Erosion Control and Reclamation of Eroded Land, Guthrie, Okla., 1930–40, *U.S. Dept. Agr. Tech. Bull.* 837, 1943.

11. Duley, F. L., and M. F. Miller, Erosion and Surface Runoff under Different Soil Conditions, *Mo. Agr. Expt. Sta. Res. Bull.* 63, 1923.

12. Duley, F. L., and O. E. Hays, The Effect of the Degree of Slope on Run-off and Soil Erosion, *J. Agr. Research,* 45:349–360, 1932.

13. Enlow, C. R., Review and Discussion of Literature Pertinent to Crop Rotations for Erodible Soils, *U.S. Dept. Agr. Cir.* 559, 1939.

14. Flynn, Richard H., Soil Conserving Practices Save Farm Labor, Power, and Equipment, *Soil Conservation,* August, 1940.

15. Hamilton, C. L., Terracing for Soil and Water Conservation, *U.S. Dept. Agr., Farmers' Bull.* 1789, 1938.

16. Hays, O. E., Clyde E. Bay, and Harold H. Hull, Increasing Production on Eroded Loess-derived Soil, *J. Am. Soc. Agron.,* 40:1061–1069, 1948.

17. Hays, O. E., A. G. McCall, and F. G. Bell, Investigations in Erosion Control and the Reclamation of Eroded Land, LaCrosse, Wis., 1933–43, *U.S. Dept. Agr. Tech. Bull.* 973, 1949.

18. Henry, Jerome J., The Nichols Terrace, *U.S. Dept. Agr. Farmers' Bull.* 1790, 1937.

19. Hill, H. O., W. J. Peevy, A. G. McCall, and F. G. Bell, Investigations in Erosion Control and Reclamation of Eroded Land, Temple, Tex., 1931–41, *U.S. Dept. Agr. Tech. Bull.* 859, 1944.

20. Johnston, J. R., G. M. Browning, and M. B. Russell, The Effect of Cropping Practices on Aggregation, Organic Matter Content and Loss of Soil and Water in Marshall Silt Loam, *Soil Sci. Soc. Amer. Proc.,* 7:105–107, 1942.

21. Kell, Walter V., and Grover F. Brown, Strip Cropping for Soil Conservation, *U.S. Dept. Agr. Farmers' Bull.* 1776, 1937.

22. Lamb, John, *Soil Conservation News* (Ithaca, N.Y.), February, 1936.

23. Lipman, Jacob G., and Adrienne B. Conybeare, Preliminary Note on the Inventory and Balance Sheet of Plant Nutrients of the United States, *N.J. Agr. Expt. Sta. Bull.* 607, 1936.

24. Lutz, J. F., The Relation of Soil Erosion to Certain Inherent Soil Properties, *Soil Sci.,* 40:439–458, 1935.

25. McCalla, T. M., Influence of Some Microbial Groups on Stabilizing Soil Structure against Falling Water Drops, *Soil Sci. Soc. Amer. Proc.,* 11:260–263, 1946.

26. Martin, James P., and Selman A. Waksman, Influence of Microorganisms on Soil Aggregation and Erosion, *Soil Sci.,* 50:29–47, 1940.

27. Miller, M. F., and H. H. Krusekopf, The Influence of Systems of Cropping and Methods of Culture on Surface Run-off and Soil Erosion, *Mo. Agr. Expt. Sta. Res. Bull.* 177, 1932.

28. Peele, T. C., Microbial Activity in Relation to Soil Aggregation, *J. Am. Soc. Agron.,* 32:204–212, 1940.

29. Pope, J. B., James C. Archer, P. R. Johnson, A. G. McCall, and F. G. Bell, Investigations in Erosion Control and Reclamation of Eroded Sandy Clay Lands

of Texas, Arkansas, and Louisiana, Tyler, Texas, 1931–40, *U.S. Dept. Agr. Tech. Bull.* 916, 1946.

30. Smith, Dwight D., D. M. Whitt, Austin W. Zingg, A. G. McCall, and F. G. Bell, Investigations in Erosion Control and Reclamation of Eroded Shelby and Related Soils, Bethany, Mo., 1930–42, *U.S. Dept. Agr. Tech. Bull.* 883, 1945.

31. Smith, Dwight D., D. M. Whitt, and Merritt F. Miller, Cropping Systems of Soil Conservation, *Mo. Agr. Expt. Sta. Bull.* 518, 1948.

32. Thompson, L. M., C. A. Black, and F. E. Clark, Accumulation and Mineralization of Microbial Organic Phosphorus in Soil Material, *Soil Sci. Soc. Amer. Proc.*, **13:** 242–245, 1948.

33. Uhland, R. E., Rotations in Conservation, Science in Farming, *U.S. Dept. Agr. Yearbook*, 1943–1947, 527–536.

34. Wilson, H. A., "Fifteen Years of Soil Losses, Run-off and Crop Yields in Page County, Iowa," Agronomy Department, Iowa State College, Ames, Iowa, 1947 (mimeo.).

35. Wilson, H. A., F. F. Riecken, and G. M. Browning, Soil Profile Characteristics in Relation to Drainage and Level Terraces, *Soil Sci. Soc. Amer. Proc.*, **11:**110–118, 1946.

36. Woodruff, C. M., and D. D. Smith, Progress Report, Soil and Water Experiment Station, Bethany, Mo., 1930–1935 (mimeod).

37. Yarnell, David L., Rainfall Intensity-Frequency Data, *U.S. Dept. Agr. Misc. Pub.* 204, 1935.

INDEX